# Memoirs of the Forties

## J. MACLAREN-ROSS

Alan Ross Ltd, London 1965

BOOKS BY J. MACLAREN-ROSS

SHORT STORIES
*The Stuff to Give the Troops (1944)*
*Better than a Kick in the Pants (1945)*
*The Nine Men of Soho (1946)*

NOVELS
*Bitten by the Tarantula (1946)*
*Of Love and Hunger (1947)*

HUMOUR
*The Funny Bone (1956)*

AUTOBIOGRAPHY
*The Weeping and the Laughter (1953)*

TALES OF TERROR AND MYSTERY
*Until the Day She Dies (1960)*
*The Doomsday Book (1961)*
*My Name is Love (1964)*

None of the people or places described in these memoirs are imaginary, though some no longer exist and for obvious reasons some of the young women concerned have been given names not their own.

©Alan Ross Ltd, London 1965
Printed in Great Britain by the Shenval Press, London, Hertford and Harlow

A quoi bon raconter une histoire qui ne porte pas en elle le poids inimitable du vrai? A quoi bon des mémoires imaginaires, de fausses anecdotes, des phrases qui se trompent de bouche, des souvenirs pittoresques? . . . Tout cela ne rend pas commode le travail de se souvenir et de matérialiser des fantômes. A ce jeu dangereux, à se retourner vers le passé qui flambe, on risque d'être changé en statue de sel, c'est-à-dire en statue de larmes.

*Jean Cocteau*
PORTRAITS-SOUVENIRS

# Contents

Prologue
*Meeting a Publisher*     page 3
*Excursions in Greeneland*     13
*Up the BBC and Down the Labour*     29

The Forties
*A Story in Horizon*     55
*They Can't Give You A Baby*     81
*The Double Death of
    William Cooper Makins*     95
*Calder-Marshall and The
    Reverend Todd*     109
*The Polestar Neighbour*     118
*Tambimuttu and the
    Progress of Poetry London*     135
*Fitzrovian Nights*     153
*The Metamorphosis of
    Peter Brooke*     163
*Painters*     183
*Topolski and Picasso*     206

Second Lieutenant Lewis
*A Memoir*     223

Some Stories
*Y List*     237
*I had to go sick*     255
*A Bit of a Smash in Madras*     272
*Five Finger Exercises*     294
*Happy as the Day is Long*     303
*The Swag, the Spy and the Soldier*     317

# Illustrations

J. Maclaren-Ross's handwriting:
Notes and rough draft of contents for *Memoirs of the Forties*
*between pages* 42/43


John Minton, Francis Bacon
David Archer, W. S. Graham, Robert Macbryde,
Keith Vaughan, George Barker, John Davenport,
Anthony Carson, Elizabeth Smart and
Dylan Thomas                          *between pages* 90/91


Graham Greene, Dylan Thomas
Stephen Spender, Woodrow Wyatt
Cyril Connolly, Anthony Carson
Jonathan Cape, Philip Toynbee
Stevie Smith, Arthur Calder-Marshall  *between pages* 170/171

# Author's Note

I am a professional writer as opposed to being a professional literary man, and those seeking scandal or inside accounts of literary politics, in which I have never taken part, would do well to look for them elsewhere.

At the same time, since writing is my business, I have come in contact with many people engaged in various branches of literary and artistic activity, and it has been my concern to portray them accurately in these pages.

I have an extremely good memory, and almost total recall where the actual material of conversations is concerned; my grasp of chronology, however, is much less exact, I cannot always remember dates, and it may well be that such and such a conversation did not take place on precisely the occasion where I have situated it. But that it took place on another, similar occasion, the reader has my word.

I have also attempted never to fall into the trap open to all writers of memoirs—i.e. to falsify an incident in the interest of making it a better story—for my further views on this, see the section entitled *The Ham*.[1]

The book excluding prologue and epilogue covers roughly the years between 1940-49; and except for the early chapters, these recollections are not presented in strict chronological sequence—my method being to follow a train of events to its conclusion, or a person episodically through the length of our acquaintance, even if this meant moving forward into the Fifties—a decade which I could well have done without.

London 1964

J.M-R.

[1] This section, and also the epilogue, were never in fact completed.

# Prologue

# Meeting a Publisher

Across the classroom stretched a banner bearing the firm's motto:

'IT ALL DEPENDS ON YOU!'

In some branches, it was said, the pupils after graduation were required to sing every morning a paraphrase of the once-popular song called that, but none of us had graduated yet. In fact we were still on the first day of the course, though this was now drawing to a close.

On the dais beneath the banner our instructor, spectacled, dapper, and dressed like something in the City, was completing his lecture on the Three Types of Dirt.

'And, most insidious enemy of all, Dangerous Destructive Germ-laden Grit,' he said (the two other types were dust and fluff, which included clinging litter). 'Tomorrow morning when we are again assembled, I will explain the Science of Positive Agitation, which may be summed up by our slogan It Beats as It Sweeps as It Cleans, and which is the only satisfactory method of combating all three types of dirt. Thank you gentlemen. Tomorrow at 9 a.m. please,' and soon I was clattering downstairs with other members of what an American author would undoubtedly describe as the Class of '38.

I was there because I had answered an advertisement which began INTELLIGENT MEN WANTED, and found out too late that it meant learning to sell vacuum cleaners. The firm, however, paid an advance of £2 10s. and the fare to London, find your own digs, so I'd enrolled at the training school.

Outside it was April in Regent Street. I emerged from a building where a car park now stands instead. Next door was a coffee house with wheels turning in the window where sandwiches of hot ham on rye could then be obtained by those able to afford them, unlike myself. Diagonally on my right was Broadcasting House where I was later to have a promising but currently unproductive interview with the Assistant

Director of Drama, at that time Moray McLaren. The clock in its tower said 6 p.m., and I flagged a taxi which I could not afford either, so as to be in time for my interview with Mr Jonathan Cape.

I had high hopes of this meeting, for Mr Cape had replied personally concerning the short stories which I'd sent him, asking me to call at the office when I was next in London; and on the telephone that morning, when I explained that I was unable for business reasons to reach him before six in the evening, he had agreed to spare me half an hour, after which he was due to attend a publishers' cocktail party.

Almost immediately my taxi stopped, chugging in a stream of traffic by the lights at the corner of Mortimer and Great Portland Streets—the meter ticked money and minutes away, and I feared Mr Cape would give me up as a bad job. I was unaware that we had halted right outside the public house called the George, where I was to spend much time when writing for the BBC in the 1950s, and that by walking in there I stood a much better chance of being signed up to write scripts by some radio producer than by having a hundred interviews at executive level.

My ignorance in those days was staggering. I had not been at Oxford or Cambridge, had no useful connections, and failed completely to realize that all one had to do at this period, according to the autobiographical pieces which various writers published later, was to ask at the office of a literary weekly for books to review, or simply to hang around Bloomsbury bookshops or Fleet Street pubs until engaged in conversation by some influential type. I believed that one had actually to produce something before being received anywhere of consequence.

I had in fact been received by Norman Collins, then deputy chairman of Victor Gollancz Ltd, but only after submitting a novel which was too far out for his firm and probably no good at that, though he thought the dialogue showed promise. This was three years before, in 1935, so Jonathan Cape would not be my very first publisher.

I went to see Norman Collins on the day Italy declared war on Abyssinia, and newspaper placards announcing this event stood on every corner as I picked my way through mud, slime and cabbage stalks in Covent Garden. Collins, pleasant, pipe-smoking, and only a few years my senior, though he'd already been novel critic for the *News Chronicle* and was the author of a critical work called *The Facts of Fiction*, greeted me jovially with his feet up on the desk, and we talked about our respective enthusiasms, Arnold Bennett and Evelyn Waugh, above the rattle of typewriters, separated by only a flimsy matchboard partition from other offices beyond.

Very soon after, Collins's own second novel *The Three Friends* appeared and began to establish him as a potential best-seller. I too embarked on a second novel as he had urged me. In the middle of it I developed mumps and I well remember his ribald letters about the possible consequences of this disease if contracted in adult life, though luckily in my case no such complications supervened. After three weeks in bed reading Thomas Wolfe, my legs would hardly support me across the room, but nonetheless I despatched to Henrietta Street my novel which could not have been less like Thomas Wolfe. Though today it might have been accepted as a Black Comedy, there was no label to tie on it then and back it came. Norman Collins held out some hope of getting it done if the ending were altered to one less macabre, I haughtily refused this compromise, and twenty years later I was the first scriptwriter he employed when his Independent Television Company was launched, though I didn't last long at that either.

The taxi drew up at 30 Bedford Square, after circling for a while the wrong side, and the door swung open at my touch as I'd been told to expect. But it also closed behind me with a hollow boom and a decisive click, the catch must have somehow fallen, and to my dismay I could not get it open again. The staff had evidently left, there was no time to be lost and again as directed I sped up the stairs in search of Mr Cape.

He rose tall from behind a big broad desk in a large high-

5

ceilinged room the beauty of which was perceptible even to one in my flustered state. White-haired with a strong square face arranged in kindly folds like an elderly American judge, the sort who on the screen tries to administer justice despite the corrupt encroachment of industrial civilization, and wearing a judge's square-cut sober black. Bookshelves round the walls framed him like a film-set, with a long window back-centre beyond.

He spoke slowly and at first in formal measured phrases, but without the kind of accent such a judge would have had: he was in reality very English. The unhurried atmosphere of comfort surrounding him calmed me down at once, though his opening sentence was not exactly what I had hoped-for.

'I'm not going to publish these stories I'm afraid,' he said, patting the green springback binder containing them which lay before him on the desk. 'To begin with there aren't enough to make a collection. As I daresay you know a prejudice exists in the trade against books under 70,000 words in length, and this applies especially to first volumes of short stories by young writers not yet established by publication of a novel.'

'I've written two novels, sir,' I said quickly as he paused. 'Unpublished and I wouldn't waste your time submitting them. But suppose I were to write more stories, to make up the length? I don't know if you've read any of these yourself. . . .'

But Mr Cape had. It so happened they arrived as he was about to leave for the country, and the pale green linen-faced paper I'd typed them on had caught his attention. The colour green was restful for his eyes. So he took the stories home for the weekend and there he had read them all. On such extraordinarily slender chances, I was to learn, much in the literary world depended.

'Have you had many opinions on these?'

'Only one,' I said. 'The features editor of the local paper, on the South Coast where I live, promised to interest one of the directors at Chapman and Hall if he thought the

6

stories were any good.'

'And did he?'

'He did not, sir.'

'What were his comments?'

'There was a whole page of them, none flattering, and headed "PLOTS—WEAK." He's a Fellow of the Royal Zoological Society too. Signs his articles FRZS.'

Mr Cape chuckled. 'Happily you've got a sense of humour.'

'I've been led to believe the contrary,' I said. 'I can laugh at myself all right, but I don't like anybody else doing so, therefore according to my friends I haven't a sense of humour.'

'Not bad at all,' Mr Cape chuckled again. 'We might use some quote like that on the blurb of your book.'

'So there's going to be a book after all?' I asked eagerly: the case was apparently to be re-opened.

'We mustn't be in too much of a hurry' Mr Cape admonished gently, and not until six years later did my first book appear under the Cape colophon—on the blurb was the bit about my having no sense of humour, and this was used by reviewers as a stick to beat me with ever after.

The book itself was certainly a collection of stories, but not those over which the publisher now bent his head, turning the green pages again as if re-examining the testimony of some key witness which might cause judgment to be reversed. I forced upon my face the dead-pan expression befitting a defendant determined to behave with dignity whatever the verdict; but as he closed the green folder and sat back for the summing up, the late afternoon sunlight framed in the long window behind him swam out of focus—isolated words only penetrated a sudden hush inside my head.

I heard 'Talent,' 'Achievement,' even 'Professional,' though this proved to refer to the actual typing of the MSS. Sight and sound came rushing back. The sunlight steadied, shining it seems to me now on spring-green leaves, though at this remove of time I cannot be certain. It seems unlikely that trees could be seen from this side of the house.

Mr Cape was smiling paternally—the case had gone after all

in my favour, or sentence was at any rate suspended. 'Have you tried the weeklies or magazines at all?' he was asking.

'Wouldn't the bad language be too much of a barrier?' I said. 'The FRZS was shocked to the core.'

'Luckily I seldom go to the Zoo,' Mr Cape smiled. 'I've no objection to language myself, used properly for purposes of realism. There are only two words I have to draw the line at, and those are Fuck and Cunt.'

'Shit?' I said hopefully.

'We've had shit in several times, that's no trouble, but Fuck and Cunt they just won't print, though young men are always trying. How old are you by the way?'

'I'll be twenty-six in July.'

Mr Cape slowly nodded, as at some further extenuating evidence. 'And, forgive me asking, have you any private means?'

'If I have,' I said, 'they're kept private even from me.'

'But you've got a job?'

'I'm at a sort of Technical Training College' I replied, careful not to let on precisely what technique I was learning.

'Then stick to whatever it is,' Mr Cape advised me. 'For the time being anyway. Because I warn you there's no money to be made out of short stories. Authors can't readily be made to understand that. Take Liam O'Flaherty for instance.'

'One of my favourite writers.'

'Oh, magnificent I grant you. But he simply will not realize that all his books don't earn a fortune. Those tales about birds and animals, best things he's done, what did they bring in? He used to call round the Accounts Department wanting ten pounds cash, and if it wasn't immediately forthcoming he'd tap his raincoat pocket and say "I've got a gun in here." The accountants usually forked out, not that there were any royalties due.' He chuckled again, and from then on his speech became more informal and relaxed—the judge, once down from the dais, was a citizen of the world.

'Doesn't O'Flaherty tell that story himself?' I said. 'Only in his version he places a bomb on the publisher's desk.'

8

'Well he never put a bomb on mine, though I've frequently been threatened with the pistol. Don't suppose he had one on him at all if I'd called his bluff, or if he had he wouldn't have used it. He's really a very nice fellow O'Flaherty. Who are your other favourite writers?'

Many of these were published by Jonathan Cape, and we spoke of Arthur Calder-Marshall, who had done successfully in some of his work what I was trying to do—namely to create a completely English equivalent to the American vernacular used by such writers as Hemingway, Cain and O'Hara, concentrating in my case mainly on the middle and lower-middle classes, an area cornered so far by V. S. Pritchett and Patrick Hamilton. We spoke of H. E. Bates, in those days working along similar lines, Ralph Bates, whose volume *Rainbow Fish* included a great short novel *Dead End of the Sky*, and the strange *Novel on Yellow Paper* by Stevie Smith which had brought me out in a rash of annoyance when Mr Cape published it two years before.

'Ah yes, Stevie. She used to work for me you know.' The chuckle had become a chortle now. 'I can see why you wouldn't like her stuff, all the same a clever girl you must admit.'

'Hanging by a sisal twist over the darkening void,' I quoted, 'lit by an electric blue flash: that's where the souls of smarties go?'

'You've left some out but still it's stuck in your memory,' Mr Cape said. 'The trouble is, she's intensely feminine and you, well frankly you're not. It'd never do for you to meet, you'd fight like cat and dog,' but many years later, when I'd re-read *Novel on Yellow Paper* and formed an opinion diametrically opposed to the one that I held then, I did meet Stevie Smith in the saloon bar of that very George outside which my cab got hung up on the way to Mr Cape, and we didn't fight like cat and dog. Quite the reverse. I quoted to her, this time in full, her own passage about the souls of smarties and the sisal twist, also what Mr Cape had said, and we agreed that for once he had been wrong. I found Miss Smith charming and

9

delightful, and she was kind enough to say she wished she'd known me when I was young.

But that day in the office I said: 'An ultra-feminine Saroyan is a gruesome thought, God wot,' which brought us round to Faulkner, whom Mr Cape had also known.

'In fact I published him, over in the States. Our New York branch did *Sanctuary*, though Chatto and Windus brought it out over here because they'd a contract as his British publishers. Faulkner wrote it while he was working as a night-watchman, and when I'd read the typescript I said to him "This is all very well, but I'd like to know more about Popeye's background, where he came from and so on, also why he's impotent like this." And Faulkner said: "Why it's all there in the first chapter, all about his parents and childhood." Well I looked back through the first chapter but damned if I could find anything like that except that Popeye was scared of birds, so then Faulkner himself had a look. "By God," he said, "If I haven't forgotten to write it after all!" '

The telephone at Mr Cape's elbow interrupted, and he said: 'Yes, speaking. Oh, I'm afraid I will be late. Delayed at the office, sorry. Later on, perhaps' and cradling the phone: 'only the cocktail party people ringing up.'

I made hastily to rise but he waved me down. 'They'll have to wait. Besides, I'm getting too old to enjoy parties nowadays. What was I saying now?'

'Faulkner had left out the part about Popeye's childhood. It comes at the end actually.'

'I'm getting to that. He went off back to his watchman's shack and over a jug of corn liquor got out the missing chapter. But by that time the book was being printed, and we couldn't fit it in at the beginning, so Faulkner said: "Let's put it in last and the hell with them." So that's how the book comes to be constructed like that. Faulkner was most apologetic about it, couldn't think how it had come to slip his mind. Charming, quiet chap. Exquisite Southern manners. Only one foot, lost the other flying with the RFC. I've good reason to remember him, I had terrible dysentery all through that trip to the States.

Thought it was ordinary diarrhoea at first, due to the change of diet, but no it was dysentery right enough. Made everything so awkward, having to run and relieve one's bowels in the middle of board meetings you know.'

'Most embarrassing sir,' I said, as he got up from his chair. 'I'm sorry to have kept you for so long.'

'It's been a pleasure,' Mr Cape said, handing my green springback folder across the desk. 'Oh and you'd better have this too': a new novel in its packet, *Serenade* by James M. Cain. 'An interesting experiment, the narrator's an opera singer but Cain makes him tell the story like a sailor off the boat. It's not out yet, and this may be your last chance of getting a copy before some prurient fool takes exception to the subject and the ban goes up.[1] However, I mustn't spoil it for you,' and though I protested he insisted on coming all the way downstairs to operate the complicated lock on the outer door, otherwise I might still be there.

Jonathan Cape has been dead for some time now, but I have never forgotten the white head and charcoal black suit, the tall spare figure standing on his doorstep in Bedford Square, one hand raised to wave goodbye and point the way to where I could best catch my bus. It was the only time we ever met, and though there was friction with his firm in after-years, I'd no quarrel with Mr Cape himself nor was he to blame.

That evening I remember he said, apropos of what I can't recall, 'I will never publish a detective thriller unless it's as good as Dashiell Hammett's *Maltese Falcon*,' and as we shook hands by the door: 'When you've got enough stories together, address them to me personally, and if I'm away on business at the time, I'll arrange for William Plomer who's one of our readers to make a report pending my return, if that's all right for you?'

I walked away, as the saying goes, on air; but getting off the bus I was suddenly taken short. It may have been Mr Cape

[1] Mr Cape was unduly pessimistic here. *Serenade*, a study in crypto-homosexuality, was never banned—indeed it was afterwards made into a sort of Hollywood musical, with all the queerness omitted and Mario Lanza in the leading rôle.

talking about his attack of dysentery that brought it on or simply just excitement. My digs in St George's Square were several streets away, but Victoria Station stood close at hand.

On one wall of the cubicle I entered a member of the BUF had scrawled: 'NO LOUSY JEWS OR COMMUNISTS ALLOWED IN HERE.' On the other, a sensualist had more carefully inscribed: 'THE SIGHT OF SCHOOLGIRLS KNEES IS HORNY.' On the third wall, above the lavatory bowl, a metal box exhorted me to 'BUY A SANI-SEAT! YOUR PROTECTION AGAINST INFECTION. INSERT ONE PENNY.'

One cannot be too careful, especially with Fascists about. Before sitting down between the perverted and the politically conscious, I dropped a penny in the Sani-Seat slot.

# Excursions in Greeneland

One day in 1956 I was walking home with a friend who lived off Clapham Common when pointing to a gutted ruin with a façade of blackened brick he said: 'That used to be a Queen Anne house before the blitz. Beautiful place I believe. It belonged to Graham Greene.'

'I know,' I said. 'I lunched there once. In 1938,' and my friend was suitably impressed.

It was noon and summer when I arrived at that house eighteen years before, aged twenty-six and carrying a copy of *Brighton Rock* wrapped in a *Daily Express* containing James Agate's review of the novel which had appeared that morning. I had not found the house easily since there are three tube-stations and three sides to the Common, Clapham Common North, Clapham Common South, and Clapham Common West, and I am incapable of telling which is which without the help of a compass. I did not carry a compass. I had moreover mislaid Graham Greene's letter which gave precise directions for getting to his house.

I would like to be able to describe the beauty of the exterior before it was blitzed, but at the time I was too busy mopping sweat from my face and then swishing dust from my shoes with the handkerchief to take anything in. The door came open suddenly and an elderly housekeeper glared at me in a manner with which, since I sold vacuum-cleaners for a living, I had of late become only too familiar. But I had also learned to stand my ground in face of unspoken opposition.

'Could I see Mr Graham Greene please?'

She said: 'We don't want anything today, thank you.'

I said: 'He's expecting me to lunch.'

'Oh. Well why didn't you say so then. Come in.' We entered a hallway and the housekeeper, having pointed silently to a short flight of stairs, was obviously making off to her own quarters when I said: 'Perhaps you'll tell Mr Greene I'm here.'

'He's out. You'll have to wait. The drawing-room's up there. Can't be taking people up all those stairs at my age you know,' and she disappeared banging a door: an old family retainer and a character to boot, as befitted the household of a writer.

The drawing-room stood open at the top of the stairs: it was the house itself. Perhaps it was the kind called a Bijou house, I wouldn't know. Someone like Denton Welch would have been able to describe the interior and enumerate the articles of period furniture which I'm told it contained, but this bit is quite beyond me. The armchair I sat down in seemed like any other armchair, though rather low, and I saw immediately in a bookcase nearby the works of Joseph Conrad, which didn't come as a surprise.[1] Also Henry James. I'd have dearly liked a smoke, but the cigarettes I carried were Brazilian, the packet done up in a twist of yellow paper and picturesque to look at, but very pungent, and they didn't seem the right sort to be smoking in these rather fragile surroundings, also what would the housekeeper say if she caught me stinking out her drawing-room?

I stood up and my reflection in a looking-glass confronted me. Not to my mind that of a salesman, nor was I wearing the official uniform of raincoat and porkpie hat: nonetheless the housekeeper hadn't been deceived. She'd known by instinct that I was only a commercial of some kind masquerading as a luncheon guest. Suppose, despite the stairs, she suddenly came up demanding credentials?

I had written to Graham Greene asking permission to adapt his Entertainment A Gun for Sale as a radio play and he had replied cordially inviting me to lunch. I now searched my pockets frantically for his letter, while realizing that I had left it on my dressing table at my digs. My digs were on the South Coast. The letter was on grey paper with envelope to match, in a small neat handwriting abounding in Greek E's.

I glanced round and as I did so Graham Greene himself

---

[1] The Secret Agent turned out to be a favourite book of his, whose influence can be traced by comparing Conrad's Assistant Commissioner with Greene's in It's a Battlefield.

appeared quite silently in the open doorway. I was startled because not even a creak on the stairs had announced his approach. Seeing me there gave him also a start, and he took a step back. He was wearing a brown suit and large horn-rimmed spectacles, which he at once snatched off as if they had been his hat. He was not wearing a hat and this was the only time I saw him wearing spectacles. I had not expected him to be so tall.

'I hope you haven't been waiting long,' he said. He had a spontaneous pleasant smile. 'Nobody told me you were here. Would you like a cigarette? Something to drink?'

'Something cold if possible,' I said accepting the cigarette avidly.

Greene said: 'We could go over to the local, if you won't find that a bore. They'll have ice there, and anyway I've forgotten to get in the beer.'

Each carrying a large jug, we set off for the pub which was on the other side of the Common and may have been the one afterwards featured in *The End of the Affair*. Greene took long lounging strides and his shoulders were well above mine as we walked across the grass. Though very lean he had high broad straight shoulders from which his jacket was loosely draped as if still on its hanger.

He said: 'I've just been asked to do a radio play myself, so I'm relying on you to show me how to write them.'

'I fear I'll not be much use. I've only written one so far and they wouldn't have that.' Then fearing that sounded too much like a total obscurity and failure, in fact the truth, I added: 'They did offer me a job on the strength of it though.'

'At the BBC?'

'Training to be a writer-producer, eventually.'

'Then obviously your play impressed them. Why wouldn't they take it?'

'Too sordid, was the general opinion.'

'Bloody fools. Well they can't say that about mine. It's to be about Benjamin Jowett, the Master of Balliol, you know.'

'Never explain never apologize?' I said, hoping I'd got it the right way round.

'That among other things,' Greene said. 'Are you going to take the BBC job?'

'When there's a vacancy. But I was warned I might have to wait a year.'

'What d'you do meantime? Besides writing radio plays I mean.'

'I sell vacuum cleaners,' I said.

Greene, almost on the threshold of the pub, halted abruptly and turned to take a good look at me. Unlike the housekeeper, it was clear that he'd not suspected this. 'Vacuum cleaners?' he said.

'Yes.'

'Are you doing it to get material?'

'No, I'm doing it because I wouldn't have any money otherwise.'

'But do you earn much as it is?'

'I don't do bad at the moment. Eight to ten quid a week.'

Greene said: 'Good for you,' plainly surprised, and we entered the pub, which I remember as a big empty barn-like place where he ordered two large Scotches with ice while the beer jugs were being filled.

He said: 'I thought of signing on myself at one time. To write a book about it afterwards of course. I never knew one could actually sell the things.'

It would have taken too long and been too boring to explain the various rackets by which selling was really done, and I simply said: 'You wouldn't have enjoyed it much.'

He said: 'Well it doesn't matter now. Because you'll be writing your own book I expect?'

This honestly had not occurred to me. I hardly ever recognize material in my immediate situation or in any events which are still going on, nor would I ever choose any course of action deliberately in order to write about it. But this, I thought then, was the difference between amateur and pro-

16

fessional, though that wouldn't be altogether my opinion today.

So I said: 'I expect I will. Sooner or later,' getting out my Brazilian cigarettes, and nine years in fact went by before I did publish a book on the subject.

Greene said: 'Oh splendid,' fumbling in the yellow pack with MENZALA on the green band around it. 'I'm off to Mexico shortly, so I must get used to smoking this type of tobacco.'

'They're rolled in real rice-paper,' I told him, but I noticed that he soon let his burn out tactfully in an ash tray on the bar.

'Mexico sounds exciting,' I said. 'To get copy for your work?' I was learning the language fast.

'A kind of travel book,' he said, the ice slid down the empty glasses and we were given the beer jugs, containing some sort of strong pale ale, to carry back across the Common.

'Not too heavy for you?' Greene asked anxiously as we halted midway to mop our faces in the noonday heat.

I said: 'It's childsplay compared to lugging one's dem-kit about.'

'Dem-kit?' Greene said, immediately alert at a technical expression he had not heard before.

'The suitcase containing the demonstration machine. It weighs a ton on its own.'

Greene said: 'One of your chaps who called at the house once carried the detachable parts of his cleaner in a golfbag. Rather enterprising of him I thought, and I suppose less heavy. I used it in a novel of mine.'

'England Made Me' I nodded, and the Queen Anne façade came in sight not a bit too soon. The housekeeper was in the hall and Greene handed her the jugs of beer with instructions to keep it cool, which didn't please her at all.

In the upstairs drawing room my advance copy of Brighton Rock was the first thing I caught sight of, which reminded me to thank him for having it sent to me.

'I brought along this review by Agate, though I expect you've already seen it,' I added, unconscious of the dreadful clanger I was dropping, for Agate compared the ending to that of Stevenson's *Ebb-Tide*, which I'd not then read but in which the villain's own vitriol explodes identically in his face.

Greene, however, merely asked: 'Do you know Agate's brother?'

'No. I don't know Agate himself either.'

'The brother's much less pompous. More amusing. He's rather ill at the moment though. In fact I've got to go and see how he is later on today.' He glanced at the review again and chuckled: 'The old boy of course has completely missed the point. It's the theological aspect that's baffled him, I've never brought it in before.'

'The Boy being a Catholic and so on?'

He nodded. 'Half of them won't understand and those who do will hate it.'

'Perhaps the Catholic critics,' I began, but he said with every evidence of delight: 'They'll probably be the worst of all.'

'You are yourself a Catholic?' I asked: it must be remembered that much less was known about the author personally in those days, and I'd been unable to obtain so far the semi-autobiographical *Journey Without Maps*, which would have answered my question.

Greene said: 'Yes, I was converted in 1926.'

I said: 'I was baptized one in 1912,' which disconcerted him more than the vacuum cleaners. I suppose a salesman with literary ambitions was strange enough, but a cradle Catholic literary salesman bordered on the extravagant.

'In that case,' Greene said recovering, 'you must have enjoyed the bit in *Brighton Rock* with Sylvie in the Lancia.'

'I haven't got to anyone called Sylvie yet.'

'Oh well, you've that to come. Spicer's girl you see gets a sudden lech on the Boy, and she wants him to have a fuck in the back of a car.'

He shot me a piercing gunmetal glance to see my reaction to his use of the word, which itself was shot out like a bullet from the barrel of Raven's automatic: presumably as a

Catholic I should have been shocked, but my face remained impassive.

'And does he fuck her?' I asked.

'No. You see when the girl asks him if he's got a French let . . .' but at that moment his wife entered the room to announce that lunch was ready.

About the meal itself I remember nothing, except that the dining room was rather dark; the blinds may have been drawn against the sun and it's possible that we had lemon pudding as a sweet. The housekeeper did not appear in person: heralded by shouts up a shaft, the dishes were borne from below by a dumb waiter and Greene himself went round pouring out the beer. Mrs Greene, handsome with black hair, was placid and sedate like a young Spanish matron, and even the repeated crash of the dumb waiter arriving at its destination in the serving hatch failed to shake her poise.

From time to time she left the table for brief periods. When she returned from each sortie her husband raised inquiring eyebrows and she nodded reassurance, but the last time she murmured something that I didn't catch; and when we rose from the table Greene said to me apologetically: 'It's an awful nuisance, but They are asking to see you I'm afraid. I wonder if you'd mind.'

'Why of course not,' I said mystified. 'I'd like to see Them very much.'

'I'm sorry but we'll get no peace otherwise,' he said, leading the way up  another, darker flight of stairs; I could hear a strange twittering sound coming from behind the door in front of which he halted.

'By the way,' I asked slightly nervous, 'What are They?' imagining giant parrots or pet vultures brought from Africa, or even elderly female relatives not quite certifiable but confined nevertheless to their rooms.

'They are in here,' Greene said, opening the door for me to precede him, and I found myself facing a large railed cot raised off the floor to about the level of my chest. From behind the bars of this cage two small, extremely pretty blonde children peered out at me unblinking. They were perhaps aged four and five, and it's a sobering thought that they must be over thirty now.

'Well, come on,' Greene said from behind me, 'Say hullo politely.'

He was addressing the children actually, but I managed a ghastly smile and a subdued Hullo. The children did not reply. Without speaking they continued to stare intently through their bars. Then to my surprise, and perhaps that of their father, they started slowly to grin, and the youngest gave a sort of gurgle.

'He looks nice Daddy,' the elder one called out encouragingly, thus haunting me for weeks with shame, for few young men in their middle twenties are sold on looking nice and I was no exception.

'That'll do,' their father said. He explained to me: 'They insist on seeing everyone who comes to the house before They'll settle down,' and to the children: 'Shut up now and have your sleep.'

They both called out Goodbye as we left and giggles pursued us downstairs to the drawing room where coffee and the rest of the beer awaited us on a tray: Mrs Greene had passed us on her way up to enforce Their afternoon rest.

'Lovely children,' I said, 'charming' in the hearty voice used by my father when he'd survived a social ordeal, and I was further relieved to see Greene had a brandy bottle in his hand.

He said: 'Who was it complained that not enough children get murdered in detective stories?' pouring me a large measure.

'A reviewer called Cyril Connolly,' I said. 'Thanks.'

'I expect you need it,' Greene said. 'There's that book of Philip MacDonald's of course, *Murder Gone Mad*, d'you know that one?'

'Plenty of kids get it there,' I agreed. 'A massacre of the innocents.'

Greene said: 'It was the old postmistress. With a swordstick disguised as an umbrella,' and over the coffee and brandy we discussed ruthlessness in the thriller, Greene's favourite example being from the initial *Four Just Men* by Edgar Wallace.

'D'you remember what they did to the Spanish priest who'd been guilty of Rape? When they condemned him to death he begged them to let him see a priest before the execution, and they showed him—a mirror!'

He had given full value to the capital 'R' in Rape and his eyes swivelled, glinting, towards me as when he'd told about Sylvie and the Boy. They had always an alert watchful quality, the eyeballs were slightly bloodshot, and one had a sense of tremendous energy and fun triumphing over inner fatigue.

I now had an opportunity to observe him more closely without staring, which I'd been brought up to believe was rude. He must have been thirty-four at the time, his lean face was unlined then, but the skin was rough and little worn: though his cheeks were carefully shaven there was still a suggestion of stubble. He smiled a lot and the set of his mouth was amiable rather than severe as in the photographs. His lightish brown hair was parted at the side and brushed in a slight curl over a broad bumpy forehead. He sat forward in the low armchair with broad shoulders hunched up high and large knuckly hands hanging down with a cigarette fuming between the long fingers. I had offered him another Brazilian which, saying he'd been smoking far too much, he swiftly refused, then had stealthily taken one of his own. I don't know how he did manage out in Mexico.

We had passed on now to ruthlessness in films, how Hitchcock got away with it often despite the censorship and how Greene himself had tried and failed to slip a ruthless scene past British Lion while scripting for Korda in 1936. From there we arrived at Paramount's prospective film version of *A Gun for Sale* and who was to play the part of Raven: if made with an American star, then Bogart, Alan Baxter, or Greene's own personal choice Eduardo Ciannelli, the Trock Estrella in *Winterset*, about which we were both enthusiastic.

'Ciannelli lends distinction to any film,' I said.

'He does indeed.'

'No, no. I was quoting your own words. From a film article in *Night and Day*.'

'Oh, so you've read *Night and Day*.'

'Every issue.'

*Night and Day* had been an excellent sophisticated weekly magazine on *New Yorker* lines, edited by Greene and John Marks the translator of Céline, and Greene had done the cinema criticism, which led to the magazine folding because some fool said that he'd libelled the child star Shirley Temple and there had been a case in court.

He said: 'I remember the article now. Wasn't it a review of *Marked Woman*, with Bogart and Bette Davis?' adding with relish: 'That was a pretty ruthless picture, where the henchman cuts the double-cross on Bette Davis's cheek.'

'Ciannelli was the Vice-Czar.'

'Lucky Luciano of course. 99 years in Sing-Sing.'

I said: 'You based your article on the resemblance between the city under gangster rule and the feudal system, Ciannelli being the latterday equivalent of the Robber Baron.'

'I believe I did. Bogart as the crusading DA made the comparison actually, it was in the dialogue.'

'But you see,' I said, 'it wasn't.'

We had finished the coffee and brandy and were now drinking up the remainder of the beer. It was, perhaps, not an awfully wise mixture and may have gone slightly to my head: the contradiction slipped out before I could bite it back.

'But surely,' Greene was saying, 'I remember perfectly. After one of his witnesses refused to talk, Bogart said: "It's feudal." '

'No. I'm sorry. He didn't say that.' It was too late to stop now, and I continued gently: 'I went to the film just after reading your article and I was waiting for him to say it. But what he really said was "It's *futel*." '

'Futel? But what does it mean?'

'It's how Americans pronounce "futile".'

Greene stared at me for a moment then began to shake with laughter. The fact that he had based a whole careful piece of social criticism on a single misapprehended word seemed to fill him with genuine glee. I was relieved that he took it like that: many a writer not so well equipped with a sense of humour would have thought I was trying to score off him, which was the last thing I had in mind.

Now he began to tell me about the Shirley Temple libel case, which he evidently found less hilarious than his error about the feudal system, but accepted all the same with ironical detachment. Apparently he'd been abroad and incommunicado at the time, and returned to find the proceedings all wrapped up and judgment given against him, together with the censure of the judge.

'Two libel suits one after the other,' he said. 'There was a case about my Liberian book *Journey Without Maps* too and Heinemann's had to withdraw the whole edition, so that seems to have been my unlucky year.'

'I've never been able to get *Journey Without Maps*,' I said after expressing my indignation: before this there had been the *Glastonbury Romance*/John Cowper Powys case and the *People in Cages*/Helen Ashton case, and as a prospective novelist I was naturally concerned. 'You don't happen to have a copy do you?' Greene began to shake his head. 'Just to borrow,' I added quickly. 'I wasn't asking you to give me one.'

'If I could of course I'd give you one,' he said. 'But honestly there's not a single copy in the house, they've all gone one way or another. I'm trying to get hold of the book myself.'

Frankly I didn't believe this, I believed that every author was well stocked up with copies of his own works; and it was not for many years, when I'd published several books myself, that I realized the fallacy of such an idea, more especially if the book in question has been officially withdrawn. But at the time I regretted having asked, and changed the subject swiftly to what I was really there for: namely the radio adaptation.

Greene said: 'Of course you'll have to clear it with Paramount, they bought the rights, including radio, before publication you see. That's just a formality though, they won't raise any objection. I'll drop the London office a line straight-away.'

'But first,' I said, 'there are some technical points, concerning the play itself, that I'd like to consult you about,' and he folded his fingers together to listen. Time and place, I explained, were easily conveyed by sound alone: Christmas carols being sung by the drunken reporters, newsboys shouting the threat of war and so on. 'But Raven's hare lip. The listeners can't see it, and characters would hardly comment on it to his face.'

Greene said: 'But they would behind his back. In the Corner House for instance, while he's waiting for Cholmondley to pay him for the murder. One waitress could say to another, "Ugh, he ain't arf an ugly bastard. That 'air lip of his makes me want to retch." '

'Excellent. Would "retch" be right for a girl of this sort, though?'

Greene said: ' "Makes me want to vomit"?'

'How about "fair turns me stomach up"?'

'That's it.'

I said: 'Then another problem. How does Raven find out Cholmondley's going to Nottwich? Hanging about the station like he does in the book is visual stuff, so it'll have to be put over some other way.'

Greene said: 'Cholmondley could drop his railway ticket. In the Corner House again, when he takes out his wallet. Then Raven would also know which station he's leaving from.'

I said: ' "Ought to be more careful dropping your ticket Mr Cholmondley. You don't want to pay the rail fare to Nottwich twice"?'

'Something like that, yes.'

These exchanges gave me an idea of the speed at which his trained mind worked: I would have taken days, perhaps weeks, to overcome such minor obstacles. Soon all the minor points had been thrashed out and we engaged in a discussion about the way in which Raven ought to speak.

'In the sort of voice some East End Jews have got,' was

24

Greene's opinion. 'Not exactly a lisp, not quite guttural, in between the two.'

'But Raven isn't Jewish.'

'No, but he'd have a voice like that. Lots of Londoners do.' He told me that, when he worked for Korda, he had been taken round various clubs in the King's Cross area by a cameraman with underworld connections, and it was there that he had heard voices of the type he meant.

'In one place the regulars only drank milk. It was owned by a great fat homosexual known as the Giant Pander,' he spelt it out for me and laughed at the pun, 'but the customers weren't queer. Very tough looking, razor scars and all that, but quiet. Very quiet. I asked if the milk was laced with brandy or anything, but they said no. Straight milk. Made it much more sinister, I thought.'

'Is that where you got the idea of the Boy not drinking?' I asked, in an attempt to manoeuvre him into talking of his own work, but he replied Perhaps, he hadn't really thought.

'D'you think you'll write any more Entertainments?' was my next question; for *Brighton Rock* was first published as one, as such despite the Catholic angle I considered it, and only much later did it become a Novel and later still a Modern Classic.

'I might,' Greene answered. 'Just one more. Based on an original idea I started to work on for Korda, only his outfit thought it would be too dangerous to film. About a Spanish Government agent who comes to London on a mission during the Civil War and finds that the war has followed him here.[1] I try to restrict myself to home ground if I can, English backgrounds, London whenever possible: I've always made that a rule.'

South America, Istanbul, Stockholm, the Gold Coast, and now Mexico went rapidly through my mind, I could hardly let this pass, but before I could speak Greene said: 'Oh I know, I've broken the rule several times. But all the same I think an English novelist should write about England, don't you?'

[1] Later published as *The Confidential Agent* 1939.

Presumably They had settled down at last upstairs, for Mrs Greene came in to join us, though not in the conversation. She sat in the armchair facing her husband, but turned sideways to him, with her legs tucked under her. She busied herself with head bent over some piece of needlework: embroidery, brocade, it may have been but not, I think, knitting.

I remember her speaking twice only: once was when we were talking about American short story writers and Greene said: 'You liked Saroyan, didn't you darling?'

She looked puzzled and said: 'Saroyan?'

'You know, the Armenian.'

'Oh yes,' she said. 'The one who isn't Michael Arlen.'

The second time she spoke was to remind her husband that the time was half-past four. Greene glanced at his watch and sprang up with an exclamation. I rose also, saying: 'James Agate's brother?'

'Yes. I'll walk you to your bus.'

On the way up the High Street, past twopenny libraries and plate glass shops, he told me several anecdotes about the brother, but I remember none of them. The brandy, the beer and the heat had hit me as we left the house and I was struggling with a question in my muddled head. Would it be an imposition if I asked Greene to look at the short stories which I'd written?

There he stood, sympathetic and friendly, stooping slightly at my side, a soft wide brimmed dented hat, like those worn by newspapermen in the movies, tilted to the back of his head. To neglect such an opportunity, of obtaining the opinion of a man whose work I so much admired, would be simply foolish and in a rather muzzy voice, as we waited by the bus stop, I made my halting request.

'Of course, I'd be glad to read them,' Greene said. 'Only difficulty, I'm going abroad tomorrow.'

'Mexico?'

'No, an assignment for *The Times*. But if you're not in a terrible hurry, you could send them on the day before I get back,' he gave me the date when he expected to return, 'and

26

I'll let you know very quickly what I think.' My bus was approaching and I signalled it to stop. 'Good luck with the housewives meantime,' he called out as I climbed aboard.

'Prospects is what we cleaner-salesmen call them,' I told him. On the top deck I fell asleep and was woken by the conductor way past the stop; then in the train going back to the small South Coast town not far from Brighton itself, I realized I'd forgotten to ask Greene to sign my copy of *Brighton Rock*, which was the reason why I'd brought it with me.

The prospects kept me fully occupied during the following week, a love affair that had never properly begun was coming to an end, and on the day it ended I received a letter from the BBC expressing interest in my proposed version of *A Gun for Sale*: by the same post came a contract from Paramount Pictures several unpunctuated pages long which, deciphered, allowed me to retain any fees from the radio play in return for their right to use in the film anything they fancied from my adaptation.[1] I signed this contract and posted it back with the uneasy feeling that, not having read all the small print, I might somehow have signed away my soul: at the same time the MSS of my stories went registered to Greene at Clapham Common.

A reply came very quickly, as indeed he'd promised. With eagerness I tore open the small grey distinctive envelope, but realized from the first line and a glance at the signature that the letter was not from Greene at all, but from his wife. An extraordinary similarity in the handwriting, due perhaps to the fact that they were cousins, had misled me.

Her husband had returned the night before, Mrs Greene wrote, extremely over-tired by his trip, and she felt it her duty to prevent him from becoming completely exhausted by taking on more than was necessary. She was sure that he would have liked to read my stories but she was also sure that

---

[1] The Paramount film version, re-titled *This Gun for Hire*, scripted by W. R. Burnett and set in America, starring Alan Ladd as Raven, Veronica Lake and Laird Cregar, was shown over here in 1942 and contained nothing from my adaptation.

I would understand why this would not be possible. She was therefore returning the MSS under separate cover, and signed herself Sincerely Vivien Greene.

I still have the letter somewhere.

# Up the BBC and Down the Labour

Moray McLaren, then Assistant Director of Drama at the BBC, wore a flowing Lavallière cravat and grey hair flowed back from his brow into a mane at the back like a musician or concert pianist. He was stockily built and sat squarely above his desk as if he'd been built out of it as an extension of the wood.

I faced him from a chair set slightly lower than the desk, as is customary in the monastic cells of BBC executives. This was my second interview with Moray McLaren, the previous one being some months before when he'd talked about a job they might have for me in the future.

'Graham Greene's novel *A Gun for Sale*,' he was saying, 'is concerned with the possibility of war, almost brought about by unscrupulous armament manufacturers for purposes of profit, but averted just in time.'

'I know,' I said. I'd just adapted the novel for radio, and the typescript lay before him on the desk.

'The book is fiction,' Moray McLaren told me, 'but the international situation in sober fact is extremely precarious at the moment.'

I knew that too, but didn't want to interrupt him again. He continued: 'Not quite the best time to broadcast a play on this subject, perhaps,' and smiled benevolently.

I said: 'Does that mean you're going to turn it down?'

He answered mildly: 'Turn it down? Oh dear me, we haven't got to that stage yet. No decision at all has been reached so far, you only sent it in a week ago. These things have to go through a lot of channels, various opinions must be obtained and so on, first.'

'But you personally have read the script?'

'I have glanced through it, seems to be a very competent adaptation, but of course it must go to the Readers for their report, then Val Gielgud the Director of Drama will want to see it if the reports are favourable,' another benevolent smile, 'and if the international situation permits of a production, why then we'll be able to decide.'

'But all this will take time?'

'Quite a bit of time, I'm afraid. It's August you know. The summer holidays. The Readers, some of them are away.'

He smiled: 'You're very lucky, yourself, living at the seaside all the year round, you don't have to take a holiday.'

'No,' I said. 'I can't afford to, either.'

'But you still have a job?'

'If you can call it that.'

'Jobs,' Moray McLaren said. 'Just what I wanted to talk to you about. Have you thought any more about the one I mentioned to you last time you came? Training to be a writer-producer for radio, you know.'

'Yes,' I said. 'I've thought about it quite a lot. Are there any vacancies?'

'Alas no, rather a long waiting list just now, but I take it you'd be willing to accept if a vacancy occurred?'

'Yes.'

'Good!' he exclaimed beaming, and made a note on his desk pad. 'Now we have all your particulars, but there's just one question I didn't go into last time you were here. The question of marriage.'

'Marriage?' I said perplexed.

'Yes, I forgot to ask if you were married.'

'I am married.'

'And,' he coughed delicately, 'do you live with your wife?'

'I don't quite see what,' I began, but he soothingly interrupted: 'I'm sorry, I have to ask these questions, it's vital to know the answers I'm afraid.'

I said: 'Very well. I don't live with my wife.'

He said: 'Separated or divorced?'

I said: 'Separated. By mutual consent.'

He said: 'D'you think a reconciliation is likely?'

I said: 'No I don't,' and Moray McLaren made another note.

'And are you going to divorce?' he asked.

'I hadn't thought about it. Why?'

'Well you see, divorces are allowed in the Corporation if they're discreet, but a really resounding one, well Sir John wouldn't care for that at all.'

'Sir John.'

'The Director-General.'

'I'll bear that in mind then,' I said. 'Not too resounding a divorce, otherwise to have one is all right?'

'Perfectly,' he smiled, we stood up to shake hands and the difference in our heights was rectified.

'As for this adaptation,' he added, 'I fear its fate is as much in Mr Hitler's hands as ours,' and I travelled back by train to the small seaside town where I was so lucky to live, and where I was greeted on the station platform by my vacuum cleaner supervisor with news of the impending sack.

'Almighty Christ old man where you been all day. Up the BBC? Jesus you'll be down the Labour soon, you're getting your cards.'

'Who says?'

'New Branch Manager, that's who,' Soapy the supervisor said. 'He's been over after your blood, that woman at Arundel put the squeak in and you're for the bleeding jump.'

'The woman we sold the secondhand cleaner to?' Flogging secondhand machines to prospects as a sideline is accounted an unforgivable sin in the cleaner world: as Soapy was well aware, which was why he'd been careful to use me as a front.

'The Arundel woman was your idea,' I said. 'You took half the cash, why aren't you for the jump yourself?'

'Have a heart old man, you don't expect me to take the can back, christ I got a wife and kids.'

'You'd flog them too if they'd fetch enough for a couple of pints,' I told him, buying a copy of the local rag at the station bookstall which was just about to close, and over a brandy in the buffet looked down the Salesmen Wanted.

Refrigerators and floor polishers (too heavy to hawk around unless you had a car); clothes-on-credit (distributing leaflets at

31

ten bob a week: a cheap advertising stunt for a newly-opened store); canvassing for a national newspaper (commission only, though it said £3); then water softeners and that was all. I didn't fancy softeners: you had to go round asking housewives 'How's your water?' and I hadn't the nerve for that.

I'd not offered Soapy a drink, though he had hung around in hopes, but I bought a baby Guinness for the old London-Irish porter who'd served in several regiments and four campaigns and could remember when my father was still alive. This didn't require a tremendous effort since my father, a man not readily forgotten for his physical size alone, had died only two years before; but the porter could also remember having hydrocele as a young recruit: an experience which he was not at all unwilling to recount.

One morning at reveille he'd gone to get out of his bunk and had straightaway fallen flat upon the floor: the weight of serous fluid on his testicles would not allow him to stand upright.

'Matter o'gravity,' he said wiping brown froth from his Old Bill moustache. 'Pulls you down, upsets the balance d'you see, all that water on your balls, it has to be let out,' and he went on with relish to describe the operation they'd performed on him: 'But it didn't stop me having kids, they got to take the leader out for that,' which brought Hitler back to mind and he ended up by saying: 'Ah well, way things are going, you'll be in the army soon yourself, I've no doubt.'

Next morning, as Soapy had predicted, I was down the Labour Exchange with my cards, which had duly arrived with a curt letter of dismissal from the Brighton Branch. I hadn't enough stamps to draw the dole, so filled up an Unemployment Assistance form and sat down to await the arrival of the Means-Test Man, who took his time in coming.

The Means-Test Man looked round the ground floor back bedsitting room to which I'd shifted, wrote down 'Rent: ten shillings,' then asked: 'Any private income?' I said 'None'; he wrote down 'Now destitute,' then said: 'Sign here, you'll be hearing in due course,' and three weeks went by without a thing.

Meanwhile Munich came, and it began to look as if the Irish porter had been right about me going in the army. Sandbagging, ARP practice and gas practice with box-like respirators were going on all round; recruiting posters pointed an accusing finger: 'YOUR COUNTRY EXPECTS YOU' and suddenly it was all too much like *A Gun for Sale* to be entirely comfortable.

I'd naturally given up all hope of the adaptation being accepted: September 1938 was certainly no time to broadcast a play about a war engineered by unscrupulous armament manufacturers for purposes of etcetera.

And yet the war, as in Greene's book, was averted just in time (for another year at any rate) and on the Friday following Chamberlain's return I was summoned to the Labour, outside which a chap in the dole queue had fallen in a faint from hunger; and the Head Clerk wearing bi-focals, a butterfly collar and grey Homburg hat counted silver coins on the counter in front of me, flinging them down contemptuously as if paying off Judas: except that instead of thirty pieces I got only seventeen.

The man who'd fainted had been propped by his mates against the kerb; on the wall above was painted: 'DO NOT LOITER IN THE STREET TO THE ANNOYANCE OF THE RESIDENTS,' and the queue stretched halfway down, shouting advice to the group around the fallen man while the Head Clerk from inside was bawling: 'Silence out there, please!' The man bled quietly by the kerb.

To cap it all, it was Armistice Day and pretty smiling girls sold poppies by the cenotaph where a service was being held and a robed clergyman spoke of Peace: 'The crisis is over,' but for me it was just beginning, and at the doorway of the digs my landlady waited, hand out for the rent.

Like the Head Clerk at the Labour, the landlady wore even in the house a hat pulled down to her eyes, but hers was of greenish felt. She always wore an old stained black dress and

33

carpet slippers, even when she went outdoors which wasn't often. Mostly she crouched over a gas ring in her back kitchen cooking kippers, the whole house was permeated with their smell; and by dint of eating this fish all day long, her dark leathery skin had begun to take on the smoked complexion of a kipper.

For me no food was provided, there were no facilities for cooking in the room, and she didn't even make the bed. I came to dislike this landlady more than any I've had since, which is saying a great deal.

I did not find hunger a good discipline as Ernest Hemingway, then my great hero, did according to his posthumous memoir of early life in Paris; moreover ten Tenners[1] a day, which were the most I could afford, seemed an inadequate cigarette ration for a man who as a rule smoked fifty normal size.

Nevertheless I wrote a short story which comprised the landlady, the Head Clerk, the Means Test and the man who'd fainted in the dole queue on Armistice Day; I called this *Peace in Our Time* which I considered a nice ironic touch.

Editors didn't agree: the typescript came back quicker than any I'd ever sent out, and in fact it was never printed anywhere until I included it in my second collection of stories by which time (1945) it was deemed, no doubt rightly, as dated or old hat. Meantime, having kept fine as usual for the crisis, it poured down outside with rain.

Returning home one really dark cold wet November day, having spent the afternoon in the public library which was warmer than my room, I stepped on two letters evidently delivered by the last post and still lying on the mat, both of them for me.

One envelope had 'British Broadcasting Corporation' printed in the left-hand corner, and tearing it open I read unbelievingly: '*Gun for Sale*, pleasure in accepting, proposed fee 30 guineas, Moray McLaren'; in the hall looking-glass, beside the seaweed barometer, I could see steam rising from

[1] A small extremely cheap cigarette, then much in favour with the unemployed.

34

the sudden heat that rushed up into my rain soaked scalp.

The second envelope, addressed in the handwriting of my mother, then still alive but hard-up herself and unable to help me much, crackled to the touch: despite everything she'd enclosed £2 in cash for me to buy some shoes.

Those that I had on squelched with the water they'd absorbed through holes as, cramming both letters into my overcoat pocket, I returned at top speed to the high-street where at that time a fairly good pair could be bought for eight-and-six. Then, well shod once more, with new dry socks, carrying parcels full of food and cigarettes, I made for the level crossing near which a friend of mine called Jaeger had his flat.

C. K. Jaeger was the same age as myself and also wrote, but unlike me he'd actually had two stories published in *The Standard* and worked on the scripts of feature films, but this was all some years ago and now he too was on the dole.

That evening I arrived just as he was hurling downstairs the son of his landlord who had called for the overdue rent and been rather unwisely rude to Jaeger's wife. The falling body knocked one of the food parcels from my hand, and retrieving it I climbed towards the first floor where Jaeger, tall and rangy in kilt and sporran, leaned by the landing rail.

'I am not a man of violence but that insolent git made me see red,' he said as the landlord's son stumbled away into the rain. 'I'm seriously thinking of giving these people notice, damned if I'm not.'

He'd been educated in Edinburgh and looked every inch a Scottish laird, although actually of Danish origin and born in Bradford. A picture of the Angel Gabriel, dressed also as a Scot and about to blow the bagpipes instead of his horn, hung above the chimney-piece in the living room, where an enormous fire blazed and Jaeger's wife stood clutching a scarlet screaming baby who in the sixties became secretary to a BBC-TV script editor.

I gave my news; Jaeger at once produced a flagon of the horrid patent wine which for financial reasons he was forced to drink; the fags were proffered, the food was eaten, the baby bedded down for the night; then Jaeger said: 'You know, Julian, Lydia and I were thinking of moving to a bungalow up the other end, I don't really think we ought to stay here after that fellow's atrocious behaviour tonight. Why don't you kick-in and share with us?' and when I agreed enthusiastically to this plan: 'Splendid, that's all settled then. Now let's have a butcher's at that BBC letter, see when you can expect the cheque.'

'Thirty guineas,' I said tendering the letter which in my excitement at its arrival I'd had no time to read myself, except in snatches.

Jaeger said: 'On acceptance, according to Jonah Barrington. But shouldn't it be *fifty* guineas for a play this length? Is that not the sum Jonah Barrington mentioned in his column?'

Jonah Barrington was radio correspondent for the *Daily Express*, and any statement made by an *Express* contributor was believed implicitly by Jaeger, who refused to talk to anyone in the morning until he'd finished reading William Hickey. Jonah Barrington had indeed quoted 50 guineas as the sum paid for a full length radio play by the BBC, and in consequence a page from a radio play in progress protruded from Jaeger's portable typewriter on a side table.

'There's Graham Greene's share to be deducted in this case, though,' I said.

'Oh of course, it says so here.' Then Jaeger, frowning down at the letter, said: 'Hold on a bit. You get 30 all right, but *payable in two halves*: 15 when you sign the contract, 15 on production. There's no contract enclosed and it doesn't say when production's going to be,' and stroking with a thin smile his small golden moustache, he added: 'You've not forgotten Mr Kilham Roberts?'

I said: 'My God you don't suppose?' and Lydia Jaeger, entering from the nursery, cried out: 'Oh not all that again!'

The name of Denys Kilham Roberts, MA, Barrister-at-Law and Secretary of the Society of Authors, was engraved indeed on all our hearts. At that time he edited a paper-back miscellany, the very first to appear, called *Penguin Parade*, to which I'd submitted a story that had been, to everyone's astonishment including mine, accepted for a future issue.

A fee of £4 was proposed by the editor and, nugatory though it seems today, would have made all the difference then, since I'd just recovered from a nasty go of 'flu and had a doctor's bill to pay as well as rent.

I asked if the cheque could be sent off by return: in reply came a letter from Mr Kilham Roberts' secretary saying that payment was not made on acceptance; on publication then, I queried hopefully, but the secretary answered that they did not precisely pay on publication either.

I wrote asking for a definite date on which I could expect to receive the money, and received instead the typescript of my story back, with a note regretting that I was not prepared to abide by *Penguin Parade's* rule regarding payment (they still did not say what this consisted of).

I was incensed, believing with Mr Edmund Wilson that 'a piece of writing should be paid for on the nail . . . and once accepted, should be printed,' though I had not then read the eminent critic's admirable *Literary Worker's Polonius*, in which this precept is cited as one of the duties of Editor to Contributor.

No reply was forthcoming to my enquiry as to whether Mr Kilham Roberts in his rôle as Secretary to the Society of Authors would approve of his alter ego's editorial procedure, and I passed the correspondence to a local solicitor for legal action. The solicitor wrote one letter on my behalf, received a short answer stating simply that Mr Kilham Roberts was a qualified barrister, and dropped the case in terror and confusion.

My mother, though herself sick and in need of cash, paid both doctor and solicitor, I was back where I started with no story published, and Denys Kilham Roberts has since been awarded the OBE.

That was the *Penguin Parade* story, with which both the Jaegers were abundantly familiar; but despite this experience

I'd yet to learn the snags surrounding payment of any literary fee, and payment in full most particularly.

We examined the relevant clipping from Jonah Barrington's column: payment on acceptance, yes, but there was nothing said about it being in two halves. Jaeger advised me not to argue the toss: 'Better write asking for the contract straightaway, only go canny, you don't want this lot sending back the bloody script as well,' and write off I did that very night.

As a matter of fact our fears in this case were unjustified: having signed the contract I did receive a cheque for half the fee, though after a certain time since cheques are prepared by accountants who are busy men. It's true that nowadays machines do most of the work, but they cannot affix signatures as well: this involves human agency, and I've known the business directors of a well-known literary weekly take longer to sign a cheque than I took to write the entire article for which they were paying.

But this 15 guineas from the BBC was the first money I'd ever earned by writing, my pride and pleasure in it mitigated only by not receiving the lot at one go. Moreover, regarding the date of production Moray McLaren simply couldn't say: with this particular subject great care had still to be exercised in choosing a suitable date for the broadcast, but no doubt this would be within the year.

I moved into the Jaeger's new bungalow at the other end of town, bidding goodbye without regret to the smell of kippers and the green hatted landlady: nonetheless, in a roundabout way she was responsible for my meeting a most intriguing character, G. S. Marlowe.

In the mid-Thirties G. S. Marlowe had published a remarkable first novel called I am Your Brother. This has been out of print for many years, copies of it now fetching £2 or more apiece among book collectors, but at the time it had not only a critical success but got into the best seller lists as well: very surprisingly, for Marlowe's staccato cinematic style was in direct contrast to that used by most bestsellers of the day. Also, since by the very nature of the story delusions were often fused with reality and vaudeville humour with scenes of Gothic nightmare, it was not always easy to tell what the novel was about or how many of the incidents happened outside the mind of the protagonist.

It was the physical appearance of my former landlady which reminded me of this work, for she strongly resembles the repulsive mother of the schizophrenic young composer, shuffling and snuffling about the Soho markets in search of offal on which to nourish her other, perhaps imaginary son: a monster product of maybe artificial insemination, who lived in an attic above his brother's studio and had to be fed raw liver and fairy stories once a day.

Having re-read *I am Your Brother*, I was struck by what a sensational radio play it would make: the episodic structure of short sections, cross-fading as it were one the other, seemed already designed for the sound medium, and I wrote asking the author's permission to adapt. Besides, even in those days 15 guineas did not last for ever, and after the acceptance of *A Gun for Sale* I imagined a career as a radio writer was opening up before me, and for a brief period it did: but in 1958, not '38.

Gabriel Marlowe, as he signed himself, replied promptly. A long friendly letter full of pertinent suggestions—a dynamo fading up, for example, to convey to the listener when the hero's delusions were about to overtake him—and concluding with an invitation to call on him in London.

Marlowe's flat was in Kensington, a brisk goodlooking girl whom he introduced as his secretary poured us glasses of Scotch, heavy curtains shut out the dark rainy residential street, and the central heating was very comforting after the cold outside.

I had formed from reading Marlowe's work a mental picture of him as a short thin waspish man of middle-age, dark and slightly sinister perhaps, certainly sardonic: also it had not occurred to me that he would be anything but English. The off-beat quality of his books arose from an extremely individual attitude to life, rather than any foreign turn of phrase.

But Marlowe was definitely not English, and the exact

opposite of what I'd imagined him to be like. He was not short, indeed when he stood up to greet me he seemed to fill the room, which was his study and admittedly not large. Marlowe however was very large. Nordic looking, in his middle thirties, amiable, ambling, almost ursine in appearance. Like a big gentle blond bear and he wore a light brown shaggy suit that fostered the resemblance. His eyes smiled short-sightedly behind shell-rimmed spectacles, his English was fluent, his voice soft and his accent heavy.

I never did find out where he came from. He could have been Scandinavian but somewhere round the Danube Basin was more likely, and I've heard all sorts of origin attributed to him including Viennese. Despite his amiability there *was* something mysterious about him after all. Not sinister, as I'd expected: just mysterious. He really was a man of mystery.

The study being lit only by a desk lamp accentuated this ambiguous aura, its visible expression the lamplight halo behind his big blond smiling face as he told me about his career in Hollywood where he'd written the script for the Freddie Bartholomew version of *David Copperfield*. There was no trace of American in his accent.

'Dickens,' he said, 'anticipated with his style the cinema. For example, *Bleak House*. The beginning, in the fog. There is no need to write a script, also *Edwin Drood*,' and one could see of course the Dickensian element in his own characters: the pawnbrokers, tailors, pavement artists and music hall performers, revealed through their own elliptical speech.

Marlowe told me about his meeting with Greta Garbo then, crossing the Atlantic abruptly, how *I am Your Brother* had originated as a bedtime story which he used to tell in nightly instalments to the children of Sir Roderick and Lady Jones while staying as a guest at their country house. I wouldn't have said the subject was all that suitable for children myself, but presumably Lady Jones didn't disapprove, since it was she who encouraged him to write the novel, which was dedicated to her under her maiden name of Enid Bagnold

Marlowe spoke warmly of *National Velvet*, the secretary

came in to refill our glasses, and he cocked his head to listen, with one finger uplifted as one of his own chararcters might have done, to the rain dripping on the bushes outside the window.

He quoted: ' "Such dank gardens cry aloud for a murder." Do you know this? Stevenson. Cry Aloud For A Murder, a wonderful title. But it's better in the suburbs. They have there laurel bushes and in the houses behind the bushes live murderers. Respectable little people, but with passions also. For love and for money. Like Crippen, Seddon, wonderful fellows. And all the time on the laurel bushes drips the rain.'

He slid open a drawer of his desk: 'I have written here about murder in the London suburbs,' taking out four typescripts clipped into manilla folders: 'Four novelettes to make a volume. But they will not be printed yet. My publishers say after the next novel only, otherwise they will not make money.'

His third book, *Their Little Lives*, had been a volume of stories and had not made money. *I am Your Brother* made money, his second novel about the pavement artist did not make so much, now the publishers were becoming cautious so the new suburban stories would have to wait. None of them was called *Cry Aloud For A Murder*, though I recall distinctly only one title, *Dead Man's Money*: perhaps the Stevenson quotation provided the overall title for the four. These were never published: later, when Marlowe disappeared, the stories apparently vanished with him. At all events neither his publishers nor his agents seemed to know what had become of them.

'Did you ever know a murderer?' Marlowe asked me sliding the stories back into the drawer.

Yes, I told him, I had known a murderer though not well. A Russian con-man in the South of France who loved to dress up in uniform and pass himself off as a naval officer, who shot the woman who kept him six times through her bedroom door: imagining, as it proved erroneously, that she'd been unfaithful. He had escaped the guillotine and been sent instead to Devil's Island, since the murder was in a sense a crime passionel, though in my opinion he should have been certified insane.

'You will write about him one day,' Marlowe said; then asked, while the glasses were refilled once more, what I was writing now. He had clearly, on the evidence of his books, endured extreme poverty himself in early days, and showed great sympathy for my present plight, offering not only to read my stories but also to effect an introduction to Sir Hugh Walpole, whom he said would be able to help.

'We will arrange a little dinner party,' adding quickly: 'Informal,' a typical example of his tact, for he guessed quite rightly that I would have no evening clothes. Another example was shown when the secretary brought in my teddy bear coat from the airing cupboard where it had been put to dry. Marlowe helped me on with it himself and as he did so stroked the material admiringly: 'A magnificent coat. How I wish I had a coat like this myself,' thus sending me out into the cold and rain with the illusion that I owned one enviable possession at least.

This teddy bear coat at first caused much amusement among the other unemployed when I wore it to sign-on down the Labour, but then I became a sort of dole queue hero, having one day told the bullying Head Clerk to remove his hat while addressing me, since a notice on the wall said that the officials of the Exchange were but the servants of the public, and we were undoubtedly the public.

After this no one laughed even when I appeared in the teddy bear coat plus Wellington boots, because the continuous rain had caused floods up our end: at one time so bad that fishermen hired out boats for residents to do their shopping in.

The floods soon froze into sheets of solid ice as the full force of December struck, there was talk of skating and winter sport, but Jaeger had obtained a shedful of coal on credit and big fires crackled loudly in the grate by which I crouched to do my adaptation of *I am Your Brother*.

Jaeger too had fallen under the spell of this strange book; it

J. Maclaren-Ross's handwriting
Notes and rough draft of contents for *Memoirs of the Forties*

## MEMOIRS OF THE FORTIES

### PROLOGUE IN MUNICH YEAR

1. ✱ My First Publishers
2. ✱ Excursions in Greene Land (?)
3. ✱ Up the BBC and Down the Labour

### THE FORTIES

1. ✱ A Story in Horizon (1940)
2. ✱ They Cant Give You a Baby
3. ✱ The Double Death of William Cooper Makins
   In Hospital with Rayner Heppenstall
4. ✱ Calder-Marshall and the Reverend Todd
5. ✱ The Polestar Neighbour
6. But and Ben with Burke and Hare
   ✱ Tambimuttu and the Progress of Poetry London
   Kitty of Bloomsbury
7. ✱ Fitzrovian Nights
11. Rude Men of the Café Royal
12. Nina Hamnett in Howland Street
13. Some Quick, Some Dead (Poets & Painters) ✱
14. Subra's Bookshop and Others
15. The Days of the Doodle-Bug
16. A Few Wartime Editors
17. Under the Cape Colophon
18. The Misadventures of a MS
19. My Second Publishers
20. ✱ The Metamorphoses of Peter Brooke
21. Encounters in Thurloe Place
22. John Lehmann at Home
23. Cyril Connolly Continued
24. Enter Alun Owen
25. Humphrey Slater and the Enormous Ham
26. Anthony Powell Plays Happy Families

## CONTENTS (cont.)

27. * Topolski and Picasso

28. Roy Campbell at the BBC

29. Alfred Hitchcock : A Voice on the Phone

30. Vignettes :
    Beverly Nichols,
    ( Eric Ambler, Henry Green, Gerald Hamilton,
    Alan
    Pryce-Jones, Joyce Cary AND A COUPLE OF KINGS =
    R-T. Campbell
    Geoffrey de Montalk and John Gawsworth )

31. Excursions in Greene Land (2)

32. Brian Howard at the Mandrake Club

33. The Last Summer in Soho (1949)

## EPILOGUE IN 1964

J. Maclaren-Ross
9-10-64

Dorothy Shirley     (apropos
                      BEYHON
+                      FILMS)
TRIBUNE competition,
Orwell sending back
mine, saying it almost got the prize etc.

Picasso said once that he who creates a thing is
forced to make it ugly. In the effort to create the
intensity and the struggle to create this intensity,
the result always produces a certain ugliness,
those who follow can make of this thing a
beautiful thing because they know what
they are doing, the thing having already
been invented, but the inventor because he
does not know what he is going to invent
inevitably the thing he makes must have
its ugliness.

                                    Directly
                                    Below this
                          On the other hand, the
                          writer should allow the editor
                          a reasonable length of time
                          in which to decide and
                                          should not
                                          pester him
                                          with

from                                   letters & telephone
Edmund                                 calls till a
Wilson                                 maximum of, say,
The Literary Worker's                  two weeks has
      Polonius         Picasso         elapsed.
June 1935. (G.B)       Picasso         (under "Duties
Shores of Light 1952.  Graham Greene    of the Writer
                                        to the Editor."
                       J. maclaren Ross
                                       RE
Duties of the Editor                   COMMISSIONING
Done
      to the Contributor.

A piece of writing should       "... any editor with a
be paid for on the nail         primary grasp of
(if the finances of the         the duties of his
paper permit it); and           position will
once accepted, should be printed.   school himself
                                    never to leave
"... it must be asserted, as a      any doubt as to
general thing that the              whether or not
writer has just cause for           an article is
complaint when an editor            ordered and to
accepts his manuscript              stick by his
& then suppresses it by             engagement,
leaving it in the "barrel".         once it has
                                    been made.
(More especially, if he             If the manuscript
hasn't been paid on the   re   turns out too badly, he
nail or otherwise         Connolly
                          &
                          film- is not absolutely bound to print
                          article  it; but he is certainly bound to
                          #        pay for it and to give it back
                                   to the writer, so that the latter may
                                   have a chance of publishing
                                                  it elsewhere."

strongly influenced his own first novel, *Angels on Horseback,* on which he was then engaged and which Routledge published in the winter of 1940. (A possession certainly envied was my copy of Marlowe's second novel *Pictures on the Pavement,* which he had inscribed and autographed for me in his enormous handwriting.)

Marlowe had also reported favourably on my stories and finally fixed the date for the Walpole dinner party, then came a last minute telegram: Sir Hugh fallen sick; when he recovered it was to go for a spell abroad, so in fact we never met. Meanwhile Marlowe, who seemed to know everyone, promised he would get Arthur Bliss to compose the music for the radio play of *I am Your Brother,* which was now finished and awaiting decision at the BBC.

'We must be careful though with Bliss,' Marlowe told me. 'Or it will be music by Arthur Bliss, conducted by Arthur Bliss, script from a novel by Arthur Bliss, with Bliss also producing. He will take over everything including the rôle of the Brother if we don't watch out,' but as it turned out Arthur Bliss didn't even do the music, because the BBC decided not to broadcast *I am Your Brother* after all.

Val Gielgud, with whom the script had ended up, wrote me a letter saying that such a play would overstrain the resources of the Corporation, requiring not only a composer specially commissioned but the whole of the BBC symphony orchestra and chorus as well, besides being of unusual length and needing an enormous cast: the only way to produce it would be in serial form and this would not be possible either as the story was not suitable for a family audience (which didn't, apparently, include the children of Enid Bagnold). Gielgud hoped however that I would send to him personally any further radio plays of mine.

I continued notwithstanding to visit Gabriel Marlowe, who moved later on to a much bigger, very modern flat near Chelsea Barracks, in a new red brick block rather resembling a barrack itself. Here, on an afternoon in Spring, I found him living in an Edgar Wallace-like opulence, surrounded by dictaphones, telephones and typewriters, with a brand new secretary even better looking than the last. Sunlight streamed in through the long window stretching across one wall, under which he sat in shirtsleeves at a huge desk covered with sheets of foolscap scrawled upon in his outsize script.

'Working overtime,' he told me. 'A play. Four acts, two complete but the other two,' he flung his arms wide: 'Confusion! I am going abroad next week, somewhere peaceful to finish this.'

'Where d'you think of going?'

Marlowe shrugged: 'It's not so easy now, with half Europe in the hands of Hitler, and I don't want to fall into them also because you see I'm Jewish. But I think I've found a place where the Nazis won't invade,' and at that moment the new secretary entered to announce that the laundry was at the door.

'Excellent,' Marlowe cried. 'Just in time, I am in great need of clean shirts, also socks. Compliment the laundry-man please on his so opportune arrival.'

'He says he won't leave the laundry, not until the bill is paid.'

'Bill paid? Ridiculous, tell him I will pay later at the shop.'

'He wants the money now.'

Marlowe sighed, fumbling among his papers until a wallet came to light, then from it extracted a one pound note which he extended with the weary gesture of one who meets, to keep the peace, some outrageous and extortionate demand.

But the secretary didn't take the note. 'He wants more than that,' she said. 'Or he'll take the laundry back.'

'This is despair,' Marlowe said throwing up his hands. 'I will go myself to reason with the man.'

He got up and ambled into the passage, voices were raised in argument outside, then the front door banged and Marlowe returned clasping to his chest a single shirt in a cellophane envelope.

'Only one. That's all that he would give. And no socks though I let him have the pound. The rest only when the bill is paid in full. Julian do you have such business with your shirts?'

I'd always taken it for granted that Marlowe was at least well off, and this scene had surprised me more than the news that he was Jewish, already astonishing in a man of such Nordic appearance; but I said: 'Where I live it's like this all the time.'

'Then how expect us to do our work?' Marlowe said chucking the shirt down among the foolscap sheets from which the secretary promptly snatched it up. 'How can a play be finished in such conditions. God be thanked, next week I'll be away from it all.'

I asked him again which country he had chosen for his temporary refuge.

'Norway,' he replied.

This was the Spring of 1940, and naturally the last I saw of Gabriel Marlowe.

The place where the Nazis wouldn't invade was invaded, and Marlowe who had meant on returning to join the British Army never returned, never published another book, was in due course written off as dead by all including his executors.

Yet was he dead? For a few years ago I was drinking champagne cider with a man who'd known Marlowe before the war, and claimed to have met him recently, alive and well, in some village the name of which I can't remember. This man had no idea he was supposed to have been lost in Norway, so asked no searching questions, and in the village inn they had together sunk a pint. Thus Marlowe contrived to enshroud himself in mystery right up to the end, if indeed it was his end.

But back to 1938 and the BBC.

Besides I am Your Brother, I adapted that winter yet another radio play, about a crooked astrologer, from a story by Anthony Skene[1] called The Predicted Murder. I re-titled this The Stars Foretell and despatched it to Val Gielgud personally,

[1] My meeting with this writer will be described elsewhere, and does not belong properly to these Memoirs.

in accordance with his wish, but a secretary informed me that the Director of Drama was by this time in the USA and no decision could be reached until his return: date as yet unknown.

1938 became 1939 with still no news and creditors battering on the bungalow door, then a big BBC envelope arrived, containing a new typescript of *A Gun for Sale,* revised and lavishly cut by a young woman in the Script Department whose name I have forgotten. In her accompanying letter she hoped I would approve as she had, in her own words, 'tightened-up' the play considerably (as if it were some kind of scrotum), adding that the main thing was that Graham Greene himself had approved her version.

I replied sharply that my own approval didn't seem to matter all that much, and that to me the main thing was prompt production, since I urgently needed the remainder of the fee.

Moray McLaren then took over, explaining that the cutting and revision had taken some time, consequently the play had got behind in their schedules, already stocked with plays awaiting production, and no date for *A Gun for Sale* could be envisaged yet awhile.

Shortly afterwards Jonah Barrington wrote in his column that the BBC Drama Department was becoming desperate in its search for radio plays, prompt decisions and payment on acceptance would be made: fees of £25 and £50 according to length being once more held out as bait to authors willing to write for sound.

Jaeger, whose effort in this direction had just been returned after a lapse of two months with a simple rejection slip, showed me this item with relish, and I decided to write Barrington citing my own case in contradiction and putting him right on several points.

The letter was sent, no reply came, but instead a few days later an incomprehensibly angry note from a firm of literary agents accusing me of divulging details to the public press of royalties paid to their client Graham Greene, in their opinion an unpardonable course of action.

I was completely in the dark; Jaeger, wearing his usual breakfast costume of black velvet jacket and black skull cap, and smoking the long stemmed meerschaum pipe which was an accessory to this morning dress, declared himself equally mystified; then suddenly gave a sharp exclamation, and clapping the lid on his meerschaum, passed to me his copy of the *Daily Express*, open at Jonah Barrington's radio column.

In this Barrington complained that he had been deluged with letters in small handwriting and would future correspondents please address themselves not to him but to the department of the newspaper mentioned when the original item had been published.

It should now be explained that my handwriting is extremely small, neat and legible: in those days even smaller than it is now, age having taken its toll of my sight, and people seeing one of my MSS would frequently ask how it was done, to which the correct answer was, of course, 'With a pen.' To make my communication more personal, I had not typed my letter to Jonah Barrington, and the present complaint in his column was quite clearly related to it.

A search through back issues of the *Express* finally turned up, on a page where it had been overlooked, since none of us expected anything of the sort, a facsimile of the opening paragraphs of my letter, under the caption: 'CAN YOU WRITE SMALLER THAN THIS?'

The portion reproduced, dealing with my adaptation of *A Gun for Sale*, ended with a sentence explaining that the total fee was divided between Graham Greene and myself: the subsequent paragraph, revealing that only half had been paid and that I was unable to obtain the rest because no production date could be scheduled, was cut off short: a reference to my being on the dole, however, had been printed to the fore.

At that time a sort of stigma or shame attached in the public mind to people receiving Unemployment Assistance: certainly it had not yet become a matter for self-congratulation as now, when any number of bearded voluntary poverty beats from Soho and the Fulham Road boast loudly of spiving a livelihood from what they call The Lark. I imagined that this was really what had upset Greene and his agents, and wrote directly to him apologising for associating his name with someone on the dole, and furthermore explaining that my letter to Barrington had been sent in the hope that he would in some way influence the BBC to pay the remainder of the fee, and having been marked 'Personal' in the first place, was plainly not intended for publication.

Greene replied curtly, on a postcard inscribed: 'Mr Graham Greene is in Mexico but will communicate with you on his return.' These words had been crossed out, and underneath he had written: 'Don't be a fool, of course I don't mind your being on the dole,' continuing that he did mind me making public the amount of his BBC royalties, and that no one would write letters to the papers if they didn't mean them to be published.

I realized that it would be useless to explain further; also I was rapidly losing patience with the whole business of A Gun for Sale, and indeed several years passed before I could bring myself to re-read what had once been a favourite book.

But repercussions from the Barrington letter had not yet died away. The holograph fragment in the Express cited my play The Stars Foretell as a contradiction of the prompt decisions promised by Barrington on the BBC's behalf, since the script had been with the Drama Department for I don't know how long; and I next found myself involved in correspondence with R. H. Naylor, the newspaper astrologer later remarkable for his prophecy that there would be no Second World War.

Mr Naylor, whose weekly horoscopes appeared under the heading 'WHAT THE STARS FORETELL,' considered the title which I'd chosen to be an infringement of copyright: I was able to correct him on this assumption, but not before he had protested also to the BBC, and the upshot was that I was summoned to yet another interview at Broadcasting House.

Moray McLaren surveyed me sadly across the desk as a housemaster might a pupil who has let down the side.

'I appreciate your difficulties,' he said, 'but we have our own as well. Rules and regulations are not easily set aside nor exceptions made, but in this case and in view of the publicity it has received, a solution satisfactory to all parties might still be found.'

'That's heartening,' I said.

Moray McLaren exclaimed, as if struck by sudden inspiration: 'An early date. That's it! If your adaptation could be scheduled for broadcasting at an early date, that would be the solution to all our problems, would it not?'

'How early?' I asked.

Moray McLaren said: 'The schedules will have to be rearranged of course, but we'll see what can be done. The play might even be produced this year!'

He rubbed his hands, refreshed as Gabriel Marlowe would have put it, more than ever resembling in attire a musician or pianist of a slightly earlier period.

I asked: 'I suppose there wouldn't be any vacancies for training as a writer-producer yet?'

Moray McLaren replied: 'Well, in view of the international situation we're cutting down on staff rather than increasing our personnel at present, but your name has not been overlooked, never fear.' Then glancing down at a note on his desk pad: 'Now there's the question of your other play, *The Stars Foretell*, and R. H. Naylor's claim that you've infringed his copyright.'

'That claim is nonsense, as you know.'

Moray McLaren nodded: 'We've already written to him on the subject.'

'And a decision on the script itself?'

'Actually,' Moray McLaren said with tremendous relief, 'that's in the Director of Drama's hands not mine. He's now back from the States and I believe has some news for you, if you'd care to go along and see him in his office.'

'What, right away?' I asked astonished.

Moray McLaren nodded vigorously, springing up as if about to mount the concert platform and perform a recital that very moment.

'No time like the present,' he said.

Val Gielgud had two beards, one sprouting from each corner of his chin. His office was very dark although it was daytime, and in the gloom he gave the impression of a character in an Edgar Wallace who might turn out to be someone else disguised. He stared at me severely through a forbidding pair of spectacles during a short silence which I broke by saying: 'I believe you have some news about a play of mine called *The Stars Foretell*.'

'I have,' Val Gielgud said abruptly. He had a deep brusque voice. 'Not good news, I'm afraid.'

'I'm sorry to hear that,' I said.

Val Gielgud said: 'The script has somehow been mislaid. Even after an extensive search it has not been found.'

'D'you mean you've lost it?' I asked.

'We hope it may yet come to light.'

'But it arrived here all right. You sent an acknowledgment.'

'My secretary did,' Val Gielgud corrected me. 'I was in America at the time. When I returned, the script was no longer in the file awaiting my attention.'

'What does your secretary say?'

The secretary was called in and interrogated by her employer, plainly not for the first time. She showed us the file concerned and even opened it for our inspection as if hoping the script might be still inside. The script was not inside, but then we were already aware of that.

'However,' Val Gielgud said dismissing the secretary, by now close to tears, 'you no doubt have a copy, so no great harm will have been done.'

'I haven't a copy,' I told him.

'But surely you keep a carbon?'

'I do my own typing, and I've no time to bother making carbons.'

'That, if I may say so,' Val Gielgud said severely, 'is a trifle careless of you.'

'More careless than losing typescripts?'

There was another silence, this time broken by Val Gielgud

saying: 'Of course you realize that, while every reasonable care is taken of MSS submitted to this Department, the Corporation cannot assume responsibility in cases of loss or damage?'

'Has every reasonable care been taken,' I asked, 'in this particular case?'

That went unanswered also, then he said: 'Perhaps you'd like to send us the original MS? From what I have seen of your handwriting...'

I said: 'The MS would have to be entirely rewritten first. I made all corrections and alterations while typing, and I couldn't undertake to do it all over again unless I were commissioned to do so.'

Val Gielgud at this rose to his feet, smiling faintly for the first time since I'd entered his office: 'That, as you'll understand,' he said, 'would be quite out of the question.'

Not long after, I received by the same post two letters from the BBC Drama Department. One was from Val Gielgud saying that, although further enquiries had been made, my script still remained missing, and he feared there was nothing more that could be done.

The other said that they had much pleasure in accepting my play *The Stars Foretell*, for which a fee of £25 would be paid on production. This letter was not signed by the Director of Drama but by a producer into whose hands the script had passed in some manner which was never quite cleared up. Having been filed under Acceptances, it was in none of the places where it should have been, hence the confusion which arose. The producer in question afterwards committed suicide, and I never found out whether or not he first produced *The Stars Foretell*.

Nor was *A Gun for Sale* so far as I know ever produced. The early date unerringly chosen by the BBC was September 1, 1939, and considering the play's subject the broadcast was naturally cancelled: since, two days later, we really did have war in our time.

# The Forties

# A Story in Horizon

A Flying Bomb later killed the girl called Bobbie whom I kissed in the back of the car, and Di who drove it is dead as well: though of natural causes, if you can call cancer a natural cause.

But that morning in March 1940 these young women were both very much alive: Bobbie's crimson lipstick tasted like scented soap in my mouth, she drew back to arch provocatively her pencilled brows over bold dark eyes, and to slap lightly with her wedding-ringed hand one of mine which may have reached too far under the rug covering her knees; while Di at the wheel, with the back of her cloud of blonde hair turned to us but her eyes intent on the driving mirror, called out gaily: 'Now then you two!'

The car was a Riley painted red, with a detachable hood which at this moment was up, and in it I was on my way to London, where I'd been invited to call on Cyril Connolly who had recently accepted a story of mine for publication in his review *Horizon*.

*Green folders, green ink*
Cyril Connolly's book *Enemies of Promise* remains a landmark to members of my generation, standing up as such today, the cautions which it contains still valid: though most of us, Connolly included, have fallen into the snares which he foresaw, while a warning 'not to capitalise indolence and egotism' reads oddly now from the author of *The Unquiet Grave*.

In the Thirties I'd known Connolly's name only through his stimulating reviews in *The New Statesman* and Desmond MacCarthy's eulogistic *Sunday Times* notice of his novel *The Rock Pool*, then unobtainable in England: though I'd tried hard to get a copy of the Obelisk Press edition, having spent my own early youth not far from those parts of the French Riviera featured in *The Rock Pool*, among characters not dissimilar from those evidently described therein.

Then quite by chance I discovered *Enemies of Promise* in the local public library, about a year after its publication during the Munich crisis. I was still on the Assistance and very dispirited; the outbreak of war seemed to put the lid firmly on any chance of a literary career, and finding a book like this was a tremedously invigorating experience.

Part of its appeal lay I suppose in the author's having read and appreciated all the contemporary novelists that I myself enjoyed (not by any means usual at this period, still less in the backwater where I lived), also some novels which I'd not read at all, such as *Living* by Henry Green and Christopher Isherwood's *The Memorial*. Here, I felt, was someone who might see merit in my work, if merit was indeed there to be seen, which I was seriously beginning to doubt : I'd even ceased to send my stories out, and there still weren't enough of them to make up a volume.

If only Cyril Connolly were an editor, I thought, and a few days later the first advertisement for *Horizon* a Review of Literature and Art, edited by Cyril Connolly, appeared like an answer to prayer in the sixpenny weeklies.

'One last chance, if this doesn't come off I'll pack it in,' I told Jaeger who had finished his novel and, like me, was awaiting call up while signing-on the Labour; Lydia his wife parcelled up the green springboard folder containing the stories, their daughter now aged two was handed a label to lick; and addressed to *Horizon* office the parcel was posted off when the price of a ninepenny stamp had with difficulty been rustled up between us.

Soon a winter even worse than the last one tightened round our bungalow its rigorous icy grip, every day the postman trudged through snowdrifts to the door : bills, demands and threats from unpaid tradesmen lay unanswered on the mat but, except for a printed acknowledgment, nothing from *Horizon* came through the letter box.

Against the advice of everyone I knew, I finally in mid-February wrote a postcard to the editor asking for the typescript's return. In prompt reply came a postcard written in green ink and Cyril Connolly's own handwriting: 'Hold on, MSS filed in error, just been found, now being read,' but I'd long ceased to be an optimist and merely gave a hollow laugh.

That weekend we were asked over by friends in Littlehampton; a play reading of *Julius Caesar* was held while a snowstorm whirled round the house; Jaeger, who was in the title rôle and suffered from recurrent bouts of asthma, suddenly turned blue and fell off his chair; and we had to stay the night since the storm had stopped all traffic on the roads.

Sunday, back at home, we found all pipes frozen, the water off, and our credit frozen also; I retired to bed with a streaming snorting cold, woke on Monday with rigid limbs and head stuffed up. A burst pipe had instantly blossomed out in icicles, and Jaeger throwing me a letter from the doorway said: 'From Connolly I think.'

My fingers had chilblains on and I found the letter hard to open. It was from Connolly all right, the green handwriting covered both sides of the page. I read the opening paragraphs and tried to produce a shout of elation, but the strangled sound that came instead was mistaken for my death rattle and brought all the Jaegers rushing in.

Particularly gratifying was the fact that the main story mentioned and accepted was one called *A Bit of a Smash in Madras* which nobody, certainly not the Jaegers and perhaps not even myself, had believed would ever be published; moreover Connolly also proposed to print in future issues *Five Finger Exercises*, the first short story that I'd ever written and one hitherto rejected by editors with cries of distress, since it described a girl of 16 being seduced by a man of 30 in a seaside town; and *Happy as the Day is Long*, around which the Denys Kilham Roberts controversy had raged. Last but not least, *Horizon* paid 2 guineas per thousand words, *A Bit of a Smash in Madras* was in length at least 8,000, and Connolly wrote that a cheque for half the fee was on its way.

'Julian's bloody well done it at last,' Karel Jaeger shouted, wringing my chilblained hand; little Karel his daughter caught the spirit of rejoicing and did an elephantine dance around my bed; and Lydia Jaeger was sent forth into the snow with the *Horizon* letter, to unfreeze further credit from the shops.

The reasons for the delay in deciding were explained in the letter as well. Apparently *Horizon's* office was also the flat of Stephen Spender, then associated with the Review and in the Fire Service at the time, and by the sort of coincidence by no means unique in my life, the typescripts of his poems were bound in green folders exactly similar to those I used. A girl secretary of the species that has haunted me throughout my professional career, beginning with the BBC, had found my stories lying on a desk and, without looking in the folder, filed them away with the rest of Spender's work in his study, where they remained until on receipt of my postcard a search was made. (This incident taught me a lesson which all young writers should learn: never to be afraid of sending editors a reminder once a reasonable length of time has elapsed: 'a maximum of, say, two weeks,' to quote again from the excellent precepts outlined in Edmund Wilson's *Literary Worker's Polonius*, a copy of which should hang over the desk in every editorial office.)

A cheque for 9 guineas duly arrived from Connolly, and with it another letter: now he wanted me to write a long 10,000 word story about the South of France and was not inimical either to considering the short vacuum cleaner salesman novel with which I'd been wrestling, and which at that time I reckoned would run out at about 25,000 words.

'A whole issue of the magazine maybe,' Jaeger said in awe as he took the cheque to a chap he knew who would put it through his bank, and that evening we celebrated with a real bottle of wine instead of the noxious patent stuff in which we usually indulged when the dole paid out on Fridays.

But suddenly there began to be trouble at the *Horizon* end. *A Bit of a Smash in Madras* concerned a motor accident in the city of that name and the legal intrigues consequent upon it; and, for fear of a possible libel suit, the locale had to be changed to E. M. Forster's imaginary state of Chandrapore and

58

the words *In Madras* were cut therefore from the title. (Actually, when the story appeared, the sole legal repercussion was a letter of praise from a retired judge in Bombay wrongly identifying by name all the protagonists in the case, which he believed he had tried himself.)

Even so, two sets of printers flatly refused to print, objecting to several expressions in the text and to the opening sentence in particular, which originally read: 'Absolute fact, I knew fuck-all about it,' and was not acceptable even when the offending words were altered to 'Sweet F.A.' Stephen Spender took up the struggle with the printers and sent me a list of the expressions for which substitutes had to be supplied and which ended, in the form of a short poem:

> 'Pissed-up'
> 'By Christ'
> 'Balls'
> 'Bugger.'

This list was in my pocket when I set off in the Riley with Di, who was driving up for a day's shopping in London with her friend Bobbie. I was lucky to get the lift, for £1 was all the cash I'd been able to raise.

## Bobbie and Burmese cigarettes

Bobbie said: 'But I don't know you well enough,' her eyes opening wide at a suggestion of mine; then later on she said: 'Well not yet,' and later still: 'We'll have to see.'

It was true she didn't know me well enough, I'd never set eyes on her until that morning. She was about thirty, a long-legged brunette, slender, with sleek hair almost black and these bold brown eyes. She had been a model before her marriage and was very well made up, using a shade of cream and powder that gave a matt, tanned looking surface to her skin. Her mouth was painted in a crimson curve that looked hard but in fact was soft and smooth. The moment we met antagonism crackled like electricity between us and a residue remained even after we'd begun kissing in the back of the car.

Di had brought chicken sandwiches for our lunch, a bottle

C

of sherry, and even glasses to drink this out of: the sherry
went slightly to Bobbie's head and on the last lap of the drive
her leg pressed hard against mine, the rug was cast aside; her
wedding ring cut into my fingers which were twined in hers,
and after all this time I can smell her scent mingled with the
petrol fumes one always got inside that car whenever the
hood was up.

Antagonism evaporated too and when we reached High
Holborn where they were to drop me off, Bobbie opened her
mouth for a final kiss that obliged me to wait for passion to
subside before I could climb out of the car. It was then that
she said: 'We'll have to see.'

Di, a born matchmaker though herself unmarried, beamed
as they drove off, the blonde and the brunette, towards the
City where Bobbie's husband worked. I walked elatedly up
Southampton Row, stopping at a tobacconist's to break into
my pound note and buy some Burmese cigarettes which
seemed appropriate to the occasion. I soon found these almost
unsmokable, and wished I had stuck to my usual Brazilians
but I had to go careful with only nineteen shillings now
to last the day: though Connolly in his letter of invitation
had promised to let me have the remainder of the fee, this
would take the form of a cheque and the banks were already
closed.

A clock said 3.15, my appointment was 3.30, and first I
entered a big Bloomsbury hotel, with green cupolas on the
roof like a Russian church, to wash off Bobbie's lipstick in a
basin down below, little knowing that years later I would live
there eighteen months.

Lansdowne Terrace was easily found and not far off, a row
of small smoky dun-brick houses built all alike, with big blank
front windows facing a children's playground on the other
side. No 6 had no plate outside, or indication that the *Horizon*
office was to be found within: the stairs were uncarpeted and
stone. I climbed them and knocked at random on a door. This
after a stealthy pause came open, a dark face peered cautiously
through a crack, then the door was banged-to in my face.

I climbed higher, knocked, another Indian appeared, small and shrivelled like the first: one look at me and his door too was smartly shut. A third occupant, Indian also, seemed to know no English; I asked desperately: 'Horizon? Spender? Connolly?' even producing the Burmese cigarettes to make him feel at home, but helplessly he shook his head and retreated bowing through the doorway.

No 6 was plainly on the fanlight but it was equally plain that *Horizon* didn't hang out there, and I tried the house next door. Here none of the occupants would answer, there was hollow silence except for my footsteps echoing up and down; if this went on I would be late: in a panic I rushed along the row, up more and more stone stairs: Indians in every flat, either unable or unwilling to give any information, and the last one a woman in a sari shrank in terror when she saw me and almost slammed her door upon my hand.

Baffled, hot and bothered in my teddy bear coat I came out onto the pavement, and my hand seeking cigarettes touched a crumpled piece of paper in my pocket. Stephen Spender's list, and at the top the correct address which I'd not troubled to check. No 6 *Selwyn House*, Lansdowne Terrace: first one in the row, I'd passed it on the Guilford Street corner and now stood right outside.

The front door was open, a carpeted hall inside, on the ground floor right another door, with the names Spender and *Horizon*. Cyril Connolly himself answered the bell.

*Cyril Connolly at Selwyn Ho.*
Connolly at this time must have been thirty-six or seven years of age. The only photograph I'd seen of him was one which formed a frontispiece to the first edition of *Enemies of Promise,* where he is wearing an Eton suit and a top hat that rests on rather protruding ears; and the only clue to his grown-up appearance was the last paragraph of the book where he tells us that his face is round.

His face was round, plump and pale, his shoulders sloped from a short thick neck, and dark hair was fluffed thickly out behind the ears that seemed no longer to protrude. He had a short snub Irish nose and under shaggy Irish brows his eyes, set far apart, looked both hooded and alert. A startled expression, instantly veiled, had entered them when he saw me standing at the door and it was clear that I was not what he had pictured (pith helmet and white ducks: a pukka sahib? capped and collarless, with muffler round the neck: the dole? A blazer and rope-soled shoes: the South of France? Or a salesman, wearing a raincoat and porkpie hat with feathers in the band?)

Under his speculative gaze, I launched into an apology for being late, describing my peculiar reception by the Indian tenants of the Terrace, which I was still at a loss to account for. Connolly explained. Apparently a new regulation that all Asiatics should be rounded-up had that day been passed: something to do with subversive activities and the war, and the unfortunate Indians had mistaken me for an official come to enforce the order.

'But of course you were able to reassure them,' Cyril Connolly was saying.

'How?' I said. 'None of them could speak English.'

'But with your knowledge of their native language, Hindustani, or is it Tamil?'

'I don't speak Tamil or Hindustani.'

'What?' A slightly sharp note became perceptible in Connolly's soft bland voice. 'Not after all those years out East?'

This was going to be a let-down, but it was too late to bluff it out. 'I've never been out East,' I told him.

'Nor to Madras?'

'No.'

Connolly said: 'D'you mean that story's pure imagination? With all the background detail?'

'Not altogether,' I said unhappily. 'I had a friend who used to tell me stories of his life out there. I picked most of it up from him.'

We were standing in the front room which overlooked the

Terrace and had been Stephen Spender's study: his books were in a glass-fronted case by the cabinet containing the green springback folders among which my stories had been filed in error. Now, to cover an awkward pause, I bent closer to the bookcase and immediately saw inside copies of *Living* and *The Memorial*, which ever since reading *Enemies of Promise* I'd been trying to obtain.

'I suppose I couldn't borrow these?'

Connolly said: 'If you're good at bringing books back. I don't think Stephen would mind, but they are his you see.'

I promised faithfully to return them (which I did), adding: 'You haven't also got *The Rock Pool* by any chance?'

Connolly said: 'Not a single copy left, I'm sorry. At one time you might have found one in a rubber goods shop but not, I fear, any longer,' and I was to find again the phrase about the rubber goods in the preface to the original edition of *The Rock Pool* when later I did obtain a copy.

Zipping the two novels up in my brief-case, I asked what Henry Green was like, since I'd just read *Party Going* and been enormously impressed.

'A nice quiet private detective in a book by Nicholas Blake,' Connolly replied.

'Nigel Strangeways?'

Connolly said: 'If Henry was an actor he'd be ideal for the part.'

Walking as if with slippered feet though in fact he wore suède shoes, he led the way into his own office at the back. The housemaster's outfit affected by many writers of the Thirties—tweed jacket, woollen tie, grey flannels baggy at the knee—gave him an unbuttoned rather than an informal air as he slumped back in the armchair opposite me. His movements like his voice were indolent, one had the impression that he should have been eating grapes, but at the same time his half-closed eyes missed nothing. He was a formidable person.

I asked him if he knew G. S. Marlowe, who had not yet been lost in Norway; Connolly not only knew him, but he told me his real surname, which was unpronounceable and might have belonged to any Central European, though Connolly thought that he was Viennese.

'We used to stay in the same country house near Marlow, and that's where he took his name from, adding an E on the end for good measure. He used to boast a lot about being a fisherman, but we never saw anything he caught.'

'That's curious,' I said. 'He once told me much the same about Hemingway, only it was shooting not fishing.'

'I doubt if he ever knew Hemingway,' Connolly said.

'What about Greta Garbo?'

Connolly made a dismissive gesture. 'Tales from the Vienna Woods,' he said, reaching out for the folder with my stories which lay upon his desk. He spoke about the father in one about childhood called *The Snows of Yesterday*, saying: 'My father was quite like yours, all regular army men are really much the same.'

'My father wasn't in the regular army,' I said. 'He was only a captain in the Boer War.'

'But you say here he was a colonel in the Indian Army.'

'That's just the father in the story,' I said.

Connolly shifted in his chair, he seemed positive that all my work was autobiographical, and I realized that this was tantamount to contradicting him. So I added quickly: 'My grandfather was an Indian Army colonel though.'

'Perhaps the character was based on him?'

'No, he died before I was born. He wrote books on big game hunting. Quite well written. They were published by Chapman and Hall.'

'So writing runs in the family?'

I let this ride, though quite certain my grandfather never thought of himself as a writer, and Connolly said: 'I suppose you'll be going into the army yourself now?'

'I'm expecting the call-up any time.'

Connolly nodded. 'The Indian army,' he said. 'Then you'll be able to go to Madras. That reminds me, I have a cheque for you somewhere.'

The cheque, already made out for nine guineas, was finally

found clipped to the stories in the folder, and he said: 'Just take it to the bank in the morning, they'll cash it for you before we meet for lunch.'

'Lunch? Tomorrow?'

'Yes, I thought the Café Royal if that suits you.'

I said: 'Of course I'd love to, but I'm afraid I must go back this evening. Frankly I can't afford to stay the night.'

Connolly said: 'But that's all arranged, everything paid for. Bill Makins our business manager has fixed up a room for you. He'll be here presently and you can go out for drinks together, unfortunately I'm engaged myself tonight.'

I muttered my thanks; I was touched by his kindness and consideration, and had a sudden urge to tell him what receiving his long friendly letters had meant to me in my unrecognized and exiled state. But I'd the sense not to embarrass him with such a speech, for I felt that beneath his immense sophistication he was very public school.

'Unless of course there's a wife at home waiting for you?' Connolly was saying.

'There isn't a wife.'

'You've never been married?'

'Once, but it didn't take. Only lasted six months.'

'Six months. You were very unlucky,' Connolly said. 'In marriage, if even moderately lucky, one can expect at least seven years of happiness. And if exceptionally lucky, why then,' he smiled benignly, 'another seven': a dictum which twenty years later I attributed, with other sayings of his, to a film producer in a novel, though I'm glad now to acknowledge their proper source.

'I'll look forward to that next time,' I told him.

'Do you mean to marry again?'

'Not if I can help it, but these things sometimes happen. As you've pointed out, the pram in the hall.'[1]

'You're not yet thirty?'

'Nearly twenty-eight.'

Connolly sighed. 'Nearer Bill Makins' generation than mine.

[1] See *Enemies of Promise*, Penguin Modern Classics Edition, p. 127.

In fact I think you must be just about the same age.'

'1911,' a voice said, as if on cue from the passage outside :
'I'm a year ahead,' and into the office came William Cooper
Makins, a man who afterwards died twice : as I will tell.

## Goat's blood in Russell Square

'Two minutes to opening time,' Makins announced glancing
at his watch outside the office; then as we turned into Russell
Square he pointed at a skyscraper type building visible above
trees on the farther side : 'D'you see that? London University,
but it's now the Ministry of Information. Graham Greene
works there!'

'Does he,' I said.

'He does,' Makins said. 'He may be in there working at this
very moment.' It was a solemn thought : we stood there looking
towards the Ministry as if it were a shrine or cenotaph. Makins
said : 'He's just finished a new novel. About a Mexican priest.
It'll be published in the summer. You'll have whisky of course,'
leading the way down into an underground bar with barrels
round the walls.

I was not loth to accept; at this early stage of the war spirits
were easily obtainable, and he'd told me going along the street
that he was amply provided with expenses and that, as a guest
of *Horizon*, I was not allowed to pay.

Hitherto I'd known the name William C. Makins only from
seeing it on the *Horizon* letterhead, with Business Manager
printed above, and Cyril Connolly told me that as a business
manager he was extremely efficient : before this he had worked
in advertising I believe.

Makins in the flesh was a redoubtable figure : tall, gaunt,
with a fierce Highland high-boned face and a dark Elizabethan
beard jutting from his chin. I borrowed his appearance for a
film director in the same novel which embodies some of
Connolly's aphorisms, and gave him a monocle much as
Gabriel Marlowe added the final E to his surname : Makins
however did not need a monocle, his eyes were piercing
enough without. They were electric eyes and deep sunk in their

66

sockets, causing his head to be even more haughtily held.

He outdid Karel Jaeger in looking like a Scottish tribal chieftain, though his accent was incisively English and he did not affect national dress. Whenever I saw him, which seemed always to be in cold weather, he was tightly buttoned in a black business overcoat and wore outdoors a stiff brimmed black hat tilted back rather in the manner of Graham Greene, whom he resembled a little in height and build and who was the novelist he admired above all others.

His admiration for Greene's work exceeded even my own, and moreover he always knew whatever Greene was doing or writing at any given time. I forgot whether he knew Greene personally, but rather fancy he did not.

It was by recounting my experiences with Greene and the adaptation of *A Gun for Sale*, thus adding to his store of information, that I became accepted by Makins as a friend, the friendship being cemented that evening with much grain and malt.

Over the scotch with beer chasers, he pointed out what I'd already noticed: the curious omission of Graham Greene's name from *Enemies of Promise*, though *It's a Battlefield*, *England Made Me* and *Brighton Rock* had already come out when the book was written; this however, Makins told me, would soon be rectified in *Horizon*, and it was: by Arthur Calder-Marshall's excellent analysis of the novels, the first critical article on Greene to appear anywhere, in which the phrase 'Greene Land' was first coined.

But Greene was not the only writer about whom Bill Makins had inside information: there was also Evelyn Waugh. I think it was on this occasion that I heard from him about the unfinished novel *Work Suspended*: 'It's told in the first person by a chap who writes very superior detective stories, he's very proud of these detective stories but he gradually becomes human, and the book's about the humanizing process he goes through.' (I don't know whether Evelyn Waugh would approve of this précis, which I remember word for word, my interest was so great; later on when the book had appeared in a limited edition only, and I wanted to write a critical article about him, he replied asking me to wait until he was dead: I respected his wish, but this was long before the spate of articles that began to be written after *Brideshead*, by critics who didn't wait for him to be dead.)

Anyway, according to Makins, at this time *Work Suspended* was to be published in *Penguin Parade*, taking up a complete number of the miscellany; and I was able to pass on the story of Denys Kilham Roberts and *Happy as the Day is Long*, which after all that had been accepted by *Horizon*. Makins, who'd been laughing at the story, stopped suddenly to pass a hand down his beard. He said: 'The one about the Count in Chelsea?' but made no further comment then, going on to relay some further advance publishing news.

He knew more of what was going on behind the literary scene than anyone I ever knew. Not the sort of malicious personal gossip that poets indulge in, but real hard facts. His finger was constantly on the pulse, moreover he meant it to remain there. He'd no intention of being railroaded into the bloody Forces, which would mean he'd years to make up after: despite his aggressively vigorous exterior he not only had genuine pacifist convictions but also an incipient stomach ulcer which had already caused one medical board to turn him down.

'If I continue to keep out,' he said putting down money for more drinks, 'I plan to start up as a literary agent, apart from my job at *Horizon*, real live-wire stuff and you can be one of my very first authors.' Real live-wires seemed to spark out of his eyes: 'I'll handle your output and push the stories to their best advantage, which you won't be able to do when they shove you in the army, right?'

'Only too right,' I agreed with whisky burning my throat, and Makins seized my hand in a powerful grip.

'Then we're in business, or rather we ruddy soon will be. Promotion, publicity, that's the thing. Tell you what I'm going to fix up for you,' and, as he proceeded to promise, the issue of *Horizon* in which *A Bit of a Smash* eventually ap-

68

peared was advertised with my name and the title of the story alone, bordered in black, instead of all the contributors being listed as previously: a matter of great pride to me at the time.

'We've got to keep your name always to the fore,' Makins explained, emptying his glass and thrusting out his beard for emphasis. 'Impress it on the public mind. I've already been working on some of the chaps, they'll be here presently,' and while toasting the new venture we were joined by two of the chaps, both of them already familiar with my name and apparently eager to be introduced.

'You see?' Makins said. 'You're famous before you've even been published,' and another round of scotch came up: whisky didn't seem to upset his ulcer, he said, or if it did all the better as he was due for another bloody Board soon.

More of the chaps appeared, I hoped some of the girls might show up as well, but the party remained all male and the conversation became a lot less literary. All at once it turned on a woman, evidently much given to experiment and well known to all, who'd been the victim of an accident, perhaps to her leg, certainly on a remote Italian hillside, and had had to have a blood-transfusion on the spot. Since none of the people roundabout belonged to the proper blood group, the doctor had been compelled to accept as blood donor some mountain animal: here my memory begins to falter, although a goat seems the most probable in such surroundings and comes most readily to mind as the kind of quadruped concerned.

Anyhow the transfusion had been triumphantly successful, and the brightest of the chaps began to declaim a limerick that he'd made up, in which the patient subsequently rejected as stimulants various sexual deviations, also gin and heroin: at this point everybody joined in chanting the last line, the bar resounded with 'I must have goat's blood—under the skin!' protests arose from the management, and a general move was made through the blackout towards a delicatessen and wine store that stayed open late, the idea being to carry on the party at Makins' place in Guilford Street.

At the delicatessen they started laying in a typical Blooms-bury meal: potato salad, loaves of French bread, paté and salami (not affected by meat rationing which had just come in), bottles of red wine and beer. I insisted this time on paying my whack, only to find that at some previous point I had dropped my one ten shilling note, probably in the tobacconist's where I'd bought Brazilian cigarettes on the way to the bar, having given up attempting to smoke the Burmese some time before.

I immediately wanted to go back there and search, but was dissuaded on the grounds that the shop would now be shut: I remember that, in an effort to divert my attention, one of the younger men pointed wildly into the darkness ahead, shout-ing: 'Look, down there's Doughty Street. Where bloody old Dickens lived,' while another leant over some railings to show me an area in which he'd once either had a fight or else been sick, dropping in the process a bottle of pale ale which shattered below.

*A good night in Guilford Street*
Another of the chaps was worried for fear he might be sterile.

The one who did something scientific and may have been a bio-chemist said: 'That's easily settled, old boy. Just take a sample of your spunk along to a hospital, and they'll soon tell you one way or the other.'

'How'm I supposed to get it there?'

The brightest of the chaps said: 'Simple. All you've to do is toss yourself off into a bottle.'

Makins managed to wrench the conversation away from the medical turn it had taken, and back to literature.

We were sitting over the remains of the meal in his large bedsitter, which had masks hung on the walls and a big box containing marionettes in one corner. A marionette play of his had been performed at a theatre club which specialized also in plays where the protagonists wore masks, and he was now writing one with four masked characters in it, entitled *The Unknown*: the latter being a fifth character who did not actually appear in the play.

Two incomplete acts in typescript were passed round the company for criticism, while a refugee antique dealer, who'd been waiting for Makins (or a free meal) outside the door when we arrived, sneered quietly to himself in the armchair nearest the gas fire, with his chin resting on the top of a tasselled cane. The food had sobered me up, and I remembered Gabriel Marlowe telling me about a play by Karel Câpek, also entitled *The Unknown*, which Marlowe had produced in some foreign capital and which was narrated by a man in a mackintosh wearing a mask; but it was unlikely that Makins had heard of this play, never to my knowledge translated into English, and I held my peace.

The antique dealer, when the typescript came round to him, had no such inhibitions. After he'd finished explaining that all worthwhile drama indeed all art had originated somewhere in Central Europe, eaten the last piece of salami and made sure that there was no more wine, he climbed with Makins' assistance into a fur collared overcoat: there was a curfew for people like him, Golders Green was a long way off, and he looked hopefully round in search of someone going in the same direction who might pay for his taxi; but no one was, and bad tempered he left.

'Poor fellow,' Makins said. 'He's been through a lot,' and even I nodded sympathetically: none of us being used to this type of person at that time, though we were to become amply familiar with it in the years ahead.

The antique dealer was, however, the only jarring note in the whole evening: the chaps were all nice cheerful intelligent young men and I regret, during all my future nights in Bloomsbury and Soho pubs, that I never came across any of them again: nor did I ever run into the woman who had been transfused with the blood of the goat. Perhaps they were all killed in the war, though I hope not.

Now we sat round drinking beer and looking at the typescript of a very long story by another of Makins' future clients, which included a complete description in blank verse of the film *The Petrified Forest*: some of the characters visited a cinema where this was showing, and while the chap who did something scientific and may have been a bio-chemist was having a pee on the landing, Makins told me that he was the original of one of the key personages in the story.

I asked him whether the story was to be printed in *Horizon*, but he said no: the reason for its rejection seemed to be that the author had a beard. But he himself had a beard, I pointed out. Yes Makins said, he had a beard but this author's beard was reddish, and wearing it he had called on Cyril Connolly and attempted personally to persuade him to publish his poems. The moral seemed to be: never employ the personal approach with editors, still less when in an aggressive mood; on the other hand there was the precedent of Wyndham Lewis reading a MS to Ford Madox Ford while Ford was having a bath. Parts of the red bearded poet's story seemed stylistically influenced by Lewis, but Connolly was evidently less easily stampeded by shock tactics into accepting material than Ford had been.

It was all fascinating to me, but there I had to leave it, for I was afraid that the digs Makins had procured for me (themselves in Guilford Street) might refuse to let me in if I made it any later, also none of us had another shilling for the gas fire. So we all trooped down into the blackout, Makins having first opened the windows to let out the smoke.

The room he'd booked for me was in a house owned by Belgians and it too was heated by a gas fire which, lacking a shilling, I was unable to light. So I got into an enormous brass bedstead while Makins, who'd accompanied me upstairs, sat by it in hat and overcoat to have a last smoke.

He said: 'After Rudi's valuable criticism, it might be a good idea to revise my play along less expressionist lines and call it *The Unseen* instead. What d'you think?'

At this, fatigue and drink sandbagged me suddenly, the noise of the pub and the party still went on in my head but with a soporific effect, as the sound of train wheels might lull a traveller; then the noise faded like background babble in a radio play and Makins' voice alone came clearly through, saying: 'Of course Cyril often changes his mind.'

'About what?' I asked sleepily.

'Stuff he's accepted.'

'Not like *Penguin Parade* it's to be hoped,' I laughed, but Makins was unsmiling.

He said uncomfortably: 'Well, you know how editors are.'

'No,' I said, 'I don't,' then waking completely: 'What's all this about?'

'Your stories,' Makins said: 'Didn't you tell me Cyril had accepted the one about the Chelsea Count?'

'Yes I did. He has.'

Makins passed a hand down his beard, like he had done in the bar.

He said: 'I'm afraid it might be my fault. I told him I didn't consider it quite up to the standard of *A Bit of a Smash*.'

'You mean,' I said, sitting up, 'he's not going to print it after all? What about *Five Finger Exercises*? He said he was taking that story too.'

Makins shrugged: 'Well, there again. But there's nothing definite either way.'

'Connolly's letter was definite enough. And he didn't mention any of this to me today.'

Makins said decisively: 'Then I wouldn't mention it to him when you meet tomorrow. Keep in touch and I'll keep you posted. It may never happen and anyway, when *A Bit of a Smash* comes out, you may feel differently about wanting to publish the other two.'

I was about to tell him that I wouldn't feel differently about having to forfeit the fees, which would help to keep me going more comfortably until the army took over from the Assistance; but he had spoken as agent to author, and I was too tired to argue any more now.

'We'll see,' I said, sinking down on the pillows: 'It was a good night, Bill.'

'A bloody good night,' Makins agreed clicking the light off at the door: 'Sleep well now.'

I did.

73

The bank cashier was counting pads of pound notes when I appeared at his grille next morning. He carefully examined the amount and signature on the *Horizon* cheque, all of it in Connolly's green ink; then asked: 'What d'you want to do with this?'

'Cash it' I said.

'Have you an account at this branch?'

'I haven't, no. But Mr Connolly has. He said you'd cash this for me.'

'Sorry,' the cashier said. 'I can't cash it, you've no account here,' and he pushed the cheque back under the grille.

'Why can't you cash it?' I asked. 'Here's my name, quite clearly made out.'

'It's a crossed cheque,' he told me. 'It's not been opened. You could put it through your own bank, would be the best way.'

'I haven't a bank.'

The cashier went back to counting pound notes. People without banks did not interest him.

'What d'you mean, the cheque hasn't been opened?' I asked.

He glanced up, surprised to find me still there: he'd thought the matter settled.

'A crossed cheque can only be paid into a banking account,' he said patiently. 'It cannot be cashed unless it's been correctly opened.'

'Against banking regulations otherwise,' said a second, older cashier, who'd come up to listen.

'And if this cheque were opened? Would you cash it then?'

The second cashier in turn took the cheque and examined every inch of it. 'But this hasn't been opened,' he said at last.

'Suppose Mr Connolly was to open it for me. I'm having lunch with him today.'

The second cashier said: 'Could I see your identity card, please?' He seemed to have taken over entirely. The first cashier had meantime got through counting a couple of hundred. The second cashier went over my identity card with

74

equal care, even reading the regulations on the back; then he said: 'Well we don't naturally like cashing opened cheques as a rule, but in this case we might stretch a point. If you can persuade our client to open it of course.'

'Of course,' I said. 'What's the procedure?'

'Well these lines here, which make it a crossed cheque, must be crossed out and the words Pay Cash written in between. And this must also be signed or initialled by the drawer.'

'I get it. Thank you.'

'Always glad to be of service,' the second cashier smiled. 'Good morning.'

'D'you mind if I have the cheque back?'

'Please forgive me,' he handed it over with a bow: 'I was quite forgetting, ha ha.'

'See you later,' I said, 'Ha ha,' then had to return for my briefcase which I'd left behind and which had not, luckily, been pinched. The first cashier was still counting: he must have got up to a Monkey by now.

I didn't realize that this incident would recur like a nightmare throughout my career, editors being what they are and banks even more so. Nowadays opened cheques as well are subjected to suspicious scrutiny and may even be refused, but that morning I'd more important things than bank officials to worry about.

I was mainly worried as to whether Connolly meant to turn down the other two stories that he'd accepted, as Makins had hinted the night before. I thought perhaps he would pay me for them even if he didn't print, though I ought to have known better than that; and on my way to the Café Royal I was determined to ask him right out, despite my prospective agent's advice.

But at sight of Connolly my resolve at once began to falter. He was in the upstairs bar as arranged, sitting on a sofa near the door with a bulging leather satchel beside him and galley proofs unfurled upon his knee. His round plump face looked mild enough and he even smiled as he saw me, nonetheless he was clearly not a man amenable to direct questioning (though fond of it himself), and had indeed a built-in resistance to such an approach.

Waving to a waiter and pointing to an armchair opposite with the thick editorial pencil in his hand, he said as I sat down: 'I hope you had a good evening, was the room all right? Did you get your money at the bank?'

'Actually, no,' I replied to this last bit.

Connolly's shaggy eyebrows shot up in surprise. 'No? Why not?'

'The cheque hadn't been opened you see.'

'No,' Connolly said his eyebrows coming down in a slight frown, 'I don't see. I made it out to you, it can be cashed across the counter surely?'

'Not unless these lines are crossed out and Pay Cash written in between. Otherwise absolutely not. Against banking regulations.'

'Never heard of such nonsense,' Connolly said, 'but of course I'll alter it at once. What did you say I had to do?'

The waiter interrupted with our drinks and while Connolly fumbled for change I looked round the bar, which I'd not been in since an evening just before my marriage. I'd sat over by the ticker-tape drinking Corpse Revivers with a man called Mooney who could quote Gibbon off by heart. We were waiting for my future wife, and at a table facing us sat a startling blonde with legs crossed so high that Mooney said one could almost read the time.

That was October 1936: now the tape ticked out war news, the bar was full of uniforms, Corpse Revivers were off the cocktail menu, and the blonde's clock had surely been stopped.

Connolly said: 'There, I've crossed out the lines and written Pay Cash, how's that?'

'I'm sorry, you're supposed to sign the Pay Cash bit.'

The galleys slipped from Connolly's knee and unfurled across the floor, I hastened to pick them up, and muttering indignantly about the officiousness of bank clerks he signed the alterations with his satchel for a desk.

'D'you think they'll cash it now?'

'Thank you. I'm sure they will,' and they did.

'You must be sure to get to the bank before three,'[1] Connolly told me, then tapping with his editor's pencil the proofs which I'd passed back to him, he said: 'Maugham.'

'I beg your pardon?'

'Somerset Maugham. His article on the Detective Story for *Horizon.*'

'When's it coming out?' I asked. The article had been advertised as a future attraction in *Horizon* itself, and I'd been looking forward to its appearance.

Connolly did not directly answer. Instead he asked: 'D'you know anything about detective stories?'

I said: 'As it happens, quite a lot.'

'Then tell me what you think of this?'

'You want me to read the article?' I said surprised.

'A quick glance through should be enough,' Connolly said and sat back impassive with hands folded on his satchel top while I read.

Maugham's article was the one afterwards published as 'The Decline and Fall of the Detective Story' in a book of essays entitled *The Vagrant Mood*; though, since only one novel by Raymond Chandler had been published at this date, the version I saw cannot have included the references to Philip Marlowe: spelt throughout by Maugham as if he were the town from which G. S. Marlowe took his name. But otherwise the material must have been substantially the same.

'Well?' Connolly asked as I again handed back the proofs. 'D'you think it's a good article?'

'Of course. Don't you?'

Connolly had folded up the galleys and was thrusting them deep into his satchel from which other proofs protruded. He succeeded at last in pulling the straps through the fastening buckles, the satchel by now at bursting point was rolled aside

---

[1] I got there before three, for it turned out Connolly had another appointment at 2.15, and I must have misinterpreted 'Lunch *time*' as 'Lunch' the day before. Later I ate a Welsh rarebit in the buffet car of the train taking me back to the South Coast.

like an antagonist whom he had bound and gagged, and he settled himself more comfortably on the sofa. Only then did he reply.

'No,' he said. 'I don't think it's a good article.'

'You don't?' I echoed in dismay.

Benignly smiling, Connolly shook his head. 'In fact I've decided not to print it.'

'Not print it,' I gasped. 'But it's by Maugham!'

'I have the greatest respect for Maugham as a novelist,' Connolly said in his soft bland voice, 'and I don't say this is a *bad* article. It's good enough to be accepted for *Horizon* but not quite good enough for me to publish.'

Then, not quite changing the subject, but dropping that of Maugham, he began to discourse on the distinction between the detective story and the thriller: a theme already examined in his early *New Statesman* essays.

I knew by the blandness of his smile that I'd been given an oblique answer to a question not yet asked. It was now plain that if a long article by an author of Maugham's eminence, obviously commissioned and already heralded in the magazine, could thus be rejected out of hand, my other two stories, irrespective of acceptance, stood little chance of appearing in *Horizon*, and indeed they didn't. I dared not ask if Maugham had been, or would be, paid.

'Of course the detective story *is* in decline,' Connolly was saying. 'Its great period, its golden age, really ended with *The Glass Key* in 1931.'

I said: 'Aren't you quoted as saying that in *The Face on the Cutting Room Floor* by Cameron McCabe, whoever he is?'

'Why yes,' Connolly said, 'I believe I am. A brilliant book don't you agree?'

I did agree. *The Face on the Cutting Room Floor* was a strange sophisticated off-beat crime novel, by its very nature pseudonymous, which came out in 1937. 'You don't happen to know who really wrote it?' I asked.

'No I never found out. Who would be your guess?'

I said: 'I'd thought of you, actually.'

'As Cameron McCabe?' Connolly stared at me astonished. 'What gave you that idea?'

'Well, knowing your interest in this type of book it occurred to me you might have had a go at writing one under another name. Whoever wrote it has from internal evidence read a lot of detective stories, and your own reviews are so often quoted in the Epilogue that . . .' Here I broke off embarrassed, conscious too late of the brick I'd already dropped.

But to my relief Connolly had begun to laugh. 'I see,' he said. 'You thought I was giving myself a pseudonymous boost. Well I'm sorry, I'd like to have written that book, but I didn't. The author's obviously an experienced film technician for one thing, and I am not.'

Our glasses were empty, he flapped a hand at the waiter, then said: 'Now tell me, how did you get on with Bill Makins last night?'

'Excellently. Though I was scared stiff of him at first sight.'

Connolly laughed. 'Yes he's very fierce looking, but wouldn't he be more so without the beard?' and we discussed Makins' beard, Connolly believing that he wore it because his face would otherwise seem too stark and Scottish, I taking the view that it added to his fierceness. Both of us discounted the possibility that it might conceal a weak chin.

Connolly said: 'But a lot of young men seem to be wearing beards these days. There's another young man who comes round to the office occasionally with a reddish beard, trying to argue me into publishing things of his. Poetical plays,' he sighed: 'I suppose I'll have to give in eventually, I'm very weak that way,' but he wasn't weak and he didn't give in, for I cannot remember anything by the red bearded author ever appearing in *Horizon*.

I drank a fresh drink very quickly to give me courage, then asked: 'I suppose there's no more news from the printers about *A Bit of a Smash*,' for when I saw Maugham's proofs first I'd hoped they were my own, but now I'd begun to fear this story wouldn't come out either. But I was wrong.

Connolly seemed to rouse himself: 'I'm glad you reminded

me, yesterday I forgot to ask. The substitutes for what the printers termed 'offensive language.' Have you decided yet what they're to be.'

'I have them here,' I said. 'You'll see I've put 'sewn-up' for 'pissed-up' as you suggested.'

'Sewn-up, yes,' Connolly said reading rapidly down the list: 'Holy Smoke' instead of 'By Christ,' 'Bunk' for 'Balls,' 'Bleeder' for 'Bugger' and 'Damn-all' for 'Sweet F.A.' That seems all right and the word 'bainchut' can stay in because they don't know what it means. It's a shame to emasculate your story like this, not my fault, all these printers are such damned puritans you know. Almost an occupational disease. But never fear,' he smiled tucking the list away, 'I'll get that piece out in *Horizon* if I have to bring printers over from Madras to do it !'

And, for all I know, he may have done. That might explain why, when the story did appear, part of my surname was mis-spelt 'Maclaryn': an error which partly reduced the pleasure I felt at seeing something of mine in print at last.

# They Can't Give You A Baby

*A big lake*

'They can do anything to you in the army bar give you a baby,' the old London-Irish porter who'd had varicocele and served in four campaigns told me as I got aboard the train in July 1940. 'But keep your trap shut and your bowels open you can't come to no harm.'

So I reported as ordered to the Infantry Training camp at Blandford, Essex, and was there enlisted as No. 6027033 Private Ross J.

Further advice was offered me on arrival by an older recruit who said: 'Take my tip, mate, when they put you down for the range don't go on the piss the night before and don't go with no woman neither 'cause you can't shoot proper with a shaking hand,' but this advice was wasted because the only drink available in the camp was Naafi beer which certainly resembled piss but was not drunk-making enough to send one on it; no women were allowed in; and we for the first fortnight weren't allowed out.

Besides, going on the range was out of the question as none of us had so far been issued with rifles: since Dunkirk, in short supply.

The survivors from Dunkirk had been billeted for a short time in the camp on their return, and the latrine walls were decorated with drawings of a death's head above a grave-mound, underlined with the caption: 'HOW D'YOU LIKE THIS YOU ROOKIE BASTARDS? (SIGNED) THE BOYS WHO BEEN THROUGH IT.'

There was also a rhyme signed by Spokeshave the Shithouse Poet, a universal figure who seems to have served in every regiment in the British Army:

'When apples are ripe
And ready for plucking
Girls of sixteen are ready for . . .

NOT WHAT YOU THINK THEY'RE
READY FOR YOU FILTHY-MINDED
FUCKERS.'

The camp looked from the air like a big lake, they told us, which hadn't prevented Jerry from dropping a load on it in the not so distant past, as craters in the surrounding chalk abundantly testified.

Every time a plane roared overhead, the blokes rushed joyfully to the barrack hut windows, shouting 'Watch out, boys, here comes Hitler!'; they made whistling noises like sticks of bombs falling, followed by concerted shouts of 'BOOM' to represent the explosion. But that summer Hitler seemed to have got sick of coming.

'That's on account of this new camouflage we got,' explained our platoon sergeant, who looked like the soldierly figure depicted on the labels of Camp coffee bottles and claimed that we resembled not a big lake but a big bloody shower.

So while we new recruits drilled in shirt sleeve order on the enormous sun baked barrack square, other more seasoned soldiers sprayed the surface of sheds and buildings round about with camouflage paint that speckled our bare arms and khaki shirts with almost indelible brown and green spots as it was blown towards us on the wind.

We drilled at first with broomsticks owing to the dearth of rifles, then an actual rifle appeared and was handed round the square, though our platoon hadn't much time to learn its mechanism before a runner came to attention in front of our sergeant saying: 'Please sar'nt our sar'nt in No. 8 says could we have the rifle for a dekko over there 'cause none of our blokes so much as seen one yet.'

We had none of us seen a steel helmet at close quarters either, they hadn't been issued to us although a consignment in the stores awaited a War Office or Command order authorizing distribution.

Then one afternoon, when parades were over and the blokes in our barrack hut were rattling their mess tins all ready for tea, Hitler came at last.

His coming was not heralded, as it should have been, by sirens (it turned out after someone had forgotten to let these off), and a series of dull detonations from the Artillery Camp across the valley caused little stir, as things were always going off over there. But this time the hum of an engine could be heard, the blokes began their whistling and booming then stopped abruptly, dropping their mess tins, as real whistles and crumps duplicated outside the sounds they'd made.

Through the window, from the hillside on which the Artillery Camp was built, a tall brown flower of earth could be seen blossoming while we watched: it expanded outwards like a firework in all directions and afterwards many swore they had seen swastikas on the wings of the lone raider that was now heading straight towards us.

There were no NCOs present, still less an officer; we dashed to the side doorway, got jammed in the entrance, then threw ourselves flat beneath a whitewashed wall outside as Jerry zoomed over low, chips of whitewash flew; and we heard for the first time in earnest the DUH-DUH-DUH of the machine gun that had been so often mimicked in jest.

The plane dived, again the DUH-DUH-DUH, then it banked and headed towards the Gunner camp while we made crouching for the trenches: there was no one to lead the way there but we knew that already since we'd helped, ourselves, to dig them in the chalk, pissing on our palms to harden them as it was said that navvies did.

More bombs whistled down, one sounding like a direct hit; and the Nazi plane returned, circling silver and so high above our heads it could hardly be seen; voices from adjoining trenches shouted: 'Where the bleeding bloody officers?' and 'Why'nt we got tin hats?' while somebody shrilled hysterically: 'Shut your row he'll hear us, he'll hear us I tell you shut your bleeding row.'

The Jerry pilot didn't hear them and soon ceased to hear anything at all, for he flew away to be caught in the Bournemouth barrage and shot down in flames so we were later told.

Directly he'd gone everyone clambered out of the trenches and began to utter guffaws of relief and bravado, then suddenly a young subaltern appeared panting, to mutters of 'Bout time too' and 'Joy your tea, mate?', and red in the face ordered us back in until the All Clear was blown, which happened after we'd stood tealess for another thirty minutes in the trenches.

There were no casualties in the Artillery Camp, indeed we almost wished Jerry had chosen us instead, for the direct hit had demolished the Gunners' empty gym whereas ours remained intact and there were many who hated PT, above all the Horse.

But the upshot of this baptism by fire was that we were issued with tin hats and small arms shortly followed. First to be given a rifle was our barrack room NCO, a lance-corporal who'd been an insurance clerk in civvy street and now felt the chance had come to show his mettle as a leader of men.

To demonstrate the efficacy of our new steel helmets and the protection they afforded, he clapped on his own tin hat then handing his rifle to a huge recruit told this man to strike him with the butt.

The recruit, a gentle timid soul despite his size, demurred. 'That's an order,' the lance-jack rapped out, 'You either hit me or go on a 252,' there was a pause while the nature of a 252, the minor offence report, was explained to the huge recruit who could expect seven days to barracks if he went on one for disobeying an order; then down came the rifle butt, blood spurted from under the tin hat's brim and the corporal sank slowly down, the sound of his fall swiftly echoed by a heavier thump as the huge recruit followed suit, having fainted at the sight of blood.

It appeared a loose screw inside the corporal's helmet had been driven into his scalp by the blow; we agreed that a screw had also been loose inside the corporal's head, and he was carted off to hospital where the huge contrite recruit visited him every day: being unable, himself, ever to handle a rifle with confidence thereafter.

Meanwhile the barrack room radio played records of Judy

Garland singing Over The Rainbow or a tune called I Was Watching A Man Paint A Fence; and the camp must have ceased to look from above like a big lake, for Jerry took time off from the Battle of Britain to bomb us day and night.

Planes came over in droves, it was no longer necessary for the blokes to whistle and boom, all leave was cancelled, and when not a lot of the ITC was left we were abruptly evacuated, destination unknown to all other ranks.

On arrival, after a roundabout train journey so long that we'd believed ourselves bound for Scotland, we were assembled on an enormous desert of asphalt and addressed in pitch darkness by the Commanding Officer of another ITC in Suffolk.

'Now you men have been through a bad time,' he told us, 'blitzed and strafed right and left by the Hun, and you've stood up to it well. But you'll be glad to hear that Jerry hasn't smelt us out so far ha ha, so you can get on with your training in peace,' and at this prospect searchlights suddenly probed the sky, a German engine nosed chugging somewhere overhead, and the sirens started to wail.

## X Company

Now what I always think of as the Brown Period began. Browned-off was the phrase one heard most often in X Company, the other recruits owing to difficulty in finding any skirt started jocosely to talk of having Bits of Brown (buggery), the RAF blokes stationed next door called us Brown Jobs, it was autumn and the leaves were brown, and everything was uniquely brown.

The Biscuits on which we fell, exhausted after all day training, were also brown and a great source of grumbling as at Blandford we'd had real iron beds with sheets to sleep in: here we kipped down on bare boards with the three brown Biscuits beneath us, wrapped in brown blankets which had been recently fumigated and stank for weeks on end; on the other hand we couldn't spend much time in them since Jerry visited us regularly every night.

Indeed, Acky the barrack room clown and butt kipped

always fully clothed and wearing boots, so's to be ready he told us 'for when the sireens start dropping their shit'. Nothing could persuade Acky that the sirens were not the cause of bombs being dropped; only dimly aware that aircraft existed, he believed that the warning was a special device which Hitler himself operated by remote control, anticipating the doodle-bugs and V-2 rockets yet to come: perhaps like many simple-tons he possessed the gift of prophecy.

The worst of the raids was not stumbling to the trenches through black night occasionally lit by bursting incendiaries, searchlight beams or flashes of ack-ack fire, but waiting in the iron cold when winter came for the All-Clear to go, for until it went we were not allowed to return to our blankets which by this time had ceased to stink.

I remember one night standing in a trench next to a corporal when all sounds of strife had long since faded and any danger was clearly past, both of us frozen to the bone despite long woollen underpants, battle dress, greatcoat, balaclava helmet and woollen gloves: we'd ceased for some time to feel our feet except as blocks of ice we stood on; but when I cursed our lot the corporal stolidly replied: 'Could be worse mate.'

I said: 'How could it be worse? We've been here two bloody hours frozen solid while Jerry drops stuff all round us, now he's gone but that bastard siren still won't blow maybe till reveille, so how could it be worse?'

The corporal said stolidly: 'Could be bleeding sight worse mate. Could be pissing down with rain as well.'

It was an unpleasant sensation after such a night to rise at six with the sky above still black and stars out over the wash-house where we shaved in icy water: the cistern of the latrines, liberally sprinkled with the works of Spokeshave, having also frozen so the plug wouldn't pull.

At these times the sense of helplessness was strong. Jaeger who despite his asthma had been allowed into the Artillery could at least defend himself: in fact he had done more. Manning a gun during an alert on the coast one night, he'd got bored and fired off a burst at random, bringing down by a lucky chance a Jerry plane that happened to be flying over at the time.

For this feat he'd been forthwith promoted bombardier; and by the same post that brought his letter announcing this, came under separate cover a copy of his first novel, out that week.

Nobody promoted me, I remained unalterably a private and had temporarily given up any attempt to write. I had however sent my green folder of stories, returned finally by *Horizon*, to a new anthology called *English Story* which was due to be published twice a year in hard-cover book-form, giving the ITC address without knowing that its editor, Woodrow Wyatt, was stationed as a subaltern in this very camp.

So one evening when we got back from shovelling snow off the rifle range where, owing to weather conditions, we'd still not fired a single shot, I received word that an officer wanted me to report urgent over at his bunk.

### Woodrow Wyatt in the Army

Last time I heard of Woodrow Wyatt MP (Lab.) he was chasing out of his house burglars who'd been incautious enough to break into it. By that time he had been not only an MP but a Parliamentary Under-Secretary and Financial Secretary to the War Office, and I hadn't seen him, except when he was interviewing someone on the Telly, for twenty years.

The photograph appended to the *Evening Standard* account of the abortive burglary told me little of what he looked like now save that it looked as if he'd put on flesh.

But when I saw him first, as a second lieutenant in the Suffolks, he was a short slender young man, precocious though not pompous, about whom everything seemed to be polished: his Sam Browne and ox-blood shoes, the buttons of his service dress, his round cheeks and reddish nose. He had a small neat head and, brushed flat across his forehead, black or very dark hair that seemed polished also, or at any rate to shine. His eyes shone brightly too behind horn rims, the lenses of his spectacles were thick and so were his lips which pouted as he spoke or puffed a cigar.

At that date he must have been twenty-two, six years younger than myself, but was apparently a qualified barrister or anyhow had studied for the bar. Altogether a bright young man and bearing already the hallmarks of one who'd far to go. But though a socialist he'd no political ambitions then, his ambition was to be himself a writer and to make a really good anthology out of *English Story* which he co-edited with his wife.

We sat smoking cigars in his bunk where a small stove burned, blissfully warm after shovelling snow all day, there may have been some drink as well and it was pleasant to talk of other things than training and what we were down for on tomorrow's Detail, though I was at first nervous of being discovered there as the Battalion took a dim view of fraternisation despite Hore-Belisha : especially between officers and other ranks, since even a newly made-up lance-jack was not allowed to 'walk out,' as they put it, with a private soldier.

'Like a bloody courting couple,' Wyatt chortled when I told him this. 'Honestly they are a pack of bloody twerps.' He had a loud angry sounding laugh and a complete contempt for routine and regulations. 'I'd damn soon send them packing if they came sniffing round my private quarters, don't you worry.'

He told me he'd accepted my only other story about Madras, much shorter than *A Bit of a Smash,* and entitled *The Hell of a Time* : it would be coming out in the next volume of *English Story,* and he planned to publish another of mine in the volume after that only they hadn't chosen yet.

He said : 'Any story except one called *Happy as the Day is Long.* I've not read that so far, but Susan's dead against it so that rules it out.'

'Your wife?'

Wyatt nodded. 'I rely implicitly on her judgment.'

I said : 'But that's a good story. Connolly nearly printed it so did *Penguin Parade.* Read it yourself and see.'

He said : 'No, no, Susan says it's no good at all and Susan can't be wrong, so I'm afraid that's that,' but that wasn't that, for much later he read the story for himself and was so enthusiastic that he sent me a telegram of acceptance: though this was after he separated from his wife.

He asked what I was writing now, I said under army conditions it was impossible to write, he said Balls, I should put in for a pip, then I'd be more comfortable and also be able to do something for the men.

I said I'd a hard job to do anything for myself let alone the men, he said Utter nonsense, he'd have a word with the Old Man; and when I got up to go it was slightly surprising to find he didn't know what time Lights Out was for Other Ranks.

But then he'd not been commissioned long, no rubbish about going through the ranks, but straight from school OTC and University to be commissioned almost on the outbreak.

I saw him twice more before he was transferred to an orderly room at Ipswich: once in the Company Lines where he showed signs of wanting to stop and talk, but with my CSM watching I saluted him and hurried on; then when he was doing duty as Orderly Officer in the cookhouse.

There he tasted a spoonful of rice pudding, pronounced it perfectly foul (which was an understatement) and tried to egg us on to make complaints, though even I buried my face in my tin plate: since to say anything against the food amounted to a Frivolous Complaint and I'd nearly done jankers for that already.

Then came his transfer to Ipswich where I later followed him: by that time he'd been posted for special training at the Staff College, but terrific tales persisted of his prowess as a Defending Officer at Courts Martial, for which he'd become much feared and respected in the Regiment.

Accused soldiers from far and wide asked for Mr Wyatt as an American in trouble might send for Perry Mason. His clients were always acquitted, he'd succeeded in getting off a chap who'd burned down his tent during an exercise under canvas and had even secured an acquittal in a case of what sounded uncommonly like murder.

When, in London on leave, I asked him afterwards how he'd

managed this, he merely laughed out loud and said the Prosecution Officers opposing him were such dimwits it was just a piece of cake. He was by then a staff captain at the War House and tried to get me a job there though he failed.

But he must have put a word in for me somewhere at the Suffolk ITC, for suddenly I was brought before my Company Commander and put on the roll of OCTU candidates as a potential officer.

The major was ex-Indian Army, enormously tall with a shaggy black moustache and he wasn't stuck on having haircuts either, though where his men were concerned it was a case of 'Don't do as I do, do as I tell you.'

He said to me in his subterranean rumble, which all of us imitated though with respect: 'Now look here Ross I've had one or two complaints about you, insubordination and so on, but I'm prepared to believe you're doing your best and so I'm recommending you to see the Commanding Officer with a view to obtaining a commission. After all I suppose soldiering must be damned difficult for you just as writing books would be for me. Couldn't write a book to save my ruddy life. However there's a war on and we're all having to make sacrifices and do things we don't care for. Take me for example, my real life was in India, been there since I was a boy, but the war was being fought in Europe so I went and got myself shot up at Dunkirk, too badly for them to ever have me back out there I'm afraid. No, when this show's over I'll be kicked out with a tiny pension, won't even be able to afford to hunt, which was the only thing I enjoyed doing in civilian life over here. I was shot in the arse too, which makes it worse. Hard to sit a horse and looks as if I'd been bloody well running away.'

*Oppenheim*

The Commanding Officer was a very small colonel sitting behind a very big desk. He screwed in an eyeglass and said: 'Educated in the South of France eh? D'you speak French?'

'Yes sir,' I said.

The CO said: 'Not much use, French, now that France

John Minton

Francis Bacon

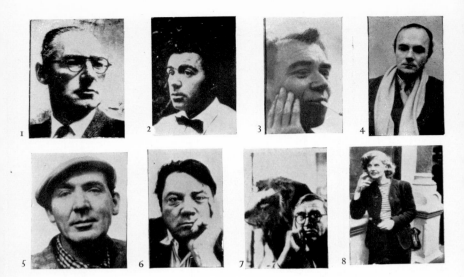

Dylan Thomas

1  David Archer
2  W. S. Graham
3  Robert Macbryde
4  Keith Vaughan
5  George Barker
6  John Davenport
7  Anthony Carson
8  Elizabeth Smart

has fallen unfortunately.'

Then he looked at my paper again and said: 'What's this, "Civilian Occupation: Author." Are you an author?'

'Yes sir,' I told him.

'D'you write spy thrillers?'

'No sir.'

The CO said: 'Pity, that. E. Phillips Oppenheim now, he writes damn good spy thrillers. Lived in the South of France too. D'you ever come across him down there?'

'As a matter of fact I did sir. At a party once.'

'*Very interesting*,' said the CO. And tell me what did he talk about?'

'Well sir he talked about agents mostly.'

'Agents!' the CO exclaimed. 'Well of course, fellow like that would know all about secret agents. Wonder to me they haven't made him Head of MI5.'

'I'm sorry sir,' I said. 'It wasn't secret agents he talked about, it was literary agents.'

'*Literary* agents?' the CO said. What the devil are they?'

I said: 'Well sir, they place the work you've written with editors and publishers you see.'

The CO said: 'Do they now.'

I said: 'Not in my experience sir.'

The CO said: 'Oh, thought you said they did. Well anyway it's most interesting to've talked to you,' and turning to my Company Commander, who stood massively beside his chair: 'Well of course he's passed all right, an author, knows Oppenheim and that, eh? Why hasn't he got a stripe?'

The major rumbled: 'No vacancy on establishment sir.'

The CO said: 'Oh, pity that. Well all right Ross, Brigadier next step, keep your fingers crossed, gooday'; the sergeant major entered shouting: 'Private Ross, Private Ross SHUN. Left wheel, quick march, left-right left-right-left,' and in getting past the CO I was luckier than many OCTU wallahs, one of whom had been failed for the following reason.

He was an instructor, young, fighting fit, two stripes,

D

splendid record as an NCO and would have made an even better officer, but at one time he'd been stationed in Scotland and the CO had therefore asked him: 'How long is the Forth Bridge, Corporal?'

'I'm sorry sir,' the corporal answered, 'I couldn't say.'

'You mean you don't know?'

'Yes sir.'

'How long were you in Scotland Corporal?'

'Six months sir.'

'And you don't know the length of the Forth Bridge?'

'No sir.'

'Thank you Corporal, that's all,' and as the corporal was marched out, to be marked unsuitable as officer material. But the real reason for failing him had nothing to do with the length of the Forth Bridge, it was because of his strong Cockney accent which the CO didn't feel would make him welcome in the Mess.

Giles Cooper, now one of our best TV dramatists and certainly the best we have on radio, was as a young lieutenant attached to the ITC for a time, though of course owing to our CO's rigid segregation of officers and men I never met him there.

Giles, as he afterwards told me, also found disfavour with the CO almost on arrival, for a reason even stranger than that which caused the rejection of the corporal.

On his first evening in the Mess, the CO had said to the Adjutant: 'That new young fellow just been posted to us. Cooper, isn't it?'

'It is sir.'

'He wears an eyeglass.'

'Yes sir. Astigmatism I believe.'

'Damned impertinence you mean,' the CO said. 'I'm the only one who's allowed to wear an eyeglass in this Mess. Have Mr Cooper posted elsewhere please, soon as you can, overseas if possible,' which is how Giles came eventually to serve in Burma which provided the setting for one of his finest TV plays.

92

But I never became an officer.

It was at the WOSBE, the War Office Selection Board Test, that I came unstuck. I'd been doing splendidly until the very last exercise when, being for the moment in command, I decided to save the lives of my men at the expense of my own.

It was a dodgy situation, all the umpires had gathered round to watch: we were retreating with imaginary Jerries on our tail, imagining bullets were whining round our heads and the only means of escape was over a bridge (non-imaginary) which we'd built across a bottomless chasm below. The chasm was not imaginary either but is was hardly bottomless, being about fifteen feet deep, so ordering my lot ahead of me across the bridge I decided to blow this up with our imaginary grenades and ammunition so the Jerries couldn't follow, thus also destroying the ammunition which might otherwise have fallen into their hands.

Therefore, straddling the tree trunk we'd stretched across the gap, I tugged it loose from the bank and clasping it in my arms fell to my death in the chasm: I'm not certain I wasn't riddled with German bullets for good measure as I fell.

Anyhow in my opinion I deserved a posthumous VC and a hero's grave at the very least; yet to my surprise, when I'd scrambled out of the chasm, the umpires were all walking away and the following day I was returned unsuitable to my unit, the report to my Company Commander saying that I'd not taken the Test seriously enough to merit recommendation for OCTU.

'Not seriously enough?' I cried. 'When I died to save my men? What more do they expect?'

I was no longer at the ITC and this Company Commander was not the major:[1] in fact he was a captain.

He said: 'You died for your men?'

I said: 'Greater love hath no man,' and told him about the bridge.

[1] The major, now a Lieut. Col., had also left the ITC and was my CO instead of OC in the new battalion.

The captain said: Seems to me you behaved with great presence of mind. Don't know what they can have found wrong.'

'Nor do I sir. Except for one thing?'

'And what was that?'

'Well you see sir, when I blew up the bridge and myself as well, I shouted BOOM as I fell into the chasm. That's what may have upset them.'

The captain said: 'You shouted BOOM? But why?'

I said: 'Sound of the explosion sir. You see everything was imaginary, the Germans and the bullets, the grenades and ammunition, so I thought we ought to have a little realism when it came to the bang, otherwise it all seemed a bit too much like a game of tin soldiers if you understand me sir.'

'I do,' the captain said dubiously, 'But all the same,' he added shaking his head, 'you shouldn't have shouted BOOM.'

# The Double Death of William Cooper Makins

But in the autumn of 1941 Bill Makins had not even died once, nor had I yet shouted BOOM. As a potential officer (though still without a stripe) I'd been transferred to orderly room duties at the Ipswich HQ where Woodrow Wyatt had secured his sensational acquittals, and Makins as my self-appointed agent was trying to find me a publisher in London.

Previous to my being enlisted, when *A Bit of a Smash* appeared in *Horizon*, a publisher had however found me.

## 30 Bedford Square Again

Rupert Hart-Davis was then a junior director of Jonathan Cape and soon after receiving his enthusiastic letter I was seated opposite him in a different, smaller office from that in which I'd been interviewed two years before by Mr Cape himself: now in America on business and prevented from returning by the outbreak of war.

Hart-Davis in those days was a large loose limbed young man, blond with small shrewd blue eyes in a big fair face: smooth shaven except for the fair moustache clipped square above a humorous mouth. He had a deep hearty voice, lounged easily in hairy tweeds and swivel chair and although he did not, like Norman Collins, actually put his feet up on the desk, gave the impression of being just about to do so.

Perhaps all young publishers affected these relaxed postures in the office, though the way Hart-Davis sat may have been due to the length of his legs, for he was perhaps two inches taller than myself besides being four years older.

One of the first things he asked me was my age, and when I told him 28, stated his own adding that I'd been quite right to publish late.

'It's much better not to publish anything until one's

properly mature,' he told me and as two properly mature men we beamed at each other across the desk. The Thirties writers were like pop singers are today, adolescent publication was if not the rule at any rate no exception, and I'm always surprised when nowadays the thirty-year-old author of some first novel is treated as if he were an infant prodigy.

I took care however not to tell Hart-Davis that my apparent wisdom in publishing late was really due to my work being hitherto rejected right and left; then we talked of Simenon, whose first books to be translated into English were just being issued by Routledge, two Maigrets in one volume to make up the 80,000 words then *de rigueur* in the trade.

Hart-Davis said: 'Of course all this business about length is absolute tripe. The Maigret novels are good precisely *because* they're short. In France 40,000 words is quite acceptable for separate publication, so he's able to cut out all the boring bits and is therefore much more readable. In England detective story writers are obliged to pad, their publishers insist on 80,000 because of the libraries, and that's why ours seem so damned dull.'

I said: 'But would you as a publisher accept a detective story or any other novel of 40,000 words if it were sent to you? Wouldn't the same restrictions apply?'

Hart-Davis swivelled sideways in his chair, stretched his legs out further, then said well they didn't publish detective stories anyway, and of course they'd done *The Postman* and other short American novels that'd been successful: he nevertheless admitted frankly that owing to pressure from the lending libraries publication of anything under 70,000 was a risk not lightly to be undertaken.

However, he said, it might be different now, with wartime paper rationing, and if ever I wrote a novel, even underlength, they'd be glad to consider it, and at parting he clapped me on the back. Despite his heartiness and genuine good fellowship I sensed he was a shrewd man besides being a likeable one, it showed in his eyes, and I thought I'd be lucky to have him for a publisher.

96

Since our meeting, in spite of army conditions, I had indeed written a short novel; but unfortunately Hart-Davis had been called up like everyone else, except Makins whom they still hadn't managed to enrol, and who wrote me that Rupert was now a Coldstream Guardsman.

## Too Short

The short novel I'd managed to complete had started as the 10,000 word South of France story which Connolly had asked me to write for *Horizon*, but ended up at treble the length.

Naturally *Horizon* couldn't print it, as it would have more than filled the entire magazine; Oliver Warner of Chatto and Windus, approached by Makins, had shown interest and then backed down because of the length: even shorter than the minimum mentioned by Hart-Davis; Allen and Unwin had rejected it for the same reason, mislaying for a while the second half of the MS during the period of consideration.

They were however much more interested in my vacuum cleaner novel, originally estimated at 25,000 words but evidently destined to be much longer, since Part One alone comprised 20,000: already written and now in the hands of Makins.

'Congratulations!' It is becoming *richer,*' he wrote to me and promised to show the MS to Philip Unwin, nephew of the Chairman, at the earliest opportunity, adding as a post-script: 'Unless the ruddy army gets me first.'

Meanwhile my second Madras piece only appeared in Woodrow Wyatt's *English Story No. 2* and had a reasonable reception when this was reviewed: I'd also managed to sell at last *Five Finger Exercises* (always difficult, in those pre-*Lolita* days, to place because of its subject)[1] to another miscellany called *Fortune Anthology*: though 'sell' is not quite accurate since *Fortune Anthology* couldn't afford to pay a fee: Makins suggesting when he heard this, that the Anthology should

[1] I was consequently surprised when a TLS reviewer later dismissed it as a conventional magazine story, out of place in an *avant-garde* miscellany like this.

appear in future under its initials only as these seemed appropriate enough.

*Museum Street*
Philip Unwin, suave and greying at the temples, shook his head roguishly at me: 'When I read *A Bit of a Smash* I said to myself "Ah, these Sahibs from out East certainly know how to tell a story," ' and paused, looking in his black jacket and pin stripe trousers like a Harley Street psychiatrist or an aesthetic member of some government department, preferably the Colonial Office.

Then he went on: 'It was a disappointment when Bill Makins told me you'd never been to Madras, but you know how to tell a story all the same I must admit.'

The implication was of an imposture or false pretences good humouredly exposed, but I was glad Makins had passed on this information as I wasn't feeling in the least like a Sahib that afternoon. I was passing through London on leave, had not yet been able to change into civvy clothes and even in my best battle dress, brightened by the yellow and red Suffolk flashes, felt no match for Unwin's formal elegance.

I was particularly self-conscious about my heavy army boots, and glad that these were hidden beneath his desk in the office at Ruskin House: other Ranks not being allowed to go about in shoes at this stage of the war.

Unwin smiled, the psychiatrist for the moment uppermost. 'Curious this fixation, however, in the novel also the narrator returns to England from Madras. Is there some psychological explanation I wonder.'

'None,' I told him. 'I just like the characters to have backgrounds that are not my own.'

'Ah yes,' Unwin nodded, 'I understand. It reduces the autobiographical element certainly,' and aligning on his desk top the MS books that Makins had passed to him, went on to say the firm was willing to make me an advance in order both to secure an option on the novel and also encourage me to continue writing it.

His smile had switched to the administratorial, his tone became more suavely diplomatic, and I felt like a small native tribe on whom a disadvantageous treaty is about to be imposed.

'How much?' I asked.

Unwin said: 'We were thinking in terms of a total advance of £25. Of which ten would be payable on signature of contract.'

I said: 'It's not an awful lot.'

Unwin explained: 'My uncle, our chairman, does not believe in making large advances to young authors. He doesn't believe that this practice lends encouragement to their industry.'

I said: 'You mean they're more likely to work if they're broke?' not knowing that this is an illusion which all publishers entertain.

In his book *The Truth About Publishing* (7th edition) Sir Stanley Unwin LL.D states: 'The hardest bargain he (a financially sound publisher) may drive is likely to prove more profitable to you than the most alluring contract with an insolvent firm.' Nonetheless I felt that, while Allen and Unwin were undoubtedly solvent, this particular bargain was a trifle too hard for me to accept.

Philip Unwin smiled thinly and spread his hands: the natives had proved less ignorant, or more cunning in their primitive way, than the administrator had expected.

I said: 'I'm sorry, in any case you'd better negotiate with Bill,' and soon found myself outside Ruskin House under the smoky autumn sky of Museum Street to which summer seldom comes.

Dusk moreover was encroaching as in my heavy boots I clumped along to the corner where Makins waited in the saloon bar of the Museum Tavern where I was to spend many evenings during the Flying Bomb period: but even then, in June 1944, the skies above that Street were always overcast and autumnal, the sun never shone, allowing the doodle bugs to slip through our defences under cover of the cloud drifting overhead.

I'd called for Makins, as arranged by letter, at *Horizon* Office earlier that afternoon. I didn't see Cyril Connolly but he apparently caught a glimpse of me, for Makins wrote afterwards that he'd said I looked very much a soldier in my uniform, which would have surprised the Suffolk sergeant-major.

Makins immediately took me on a conducted tour of the Bloomsbury bomb sites, for I'd not been in London since the Blitz and during it they wouldn't give me leave (I must emphasize this point, since in a taxi once I was called 'a Soho non-blitzer' by a very stout young woman known to us as Are They Real Or Are They False).

We inspected stretches of rubble from which rose shells of blackened brick that seemed to stay upright only by an effort of will. In one of them the privy was revealed complete with undamaged lavatory bowl, cistern and chain, halfway up a landing under which stairs had collapsed with the outer wall that bomb blast had neatly stripped away.

Makins reported that Graham Greene himself had been seen staring with peculiar intentness at this particular ruin, and from this deduced that he might be writing something about London in the air raids: though at the moment Greene was said to be going to Africa on some Top Secret Foreign Office mission, or had perhaps already gone.

Africa combined with Top Secret rang a bell, and I described to Makins how at the ITC, not long after my Oppenheim interview, I'd suddenly been summoned by the Adjutant who proposed that I should volunteer for Special Service with a cipher Department somewhere on the Gold Coast, starting with the rank of Sergeant, allowances, and several rates of additional pay.

'It's the White Man's Grave,' the Adjutant told me. 'Pretty ropey billet, terrible heat, malaria, leprosy and cholera plague, you've got a week to think it over and I won't blame you if the answer's no.'

I said instantly: 'I'll take it sir'; 'What?' the Adjutant

cried disconcerted, 'Better not decide anything in a hurry you know, White Man's Grave remember, it'll be too late once you're on the roster,' but I told him: 'I've decided sir. You can put me on it right away,' then went down promptly with pneumonia and according to the MO service in Africa was out for me, at any rate that year.

So I was struck off the Special Service roster, reinstated on the roll of OCTU candidates, and posted to the Ipswich HQ on my return from convalescent leave.

'Christ you must have been delirious already,' Makins exclaimed, 'to volunteer for duty in a place like that'. 'Anything to get away from the Home Front,' I told him. 'My dear Bill you've yet to find out what the army's like.'

'Yes and I'll make ruddy sure I never do,' Makins retorted: Evelyn Waugh was in the army too he told me, a novel with a wartime setting due out soon, and we arrived at the hall where a concert was being held and Makins' wife whom I'd not previously met awaited us.

Carlotta Makins, plump, short, and Spanish-looking, had shiny black hair and wore black with gipsyish adornments; inside the hall instruments were tuning up, people anxiously consulted scores and several heads craned round startled to see a private soldier clumping in and taking up a seat on one of those fragile little chairs.

My awkwardness at being in khaki, temporarily forgotten, revived at this: the concert too turned out to be chamber music, which I support only with difficulty, but I attempted to look appropriately soulful until the last item, when Mrs Makins immediately left us and it was time for my appointment with Unwin.

'Well?' Makins asked ordering Scotch as I entered the Museum Tavern. 'Far from well,' I answered and he stroked his beard soberly while I described the interview.

'Not to worry, they'll come round to paying more in time,' he told me and come round in time they did: though not for another two years, when Philip Unwin over the telephone offered me an advance of £50 on a volume of army stories which I'd already sold for twice that amount to Jonathan Cape.

'Drink up, my round,' I told Makins who emptied his glass at a gulp; luckily before going on leave I had drawn some pay which I'd managed to save and had thus been proof against Unwin's proffered tenner.

Makins' beard bristled with optimism as he downed a toast to our future; he was coming up for yet another bloody Board but they'd not a chance of nailing him; and in a haze of whisky fumes I clumped off through the black-out to pick up my kit and catch a train for the South Coast.

### Old Bill
Catastrophe followed swiftly on, for they did nail Makins after all.

X-rays at the Medical Board showed his stomach ulcer to be either healed or non-existent, he was re-graded as A1 and a terrible letter of farewell, such as one might receive from a lamb on its way to the slaughter, arrived announcing his departure for an army training depot somewhere in England: the worst being of course that he would *have to shave off his beard.*

Silence supervened, and almost simultaneously I was myself re-posted as clerk to the Second-in-Command of a Young Soldiers Battalion on the Suffolk Coast: billeted in a requisitioned hotel facing the sea-front where mines bobbed about like buoys beyond the coils of rusty Dannert wire.

The Young Soldiers were delinquents to a boy, always deserting or committing robbery and rape; the Regimental Jail, also in our building, had a 'FULL UP' notice on it like a Bloomsbury hotel, and all winter I was kept fully occupied typing out reports of various offences.

Then once more I heard from Makins and opening the letter was dumbfounded.

Makins *liked* the army. He'd received top marks on his training, given up drink and tobacco ('Must keep fit you know'), wrote in praise of discipline, and couldn't understand what I'd got against routine and regulations without which after all the army couldn't function. The loss of his beard seemed more than compensated for by corporal's stripes, and he wound up by saying I'd given him a completely false impression of a damn fine outfit.

After receiving several letters in this strain I replied sharply saying I'd have to think of him as *Old Bill* if he carried on like this any further: unperturbed Makins replied that he'd just returned from an MT course and been promoted Sergeant.

By this time it was Spring and in charge of his platoon he was shot off to North Africa where, according to Lydia, Bombardier Jaeger had preceded him.

*Cairo*
And then for the first time he died.

He was burnt to death in Egypt. I heard the news from Carlotta Makins whose handwriting I remember was enormous and who wrote in crimson ink. She enclosed the MS books of the vacuum cleaner novel, left behind at their flat when he joined up, also a press cutting from a Cairo newspaper describing how William C. Makins, a journalist on leave from the Middle East Forces, had died from asphyxia in a hotel bedroom set on fire, apparently, by a cigarette left alight whilst he was asleep: thus he shared the same fate as Louis Joseph Vance, author of *The Lone Wolf* novels so popular during the First World War and which, adapted as films featuring Warren William, were circulating cinemas at the very date of Makins' death.

That summer I seemed surrounded by death: my mother had just died, returning from the funeral I received Mrs Makins' letter, and I'd nearly died myself: a live round fired on the range had struck my steel helmet while I was marking in the butts, and for years I carried this bullet about as the One With My Name On It: possession of which, according to army superstition, guaranteed immortality at any rate for the duration.

I packed away the MS books together with all Makins'

letters and the other completed portion of the vacuum cleaner novel: it was though a file had been marked closed or as if the death of Makins had for the time being severed a thread binding us both to this book, and not until four years after was I able to work on it again.

## Tales of Army Life

Meanwhile Tobruk had fallen; my boss, the Second-in-Command, sauntered about in white flannels carrying a tennis racket or cricket bat; the Young Soldiers set fire to the Gym; and having failed the WOSB Test I gave up any hope of active participation in the war.

Instead I started writing a series of army stories and typing them in the evenings on my portable typewriter which I carried with me throughout my service: on this I also did the Second-in-Command's paper work while he played cricket or tennis and arranged various fixtures as Battalion Sports Officer, a position which no one envied him since the Young Soldiers didn't take kindly to organized games.

I wrote the stories after duty in a large café restaurant on the sea-front, always full of handsome Wrens vying with each other about the RAF officers who'd taken them out the night before. RAF officers rated tops, being classified in turn by rank and number of decorations; naval officers came second and Brown Jobs a long long way behind. In any case it was Officers Only though the Wrens were not themselves commissioned: one presumes that those who were went out only with admirals and air-vice-marshals.

To my amusement, many years later one of these young women, having read my book of army stories, wrote to me and said she had recognized my description of the town, that she'd herself been stationed there, and claimed to have seen me often writing in the café. In fact none of the Wrens even looked in my direction, for a private soldier was not so much beneath their notice as practically invisible.

But while they enjoyed briefly their brightest period,

before the claims of suburban home and kitchen sink enclosed them, I wrote grimly on; and when the first of these stories *I Had to Go Sick*, published by *Horizon*, brought a letter of congratulation from Evelyn Waugh, I thought how pleased poor Makins would have been.

There were, in that peak year of 1942, excluding *Horizon* and *Penguin New Writing* where I was also published, no less than 16 markets for a short-story writer to choose from, unlike today; and stories of mine came out in all these periodicals and magazines including *Lilliput*.

Kaye Webb one of the *Lilliput* editors, who afterwards discovered and married the artist Ronald Searle, told me later how they came to publish me.

I'd submitted three stories, two months passed with no reply; so, bearing in mind my initial experience with *Horizon*, I wrote a letter to the Editor reminding him of my existence. In answer came a note from Kaye Webb's secretary saying she was sorry my stories had got caught up in the back of a drawer, but they'd now been found and she was returning them herewith as not suitable for publication.

The stories however were not returned therewith, instead on the following day a letter of acceptance arrived enclosing with apologies a cheque for all three stories.

What had caused this change of mind was that Kaye Webb had been lunching with a man who complained how few humorous stories of Forces life were appearing in her magazine. She replied that they were not receiving many, citing mine as some that had been mislaid and were now being sent back as she really had not had time enough to look at them.

Her luncheon companion said: 'Maclaren-Ross? But haven't you read his army story in *Horizon*? Don't mean to say you're *turning him down?*'

Kaye Webb who in fact had never heard of me, since editors do not really read a lot, returned to the office, went swiftly through my stories and dictated at once the letter of acceptance: thus beginning a long and, for me, profitable association, since Hulton Press periodicals paid twice as much as anybody else.

Hitherto I'd been selling some of my best early stories to the new paperback miscellanies, such as Reginald Moore's *Modern Reading* and *Selected Writing* or the short-lived *First Eighteen* (edited by the intriguing and attractive Patricia Joan Bruce) for as little as three guineas flat: a guinea of course being worth double in those days, nonetheless I did not become exactly rich.

At the same time I was fulfilling my ambition to earn a living by my work, and the appearance of the stories caused Rupert Hart-Davis, now a captain and adjutant in the Guards, to contact me again and arrange for their later publication in volume-form: so it came about that after all my first publisher was Cape.

I often remembered Makins at this time when I didn't need an agent, and reflected on how glad he'd be that my name was undoubtedly before the public now.

Then, in the winter of 1944, I heard again from him.

## A Dead Letter

It was a horrid winter; that night all traffic had been stopped and the Edgware Road, which I had to cross to reach my flat, was an empty stretch of polished ice. I was the only pedestrian afoot in a frozen world, crossing the road I fell down twice, and awaiting me at home was Makins' letter.

The angular handwriting was unmistakable, besides his name rank and number were written on the back. The postmark on the envelope, bearing Middle East stamps, was obliterated but, from the amount of re-addresses including old army units scrawled thereon, it had obviously been following me about for years.

It was a thick letter, crackling I thought with the optimism and future hopes contained inside, and I surveyed it with misgiving. I'd been fond of Makins, had mourned him already in my way, and I didn't feel at that moment up to reading a letter from the dead. As I put it away unopened a V2 rocket exploded dully, I remember, in the distance like a gun being fired over a soldier's grave.

Then when the war ended, one evening at the Wheatsheaf pub in Rathbone Place, I became aware of a tall pale man wearing a long pale mackintosh and grey hat, from under the straight stiff brim of which he'd been staring fixedly for quite a while.

'D'you remember me?' he asked.

'No,' I replied, sighing inwardly Here goes, for his long shaven chin jutted like a boot and he looked formidable and severe, bearing all the signs of a fellow seeking an argument or fight.

'Makins,' he announced abruptly. 'You've surely not forgotten? I'm Bill Makins.'

'No,' I said backing away alarmed, for a fight was one thing and a ghost quite another. 'Not possible. You are dead.'

'How can I be dead,' the ghost of Makins asked. 'When I am standing here?' and despite the beardless chin I recognized that piercing stare and eyes. 'You know bloody well I didn't die, you must have read my letter.'

'But the press-cutting,' I stammered. 'Carlotta sent it me, burnt to death in Cairo.'

'A mistake,' Makins explained with a long arm waving this away. 'It was a bloke called *Makin*, William C. Makin, who died not me.'

'W. C. Makin,' I cried. 'Who wrote a book called *Red Sea Nights*.'

'*Red Sea Nights*,' Makin nodded, 'and it was he who burned to death in that hotel,' then while I called shakily for Scotch, he went on further to explain.

W. C. Makin was a journalist and war-correspondent; at the time of his death Makins was Missing Believed Killed, when actually he'd been taken prisoner by the Eyeties, and the similarity of names had caused this confusion that in a work of fiction would have strained the bounds of possibility.

So the resurrected Makins and I began to drink together, gradually his austerity relaxed and he became once more his old dynamic self; it was a memorable reunion: cut short only because the supply of Scotch at this period was hardly inexhaustible, and also Makins was due up North that night.

He'd escaped in the end from the Eyetie POW camp, had however in the meantime learnt Italian, a language on which he'd always been keen; and now that he was repatriated, out of the army and prospectless, a job in Rome had cropped up for which he had to apply in some Northern city.

'I'll let you know what happens,' he said at closing time and the tails of his long mackintosh vanished into a taxi en route for Euston Station.

But he didn't let me know and ten years went by before he wrote to me again.

*Rome*

In 1955 I published in *The London Magazine* a memoir of Frank Harris, and on its appearance received a letter from Makins whom I'd begun to give up once more for dead.

But no, he was still alive and domiciled in Rome. He'd a new wife now and lived in a wing of a converted marble palace where they sometimes held private concerts of chamber music and where, should I ever come to Italy, I would be welcome as their guest.

Makins also said that he'd been asked by the editors of *Botteghe Oscure,* an Anglo-Italian miscellany then published twice-yearly in Rome, to write his memories of the old *Horizon* days, and could he have permission to describe my first appearance there.

I replied 'Of course'; then seeing a copy of the current *Botteghe Oscure* in a Charing Cross Road bookshop sometime later, opened it at the Contents to see if his *Horizon* piece was in.

His name was certainly there but appended to three prose poems only, and underneath in brackets were the dates, writing Finis to the story of William Cooper Makins:

*(1911-1955)*

# Calder-Marshall and The Reverend Todd

'So you're out of the army and you've sold your book,' Arthur Calder-Marshall said depositing the drinks on the table. 'What d'you intend to do now?'

His voice was slightly nasal and although in the vast anonymous pub acres of bare floor and empty tables surrounded us, he spoke conspiratorially from the corner of his mouth as if we were convicts in danger of being overheard by the screw.

We'd met by appointment, it was six p.m. at the Horseshoe Tavern, next to the Dominion Cinema in the Tottenham Court Road; and for once I can even be certain of the date: the Thursday before August Bank Holiday, 1943.

'Get a job,' I told him.

Calder-Marshall's eyes narrowed, he seemed about to make some comment which he however withheld: instead picking up his pint of bitter which was served in a straight-sided glass without a handle and seemed one of the biggest pints I've ever seen.

As he drank a straight lock of hair like that shown in the early photographs of W. H. Auden fell across his eyebrow and he looked not unlike these photographs although never having met Auden I cannot say whether a resemblance in fact exists. Calder-Marshall's face was of a smooth uniform pallor including the lips, the eyes were webbed at the corners with tiny lines, his expression was that of one squinting against strong sunlight; and like other Left-Wing writers of the Thirties—Randall Swingler in particular— it was arranged to look like the face of a working-man without the features in themselves being all that rough-hewn. He wore a brown suit, was thick-set with broad shoulders shrugged up high and had about him an air of great circumspect wisdom and self-imposed control.

He was a novelist whose early work I'd much admired, *About Levy* especially being a technical tour-de-force and a remarkable study of anti-semitism in which the phrase is never actually mentioned.

Eyeing me narrowly over the pint glass rim he asked: 'And Cape is doing the book? Who are you dealing with there?'

'Hart-Davis,' I said, 'but now he's gone to America as a King's Messenger I'm dealing with Mr Wren Howard.'

'How d'you get on with Rupert?'

'The book's dedicated to him.'

'And Wren Howard?'

'Less well,' I said.

Calder-Marshall nodded but no reflection upon Mr Wren Howard was implied: it was rather that he did not really expect me to get on with anyone. The rôle which I'd been assigned at our very first meeting was that of a wild intransigent clever but foolish young man unable to cope realistically with the world and its ways; and this part was one in which I'd been unwillingly cast so often that I assumed it almost as second nature. Besides my admiration for Calder-Marshall's novels was such that I wouldn't have dreamt of contradicting him by behaving out of character.

Now he said: 'Go easy with Wren Howard and you'll be all right, when dealing with publishers you have to compromise,' though his tone contained no hope that I'd take this advice to heart. 'Did they give you any money?'

'A hundred quid,' I told him, 'but it's started to run out a bit now.'

'I can well imagine,' Calder-Marshall said, his narrow glance taking in the clothes I'd recently bought since those I'd had before joining up were not many and had moreover got too small. His glance was not approving nor did he approve of my attitude towards the army or the manner in which I'd got out of it: via the glasshouse which excited in him no surprise, since he considered some of my stories, particularly one called *Dodging the Column*, had also gone too far.

He himself had been in the army and had got out of it too,

but in a much less sensational fashion. When in the ranks he had written anonymously for *Horizon* a bitter indictment of the system entitled *Ours Not to Reason Why;* but later as an OCTU cadet his views had become modified and another piece called *Marching,* published under his own name in *Life and Letters,* ended on a Kiplingesque note in praise of discipline not this time satirically intended. Not long after he had been transferred to the Films Division of the Ministry of Information where it was felt, quite rightly, that his talents could be better employed.

'What sort of job had you in mind?' he asked.

I swallowed my whisky and said: 'Well actually Cyril Connolly thought you might get me one.'

'I?' Calder-Marshall said startled. 'How?'

'In films. With your Ministry.'

Calder-Marshall recovering seemed again about to make some comment which he once more withheld, or perhaps re-phrased as: 'And what d'you think you'd do there?'

'I could do scripts,' I said eagerly, 'and I've got a lot of ideas about films in general.'

Calder-Marshall said dryly: 'I don't doubt that, but whether they'd be ideas that would find favour with the powers that be,' and at this we were joined by his wife Ara, who also worked in Documentary and was employed by a company called Data.

'Julian wants a job,' her husband told her, she nodded smiling wanly, and while he went to get her a beer shook back her curtains of blondish hair which she wore shoulder-length in a style much affected in those days and which indeed she may have originated.

Ara Calder-Marshall was a slender woman of considerable chic and beauty, genuinely serene where her husband seemed banked-down, his calm rigorously imposed by an effort of the will in which he was a great believer. She had a lovely wryly-drooping mouth and chiselled features like a statue yet gave an effect of great sympathy and warmth. She wore a black tailor-made business suit and spoke in a husky voice so low

111

as to be almost inaudible: once in a crowded pub I had a long conversation with her at the end of which I was mortified to find I'd been inadvertently supporting fascism.

'The routine,' her husband said to me returning with replenished drinks, 'the Ministerial red tape wouldn't suit you at all you know.'

'I got used to red tape in the orderly room,' I said.

Calder-Marshall said: 'Another thing. I doubt whether they'd let you do scripts straightaway. They might if you qualified as an assistant director first, but I don't think you'd care much for that either.'

'What does being an assistant director entail?'

Calder-Marshall said: 'A sort of general dogsbody,' his wife nodded confirmation, I on the other hand shook my head, then Ara suddenly said quite loud and clear: 'Why don't we all go to the Highlander?'

I felt like saying 'How will that get me a job?' since she had spoken as if a solution to this problem had been provided: her husband glanced quickly at her, she smiled serenely back and receiving some unspoken message he said: 'Yes but d'you think he's likely to be there?'

'He'll be there,' Ara murmured nodding with conviction.

'Who'll be there?' I asked.

'Never you mind m'lad,' Calder-Marshall told me by now on his feet and intent on lowering his pint in one long draught like a lorry-driver would a quick wet, having succeeded he said: 'Just drink up and come with us,' and with his arm linked in mine on one side and Ara's on the other I was frog-marched in friendly fashion out into the petrol-fumes and pink evening light of the Tottenham Court Road.

'D'you know the Highlander?' Ara asked me as we cut past the Astoria across Soho Square.

'Yes I know the Highlander but no one goes there until half-past ten.'

'That's where you're wrong my boy,' Calder-Marshall who now appeared thoroughly relieved and in high spirits told me; and wrong I was.

The Highlander in Dean Street, which until then I'd believed to be a pub where one went only after those on the other side of Oxford Street closed at half-past ten, was jammed to the doors. This early evening clientéle was composed mainly of people younger than myself: the boys in tweed jackets with leather inserts at the elbows, the girls in white blouses and slacks with shoulder-slung bags. These I afterwards found out were university-educated assistant-cameramen, sound technicians, secretaries and continuity-girls from various documentary companies affiliated to the Ministry.

A pint of bitter was immediately waved in greeting at the Calder-Marshalls by a febrile young man slightly older than the rest and seeming not to belong among them although on friendly terms, whom Ara introduced in her husky murmur, made even less audible by the clamour in the bar, as the Reverend Todd.

The Reverend Todd did not look especially clerical yet there was something curate-like, a suggestion of primness and precision, about the long straight mobile mouth from which issued with great rapidity a loud strident voice. He seemed able to conduct several conversations at once and to have ears in the back of his head: frequently firing over his shoulder a retort to someone at the opposite side of the counter, as a gunslinger in a Western might carelessly drop an opponent who is drawing a bead on him from behind.

He had a shock of black hair piled high above a narrow pale wedge shaped face and the side struts of his large square framed spectacles were the thickest I'd yet encountered. It was impossible to see whether he wore a dog-collar as his navy blue woollen pullover cut him off at the point where the knot of a necktie might have been.

He was evidently not the mysterious person whom we'd come there to meet since the Calder-Marshalls were still watching the open door, then through it there stepped in from the street a bulky man of middle height, conservatively dressed and wearing a bow tie, who came towards us smiling.

Into his hand Calder-Marshall at once thrust a large whisky

113

which he appeared to have in readiness, at the same time saying: 'Donald this is Julian, he's out of the army and looking for a job, I thought you'd better get together.'

The man with the bow tie had thick arched George Robey eyebrows, his smiling face was blue chinned, round and bland. He made a formal almost foreign jerky bow, though without quite clicking his heels.

'Taylor,' he said in a deep pleasant voice that was not at all foreign. 'Donald Taylor.'

'Maclaren-Ross,' I said.

Donald Taylor said: 'I'm happy to meet you,' his smile curving now to resemble that of the Cheshire cat. Like the Reverend Todd he had thick black hair and dark rimmed spectacles but his hair was swept back smoothly into a curved mane at the back and the rims and struts of his spectacles were of ordinary thickness and shape.

Taking a sip of whisky he said: 'So you're looking for a job Arthur says.'

'Yes,' I said. 'Can you give me one?'

'Documentary films?'

'Yes.'

'Scripts?'

'I can do scripts, yes.'

'Then I'll be happy to give you a job,' Donald Taylor smiled. 'As a matter of fact I've been hoping we would meet. Here is my card, come to the office about 10.30 tomorrow morning and I will sign you on then. Sorry I have to dash now, good-night,' and replacing his empty glass on the counter, he gave again his jerky bow and stepped back through the doorway out of sight. His Cheshire cat smile had not faded throughout and I expected to see it lingering in the air even though its owner had disappeared.

Convinced this was some kind of joke, I turned to the Calder-Marshalls for an explanation but they were no longer in the pub, and as I was about to examine the card given me by Donald Taylor I was startled by hearing the Reverend Todd use a most unecclesiastical expression of contempt close to my ear.

'And what *d'you* think about it?' he said sensing someone behind him and swivelling his spectacles towards me like the sights of a .45.

'About what?' I asked placing the card unread in my breast pocket.

The Reverend Todd was occupied in tipping back a fresh pint of bitter, unlike Calder-Marshall it took him two goes, then wiping foam from his lips, he said: 'Poetry.'

'I don't know anything about poetry.'

The Reverend Todd said: 'Then you must be a poet,' emitting a strident peal of laughter. Sweat stood out like pimples on his pale cheeks and forehead. 'Are you a poet?'

'No,' I said. 'Are you.'

'Of course I am.'

I said: 'Well there are precedents, Donne for instance.'

'Donne?'

'John Donne. He was a clergyman too.'

'I know he was a clergyman,' the Reverend Todd began then broke off to shout behind him, in answer to some remark I hadn't caught: 'No, no, I write my own novels not anybody else's, thank you.'

I asked him: 'Are you a novelist as well?'

'Two novels,' he told me and I tried to think of a precedent for this, but clergymen who wrote fiction were fewer and only one name came to mind.

'S. Baring Gould,' I said.

The Reverend Todd repeated 'Baring Gould?' blankly, his mouth open in what seemed to be bewilderment.

'He wrote *In the Roar of the Sea.*'

'I know that. So what?'

'Well he was in holy orders.'

'Holy what?'

'Orders. He was a parson.'

'What,' the Reverend Todd demanded and his voice rose to hitherto unclimbed heights of stridency, 'is all this about bloody parsons?'

'Well aren't you a parson. The Reverend Todd?'

'Reverend Todd be damned,' shouted Todd. 'I'm *Ruthven* Todd.'

There was a short silence during which he glared and I in turn drained my glass, for I knew the work of Ruthven Todd who was a good poet, also the author of an excellent book on William Blake and an allegorical novel called *Over the Mountain* : one of the first in the neo-Kafkan manner to be published in this country.

But before I could apologize for having misheard the introduction, Ruthven Todd who now held a whisky in his hand said : 'I didn't get your name either. Who the hell are you anyway?'

I gave my name, Todd's whisky went down the wrong way, and when I'd patted him on the back he spluttered : 'But I discovered you!'

'I thought Cyril Connolly discovered me.'

'On my recommendation,' Todd shouted, his voice still pitched to carry above a crowd though the pub had now emptied around us. 'I happened to be in *Horizon* office when your stuff came to light, I sat down and read it through, then I went straight to Connolly and told him : "Whatever else you do you've got to publish this bloke." And he did.'

There was no denying that, although the name of Ruthven Todd did not figure in the story as Connolly had told it to me by letter or on the occasion of my first visit to Selwyn House.

Meantime dusk had fallen outside and, anticipating the landlord who was eyeing him as if about to refuse further service, Todd said : 'Come on, this place'll be dead now until the others close. Let's push off to my flat, I've got some food and beer in and we can carry on drinking there.'

Todd's flat was in Mecklenburgh Square, not far from the *Horizon* office, a wall of books confronted us as we entered the narrow hall and in the living room there was hardly space for the truckle-bed on which he slept.

'Borrow anything you like,' he shouted from the kitchen where he was clattering plates and glasses, so I detached a blue and silver paper covered obelisk press copy of *The Rock Pool* followed by an Alfred Knopf edition of Dashiell Hammett's first novel *Red Harvest*, not then available in England; and began with awe to examine what appeared to be a complete signed set of Wyndham Lewis on a lower shelf.

Todd, returning with salami, French bread and a gallon jug of beer, told me how, when he first came to London from Edinburgh, Wyndham Lewis had not only presented him with the books, but when he was broke put him up in the basement of his flat, bringing down the breakfast himself every morning for a week before introducing Todd to his wife, after which they all breakfasted together upstairs.

It was not a story which confirmed the popular view of Lewis as everyone's implacable enemy, but Todd was full of tales like this: famous names erupted rapidly from him, he seemed on friendly terms with every conceivable literary figure and, although still in his late twenties, to be himself a figure more of the Thirties than of the Forties.

Now he worked as a bookseller's assistant at Zwemmers in the Charing Cross Road but also acted as a consultant on antique furniture to a Feature film company which paid him a small retainer, and had a new novel coming out from Wrey Gardiner who owned the Grey Walls Press.

Mention of the film company reminded me of my own search for a job, and I said to Todd: 'D'you know a man called Donald Taylor?'

'Of Strand Films?'

'Yes that's it,' I said taking out the card Taylor had given me in the Highlander. 'Strand Films, No. 1 Golden Square. Is he really a producer?'

Todd shouted: 'Good God of course he is. Strand's the best documentary company in London.'

I said: 'Well he told me if I called there tomorrow he'd give me a job doing scripts. D'you think he might?'

Todd shouted: 'Of course he will. For God's sake go and see him. Dylan Thomas works there as well.'

# The Polestar Neighbour

*On almost the incendiary eve*
*    When at your lips and keys*
*Locking, unlocking, the murdered strangers weave,*

*    One who is most unknown,*
*Your polestar neighbour, sun of another street,*
*    Will dive up to his tears.*

(DEATHS AND ENTRANCES)

Dylan Thomas in 1943 did not greatly resemble that much-reproduced early photograph known to him as the Fucking Cherub. Certainly I failed to recognize him from it on the morning we first met.

It was the day after August Bank Holiday: the date when I was to start work at Strand Films where Dylan was already employed as a documentary script-writer. He was then going on twenty-nine and I had just turned thirty-one.

We travelled up together in the lift at No. 1 Golden Square without speaking, neither knowing who the other was. Dylan wore a green porkpie hat pulled down level with his slightly bulging eyes: like the agate marbles we used as Alley Taws when I was a boy in France, but a darker brown. His full lips were set low in a round full face, a fag-end stuck to the lower one. His nose was bulbous and shiny. He told me afterwards that he used to rub it up with his fist before the mirror every morning until it shone satisfactorily; as a housewife might polish her doorknob or I the silver-topped malacca cane that I affected in those days.

Dylan's gaze lit on this cane and he huddled back into the very soiled and much pleated raincoat worn capewise round his shoulders. He had his left arm in a sling and judging by the greyness of the linen had evidently carried it thus for some time. He later told me that, although his sprained wrist was now all right, he had become attached to the sling and hoped to wear it until it turned completely black.

Side by side we stood while the lift creaked upward in a series of jerks. It was a very old, capricious lift with a great deal of personality, but it did not on this occasion give up halfway as happened one evening in the weeks to come when Dylan and I were trapped in it between two floors for twenty minutes, until someone working late below pressed the button to release us. Now we jerked slowly past a sign advertising the manufacture of Free-Japanese Lampshades, and Dylan's eyes rolled sideways in alarm as through the open grille we saw an actual Japanese in native dress emerge from the door that bore the sign. Dylan's glance took in also my white corduroy jacket and he turned his head discreetly away as if at some obscene sight: indeed, I looked hastily down to make sure my flies were buttoned.

At that moment the lift gave out a sigh of exhaustion, rose a few inches above floor level, then sank to a stop facing the double doors marked 'STRAND', against which Dylan, clashing the lift-gate back, launched himself at a fast lick. By the time I had finished closing the grille he had disappeared, and the lift followed suit down its shaft at double the speed with which it had ascended.

I in turn passed through the Strand doors, still swinging back and forth like those of a saloon in a Western, and was brought up short by a switchboard desk and behind it a good-looking red-haired young lady, who later married a feature-film producer with whom I, long after, became associated. But before I could announce my name, a buzzer sounded and the disembodied voice of Donald Taylor, the boss asked whether I had yet arrived.

'Reporting for duty,' I said and was waved towards an office on the right where Dylan had preceded me and Donald Taylor now introduced us.

Divested of hat and raincoat, though still wearing the sling, Dylan was revealed to have on a very respectable dark blue suit and a white shirt with a bow tie and celluloid collar, too tight round the neck and giving the effect of someone strapped in the stocks. In these clothes he might have been a young provincial tradesman or perhaps a farmer up in London for the day on business. He was stockily built and robust looking rather than fat, though beginning to put on a bit of a pot. His hair, light brown in colour and not dull gold as the romantics would like it, was no longer centre-parted and wavy, as in the cherubic photograph. Now it covered his round skull in tight woolly curls. His full cheeks were carefully shaven. He replied in a rapid mutter to the introduction that seemed acutely nervous and uncomfortable. Of course it was my general get-up that embarrassed him, I had on a cream silk shirt and peach coloured tie besides the white corduroy, but I didn't realize the cause until much later; and Dylan was by nature far too polite to make any comment at this stage.

Meanwhile Donald Taylor was speaking: 'Well you boys had better get to know each other as you're going to work together'—at this Dylan visibly recoiled, and it came as startling news to me as well—'You can share that office through there, Dylan show him where it is, I'm sure you can sort out between you the best method of working.'

'What are we going to work on?' I asked.

'The Home Guard script. Feature length. Dylan will explain. I expect it to be a most fruitful collaboration.'

Donald gave his Cheshire-cat smile and little jerky bow. The interview was over, and in the office assigned to us Dylan and I stood uneasy and shame-faced, like two strange children sent off to play alone by a benevolent adult, in the belief that because they are contemporaries they're bound to get on well. We looked out of the one long window, which had a splendid view right across the rooftop to the blitzed church of St Anne's in Old Compton Street, Soho. The weathervane on the spire was still intact and glinted, a golden arrow, in the sun.

'Have you been in the Home Guard?' I asked.

'Never.'

'Neither have I. I was in the Infantry.'

'I know. I've read your stories.' He didn't tell me, nor for a long while did I find out, that he'd read the stories aloud to

Donald Taylor, insisting that I be taken on at Strand when discharged from the Army: that, in other words, I owed my job to him.

He said: 'One of the directors here was in the Home Guard, but he's doing the script about the RAF.'

'Haven't you an RAF man?'

'Yes, but he's doing a script about the Tank Corps.'

'How many are there in the Script Department?'

'Only ourselves and Philip Lindsay. The rest are directors who sometimes write a script. You can see them all on this.'

He led me to a large coloured cartoon framed on the wall behind the big broad desk, captioned 'A High Wind in Golden Square' and showing various members of Strand Films personnel being blown about in all directions. I recognized the work of John Banting, a painter and illustrator whom I'd met once or twice in bars.

'I didn't know Banting was on the staff.'

'He's not any longer,' Dylan said. 'Bit of a disagreement, don't know the details. See, there's Phil Lindsay, that little bloke floating away over the trees.'

'I'd like to meet Lindsay.'

'You're certain to sooner or later. If you spot a little leprechaunish chap with a big bump on his forehead and dried blood all over his face, that'll be Phil for sure. He was born with the bump I believe, but the blood comes from falling downstairs. He's always falling down, old Phil.'

'Is that how you did your wrist?'

Dylan nodded delightedly. 'Trying to hold Phil up. I was sober too, makes it seem more silly.' It was then that he told me about his wrist and how long he planned to wear the sling.

'Coming along nicely, ought to be jet black soon. They wanted me to go along to the hospital for treatment twice a week, but I said to myself No bloody fear. Start going to hospitals and you never know what they'll find wrong. Might begin taking my liver out and scraping it again.'

'Again? Have you had your liver scraped?'

'Every so often,' Dylan said with relish. 'Get it put back

afterwards and sewn in of course. I'm always scared they'll leave out a bit. Whenever the boys here get a tough piece of liver for lunch, and there's a lot of it about just now, they always say Now we're eating a bit of bloody old Dylan. Actually they'd have a job to eat mine.'

'But what's wrong with your liver?'

'Cirrhosis I expect.' When he laughed his cheeks puffed out but the cigarette remained squarely in the centre of his mouth. 'Hard as bloody leather. It's the booze. D'you drink at all yourself?'

'When I can get it.'

'Beer?'

'Scotch.'

'Oh of course. Your national drink.' He added: 'You don't seem much like a Scotsman though. I thought you'd be very small and tough, with steel rimmed specs, that sort of thing.'

'A kilt?'

'No, not a kilt. But a Scots accent. Glasgow perhaps.'

'My parents didn't come from Glasgow.'

'Have they got accents?'

'They're dead. But they hadn't accents.'

Dylan flushed and muttered 'Sorry.' His cigarette waggled up and down as he spoke and his face was screwed up in a frown against the smoke, but he removed the fag end only when it was burnt right down. But even when he mumbled you could understand every word, though his voice was low-toned and he spoke fast. I've heard people who should know better do imitations of him with a sing-song Welsh accent, but a slight intonation on certain words— 'Daughter,' for instance —was all he really had.

'You haven't an accent yourself,' I said to him.

He puffed out a laugh. 'Cut-glass, they'd call it down in Wales.' I didn't know this expression but rightly assumed it to be the equivalent of talking pound-noteish or having a half-crown voice in the Army. 'I don't speak Welsh either,' he added, pulling open a drawer and searching inside. 'Now where's this bloody script got to. Ah here we are. Home

Guard,' coming up with a green foolscap folder which we were to get to know too well. 'I expect you'll want to start work right away?'

'We could discuss it over drinks. They'll be open time we get there.'

Dylan seemed delighted with this suggestion, which he'd plainly not wanted to be the first to make. He told Donald Taylor afterwards that it was the first sign he'd had that I was halfway human; until then, he'd seriously considered saying he couldn't work with me at all, as for some reason never stated, and quite apart from my appearance, I reminded him of Gaudier-Brezska.

'We mustn't get tight though,' he added.

At that time when drink-shortage was starting it was not easy to get tight, nor even to get Scotch; the back bar of the Café Royal had, however, Irish in abundance. As I lowered glass after glass, while Dylan rationed himself to a single pint of bitter, his anxiety increased; but we regained the office at two o'clock with me sober enough to join in roughing-out the Home Guard story outline: the shooting script we swore to start next day.

Meanwhile that evening Dylan did get tight. In the back bar he abandoned beer and went on the hard stuff himself; as we worked our way up Soho in search of Scotch, towards the Wheatsheaf where we were certain of Scotch ale at any rate, his celluloid collar seemed to be constricting him more and more until when we reached the Highlander and there discovered gin, he was scarlet in the face and I suggested he should take the damned thing off.

'Why don't you take that bloody jacket off?' Dylan said.

'What's wrong with my jacket?'

'Fucking dandy. Flourishing that stick. Why don't you try to look more sordid. Sordidness, boy, that's the thing.'

'If you'd just come out of a glasshouse you wouldn't want to look more sordid.'

Dylan paused with a double gin suspended. 'The glasshouse?' he said. 'That where you've been?'

E

'They called it a Detention Barrack, but the glasshouse is what you'd call it.'

Dylan set his gin carefully on the counter, and reaching up wrenched the celluloid collar from its stud. 'Jesus boy,' he said, 'I'm sorry.'

'That's all right. You weren't to know.'

'Why didn't you tell me?'

'No reason why I should.'

Dylan stood there gulping and goggle-eyed, the celluloid collar dangling from his hand. 'But Jesus, the glasshouse,' he said.

He remained abashed for the rest of the evening and later on I somehow lost him.

But when next morning I arrived at the office he was there before me, hunched up over the desk as if he'd been stabbed at it. Like one of those characters in films who when touched slump stiffly back with a knife handle sticking out in front. Then I saw that he was moving. He was grasping a pencil and attempting to insert it in the holes of the dial-telephone, but without success owing to trembling of his hand.

'What on earth are you doing?'

'Jesus you made me jump. I'm trying to dial TIM, what d'you think?'

'Tim?'

'To get the time. Find out if they're open yet.'

'They're not. It's only half-past ten.'

'Oh God another hour.' He groaned. His eyes were globular, rimmed with red right round, nor had he shaved. His left arm was still in the sling but this morning he wore a brown check tweed jacket and grey flannels, these remaining his office uniform from then on, except when he was in shirt sleeves. 'Was I rude to you last night?'

'No.'

'I bloody was. I was rude to you about your coat. Is the coat all right? You weren't sick down it or anything?'

'No.'

'What about the stick? Don't say you've lost the stick?'

I showed him the stick and he seemed genuinely comforted. Henceforward he adopted the cane and jacket as though they were his own especial properties, making sure I didn't leave the cane behind in pubs and becoming belligerent himself when a chap in one of them took exception to the jacket. When one day as we walked along the street soot fell from a roof all over the white corduroy, he was horrified, and insisted on rushing me to a firm of cleaners who restored it as good as new within 24 hours, a miracle in that time of war.

Now he started suddenly to sneeze. Sneeze after sneeze convulsed him and he tried to smother them in a large red bandanna snatched from out of his sleeve.

'That's a nasty cold you've got.'

'Not a cold. It's the drink coming out.'

The drink was also coming out in sweat, and I said: 'Look here Dylan, I don't feel too good myself. Why don't we have a bottle up here, guard against these hangovers in future?'

'A bottle?'

'Whisky. We could go halves. I know a fellow can get it on the black market, I'll ring him now if you like.'

'Whisky? *In the office?*' He seemed absolutely appalled.

'Don't be silly, why not?'

But Dylan firmly shook his head. 'Not for me. You please yourself of course, but I won't if you don't mind.'

So the bottle was not imported. Actually, one double Irish when the Back Bar opened and a pint of bitter over lunch were sufficient to pull Dylan together and enable him to work that afternoon; incidentally this was one of the few times when I saw him eat anything bar a ham sandwich or a sausage roll.

Lunch was Spaghetti Bolognese at Fava's Restaurant in Frith Street, much frequented by our staff, especially junior members and minor technicians, most of whom had been at Cambridge and enjoyed trying out their Italian on the waitress. Dylan did imitations of all these, including the waitress, as we strolled along outside: a considerable feat since he himself spoke no Italian; but first he led me across the street to examine in a shop window what seemed to be a woman's severed head, also tresses of hair, cut, apparently, from the decapitated head: itself dimly visible beyond the dusty pane. By the time we had discussed the disposal of the body, involving goulash and stuffed heart served off the ration to gourmets in a black market basement, we'd arrived in Soho Square, where Dylan said he'd something even more gruesome to show me.

'See that doorway on the other side? That's Film Centre, that is!'

'A sort of documentary club?'

'In a way.'

'Well what's so gruesome about it?'

'Don't you know?' He sank his voice to a hollow graveyard whisper: 'It's where we go when we've no jobs.'

For the time being, however, we did have jobs and it was on my first payday with the firm, when I happened to be alone in the office, that a large bulb-shaped head, with a big carbuncle on the forehead, was poked cautiously round the door jamb. The nose was noduled with purple veins, clots of dark dried blood surrounded the carbuncle, and I said: 'You must be Philip Lindsay.'

'That's right. Not seen a huge tall woman armed with an axe anywhere about, have you?'

'Not today. Why? D'you want one?'

'No, but she wants me. To chop my ruddy block off.' Lindsay now came all the way in, the rough swagman's face and short skimpy frame might have belonged to two different men, and I saw that he too was carrying his left arm in a sling.

While I was introducing myself, Dylan appeared in the doorway. His eyes rolled at sight of Lindsay's sling, with a shrug he stripped off his own and dropped it in the wastepaper basket by the desk.

'Can't all go round looking like a bunch of bloody cripples,' he said. 'What happened Phil? She catch up with you at last?'

'No, or I'd be lacking a head. Missed my footing going down the gents, that's all. They say it isn't broken, though.'

'How's Crippen? Crapping?'

'Just about to bump off Belle.' Lindsay said in his hoarse staccato voice. The phone rang and he skipped back in alarm : 'Christ suppose that's her,' but instead it was Donald Taylor asking for him on the inter-com.

'Phil's on the Crippen script, one of Donald's feature projects,' Dylan said when Lindsay had answered the summons. 'Works at home nowadays and only shows up Fridays to collect his dough.'

'Doesn't this woman with the axe know where he lives?'

'No, he's safe so long as he stays indoors.'

Then Dylan told me how, some weeks before, the backers of Strand had held a board meeting at which Donald Taylor as Managing Director presided, but apparently beforehand they had called a sort of scriptwriters' roll call at Golden Square and Philip Lindsay had been marked absent on parade. Donald had been asked the reason and replied that he never insisted on writers clocking in daily, so long as they delivered the goods on schedule that was all he was concerned with.

But an accountant said: 'Surely it would be preferable Mr Taylor if these, er, writers performed their duties in the office like any other employee?'

'Yes it would,' Donald said.

'Thank you Mr Taylor,' the accountant said in triumph. 'I thought you would agree.'

But Donald said: 'I'm sorry, you didn't allow me to finish my sentence. It would be preferable—if we were making let's say sausages. Instead we are making documentary films, or am I mistaken?'

'Well no, Mr Taylor, but . . .'

'Thank you,' Donald said, bowing jerkily with his blandest smile, 'I thought you'd agree,' and there was no more question of compulsory attendance for writers at the office after that. Nonetheless Dylan and I did come in every morning, and the Home Guard script was proceeding apace.

This script was never completed, and it's hard to tell what the Ministry officials who'd commissioned it would have said had they seen the sequences we wrote. Neither of us having served in the Home Guard we'd had to invent our own, like Kafka's *Amerika*; and what we concocted was a lively comedy-thriller set in a village 'somewhere in England,' stuffed full of eccentrics and containing also a fifth column group, a delayed action bomb, and a German parachutist who'd been in civvy street a music hall Master of Disguise. Those ruled sheets of Government foolscap might even be worth money should they ever come to light; for Dylan with his usual unselfishness did much of the actual donkey work in longhand, while I dictated from the other side of the desk the dialogue of the characters assigned to me: an old sweat who'd served in several wars, etcetera.

Dylan wrote in soft pencil with a BB lead, and carried a sharpener about in his trouser pocket; long coils of cedar-wood filled the ashtray and the blotter on his side of the desk was covered with quick sketches, some highly amusing if obscene, made while he was thinking out a scene. He often bought sketching blocks of cartridge paper, but these were used exclusively for writing poetry: also in pencil, in those days before the invention of Biro or Bic; and he was determined that his handwriting, already neat and clear, should eventually become smaller than my own.

Contrary to what is often said, he was extremely interested in the film medium while I at that time was obsessed by it, though it's doubtful whether we either of us had the true Documentary Mind. What we really wanted to script were Features, and together we planned among other subjects a mystery film to be written in collaboration, entitled *The Whispering Gallery* or *The Distorting Mirror*. We both had a penchant for pictures of this sort and spent much time in tracking down the vintage examples all over London; a typical dialogue when we met in the morning would run like this:

'Dylan have you seen *The Cat Creeps*?'

'No but I've seen *The Crimson Claw*.'

'D'you recommend it?'

A violent shuddering shake of the head. 'NBG. Was your cat creepy?'

'Don't go anywhere near.'

Our own film was to be a deliberate throwback to *Caligari* and *The Cat and the Canary* in its original Paul Léni version, and Dylan provided the basic idea. A party of assorted people are being shown by a guide round the whispering gallery of a stately home open to the public, when suddenly a voice says out loud: 'I'll have this place.' Owing to the acoustics no one can tell who spoke, camera pans the various faces, and the film begins, with the heir many times removed ironing out methodically and by remote control all those in his way. He was to recruit his murderous accomplices in a deserted amusement park, and to be seen unrecognizably reflected in the Hall of Mirrors, hence the alternative title. We could never decide whether this super-villain was to be male or female, and Dylan was in favour of both: i.e. a character whose sex was changed by an operation halfway through, even though this meant censorship trouble and at very least the 'H' Certificate which then did duty for the present day 'X'.

We also shared another ambition, which was to write a film-script, *not* a Treatment as the story-form is called, but a complete scenario ready for shooting which would give the ordinary reader an absolute visual impression of the film in words and could be published as a new form of literature. Carl Meyer the co-author of *Caligari* and creator of many of the great early German silents, who invented the mobile camera or rather caused it to be moved about, is said to have written such scripts; but neither Dylan nor I could get hold of a script by Meyer, and the only ones we knew which almost succeeded in doing what we had in mind were those printed in *The Film Sense* by Sergei Eisenstein.

The rules we laid down ourselves were that the script had to be an original specially written in this form and not any kind of adaptation, and that actual film production must be possible. Our main obstacle consisted in the camera directions, which if given were apt to look too technical, and if omitted would lose the dramatic impact of, for instance, a sudden large close-up, which Dylan however hoped could be conveyed by one's actual choice of words. In fact we were attempting the wellnigh impossible, as anyone who has read the printed versions of *Marienbad* or *L'Immortelle* by Robbe-Grillet will realize, and perhaps Dylan himself in *The Doctor and the Devils* came as close to it as any writer ever will.

Donald Taylor encouraged us in all this, he too wanted to make Features and was trying to persuade our backers to make this financially possible. Apart from Dr Crippen and the Burke and Hare film, which even then kept cropping up, one of his pet projects was to put on the screen Dylan's novel *Adventures in the Skin Trade*, and I read with much enjoyment the portion which was published posthumously and which he had written some time before. The book, Dylan told me, was to end with the hero shivering stark-naked on Paddington Station, having lost all his clothes at strip poker in the course of the story, and in the last shot of the film-version the bottle caught on his finger was to slip off and shatter on the stone-cold platform.

Donald had had typescripts made and bound up, only two of these remained and Tambimuttu the editor of *Poetry London* borrowed one of them with a view to obtaining an advance for Dylan from the firm he worked for. Anything involving Tambi took more time than anyone could possibly have to spare, months, maybe years could go by with nothing done, and when Dylan terribly hard up finally had another offer for the book, it turned out Tambi had lost the typescript, or at any rate this could not be found. It was the only time I ever saw Dylan angry, the scene took place in the Wheatsheaf and one could not help overhearing it. Luckily I remembered borrowing the other copy some months before, so I took Dylan home quickly in a cab and gave him the typescript which I had there, thus enabling him to draw his advance next day : or so I hope, publishers not being renowned for speed in this connexion.

Meantime we were still stuck with the Home Guard, and Dylan wanted to incorporate the Free Japanese who made lampshades below our office. He said he had heard of Free

French, Free Poles, Free Dutch, Free Italians and if not actually Free Germans at any rate Free German-speaking people, but never, no never Free Japanese; and he tried very hard to have them in the script, while I objected on the grounds that their kimonos might lead to their being lynched in a typical English village and which of us would write their bloody dialogue?

These questions were debated often in the office and occasionally, when we'd done a good morning's work, in an afternoon drinking place called the Horseshoe Club, which now no longer exists in Wardour Street. This was approached by the most sordid staircase that I've ever seen, on either side were leprous walls, and it was down these worn stone steps that Philip Lindsay most frequently fell. The club also had a Judas window in the door. Dylan led me proudly up to this, a panel slid aside and the eye of the proprietor appeared at an aperture which had previously seemed to be a knothole in the wood.

'You see?' Dylan hissed. 'Like a speakeasy or an opium den,' but behind the spyhole nothing much went on: bookies' touts or ageing Lesbians sitting on leather settees and sometimes some elderly character such as an art critic famous when President of the Union for subtle deadpan wit, of whom Dylan was particularly fond. I personally found this man a thumping bore, with his strange furry cap of hair, round staring eyes, and thread-like lips from which issued at long intervals a tiny insect voice; one strained one's ears in vain to catch some smart crack that never came, but then of course his Oxford days lay far behind. Dylan liked elderly men as a whole, he spoke often of his old mentor, the senior reporter so affectionately described in *Portrait of the Artist as a Young Dog*, and seemed generally to equate age with sage; in the early days he'd drag me off to Tidal Basin pubs to meet decaying ship's doctors or potato-nosed skippers who must have sailed with Bully Hayes; sometimes these were also present in the Horseshoe, and in the end I largely cried off the club.

We gradually evolved a system of holding the fort on alternate afternoons, he spent his in the Horseshoe and mine were taken up with various young women, as my love-life was getting rather complicated and I had to be sure that in the evenings nothing overlapped. Dylan was too discreet to ask me any questions, though he knew the names and, when it was his turn to stay behind, answered the occasional phone calls without divulging information, as indeed I would have done for him.

Dylan was said, when fire-watching one night on the roof at Golden Square, to have smuggled a girl up there in his sleeping bag, but when asked point blank he replied with equal blankness: 'Then she must have been a very *little* girl.'

He would talk bawdily about sex in general but never about any woman in particular. For example, I once had a girl, a great admirer of his poetry, whose pride it was that she had slept with Dylan when she first came round Soho. Being less discreet than he, I asked what it was like. She said that he undoubtedly knew what to do, was gentle, considerate and even tender, but oh the guilt when morning came. In her opinion the only woman he ever really cared about was his wife Caitlin, and that is also mine.

Anyhow, in due course I brought this girl to the Back Bar where Dylan was, he greeted her with great formality and afterwards, when she'd gone to make a phone call, said: 'Congratulations, she's a sweetie. Course I used to know her slightly and don't mind telling you I tried a pass, only she wasn't having any, and that's what most of the boys have found. Lucky bugger, I hope you'll both be happy.'

We weren't happy for long, but that was hardly Dylan's fault, and in his place how many could have foreborne to boast, or drop a winking innuendo? The only woman I ever heard him speak about at length was his wife, and of her he said: 'I managed to marry the prettiest girl I knew, and can a bloke do more?'

Caitlin was indeed pretty, pink-cheeked with brilliant blue eyes and a few blonde strands always straggling loose from an otherwise neat hair-do: Dylan's Irish Rose. I never got to know her well, she didn't often join us and may even have been away, though I remember a quarrel one evening at the

Café Royal and another time in the Antelope at Chelsea when Augustus John, expected, failed to appear. I was alone with her only once, in the Mandrake Club after Dylan's death: it was the night *Under Milk Wood* was to be broadcast for the first time. She spoke mainly of her children and a Trust that was being set up for them, then I gave her a lift in a taxi to the George, the BBC pub where Roy Campbell was to be. Campbell however didn't show, and without him Caitlin suddenly said she couldn't face the broadcast. Louis MacNeice and Dr Daniel Jones, who'd done the music for *Milk Wood*, then tried to carry her bodily off to Broadcasting House but she kicked out at MacNeice, twisted free of Dr Jones and they had to go off without her. Caitlin said to me with dignity: 'Now Julian we'll go and see some nice Irishmen I know. There'll be a party at their place. Just wait here while I ring.'

Happily Margaret Taylor (no relation to Donald but then married to A. J. P. Taylor the historian), who'd been a good friend to the Thomases in Oxford and elsewhere, came in just then and promised to look after Caitlin when she got back from the phone. I slipped off out, rather pleased since I couldn't have felt less like a party with nice Irishmen that night; and I've not seen Caitlin since.

But back to Strand, the autumn of '43 advancing, and Dylan still alive.

Suddenly we were taken off the Home Guard script. The subject of course was out of date to start with—Dylan told me that the Ministry of Films Division had sat on the proposal for two years before okaying it—and abruptly it was cancelled by higher authority. The green foolscap folder was stuffed away in a desk drawer and did not re-emerge. Philip Lindsay started coming to the office again, Crippen had been hanged and Le Neve acquitted, also the woman on his tail had abandoned her axe and married someone else. This oddly enough piqued Phil instead of pleasing him, perhaps he missed the excitement of being a hunted man: though he often proclaimed, Dylan and I disagreeing, that Terror as a literary theme was Out.

'You boys sit tight,' Donald Taylor told us. 'We'll be making Features soon.' He was often called to board meetings with the backers these days and an acrimonious correspondence with the Ministry had started up. Winter was soon upon us; fog enveloped the golden arrow of St Anne's which could no longer be seen out of the window, and the office began to fill with directors and cameramen who'd been taken off the subjects they were preparing to shoot.

The air was thick with coughing and tobacco smoke and the young red-headed lady from the switchboard desk, who had not yet married my future producer and had to make and carry in the cups of tea, often complained that Strand had not been like this in the days of Reg Groves, a documentary man of the old school and formerly Head of the Script Department: headless now since his departure some months before.

Dylan: 'It's become like bloody Film Centre,' not realizing how near to Film Centre itself we all were heading: for before the Spring Strand Films had folded.

# Tambimuttu and the Progress of Poetry London

J. Meary Tambimuttu, poet and founder-editor of *Poetry London*, was according to himself a Prince in his own country. He was an Indian like his friend the short-story writer Alagu Subramaniam, but both of them came from Ceylon: the nearest parallel being perhaps the Glasgow Irish, Subra was a Hindu, Tambi a Christian, and some said that the initial preceding his name stood for Jesus. I never found out what it actually stood for.

A girl known as Kitty of Bloomsbury told me that Tambi's family seat was called Tambimuttu Towers. She said that at one time he used special crested writing paper, with a picture of the Towers embossed in the top left-hand corner. This was when he first came to London, abdicating his territory to become a literary pundit and famous figure of the Forties.

'A poet,' he would say, 'is a citizen of the world. All mankind is his country,' or 'My principality is everywhere. The Principality of the Mind.'

When Kitty came down from Oxford and was looking for a job, he took her to a bare basement room containing a half-collapsed camp bed, a kitchen chair and a wooden table on which were a bottle of blue-black ink, a chewed post office pen-holder, and stocks of the embossed crested paper.

'This was my office,' he said. 'Now it is yours. I engage you as my secretary and poetry-reader.' Squashing a cockroach on the sweating wall with a rolled-up copy of *Poetry London*, he waved this at a chaos of accumulated MSS in a corner.

'Poems,' he said. 'Contributions. You know? I have not time to read them. If they're no good perhaps they should be returned. They have been here a long time, the rats have eaten some. We have no typewriter yet but there is ink and paper to write the authors. You will be paid fortnightly, on Fridays.

Do you have any money?'

'Yes thank you. I've got £5.'

'That is good,' Tambimuttu said. 'I am a Prince in my country and princes don't carry money, you know. Give me the fiver and later the firm will refund you. I am going to lunch with T. S. Eliot. You know who is T. S. Eliot?'

'Yes indeed.'

Tambi stowed away the fiver. 'He takes interest in me and in the quarterly,' he said.

This was true. On arrival in England (completely penniless according to legend: there was garbled talk of privation and an open boat) he secured an introduction to Eliot who had been impressed by him and helped in the starting of *Poetry London*. The great grandson of a great Victorian novelist helped the most, and Tambi was no longer penniless though the grandson as a result became relatively so; but the tale has many versions and there are many more competent to tell it than I. The grandson had enlisted in the army and gone overseas during the war, and I only saw him once, in the uniform of a captain and looking ineluctably sad: as well he might if the stories are true.

Kitty's £5 was supposed to last her a week. She slept on the camp bed in the basement, living on bread and cheese: not an ideal food as it attracted the rats who'd got bored with gnawing a way through the poetry contributions and needed a change of diet. But Kitty survived without being eaten and when after ten days Tambi returned, he surveyed with approval the pile of stamped addressed envelopes that almost hid his secretary from sight.

'But the stamps?' he said. 'Where did you get them? I did not think that there were any.'

'I bought them.'

'Then you still have some money?'

'An aunt sent me £3.'

'That is good. Give me what remains, I am tonight entertaining Edith Sitwell. You know about Edith Sitwell?' He added, dropping the money into his pocket: 'Remember, next Friday is settlement day. Payment every fortnight.'

But when he did look in, after a further fortnight, he found a polite note of resignation written on the embossed stationery and the basement floor deep in peevish letters from rejected contributors addressed to K. Banks, Esq, Banks being Kitty of Bloomsbury's surname. She hadn't been able to send back all the poems, having no more money left to buy stamps, so she'd gone and got herself a job in the foreign office.

'All the same,' Kitty concluded, telling me this in 1943, 'he's a great editor. No stop laughing, he is. He has such *flair*.'

By that time the basement had long been abandoned to the rats and beetles, and *Poetry London* was subsidized by Messrs Nicholson and Watson (a publishing firm now defunct), who allowed Tambi a free hand in running it, plus salary and expenses as editor. He now had an office in Manchester Square, had published a very slim volume of his own verse called *Out of this War*, and was sometimes commissioned by the BBC to speak on poetry in wartime.

Every night he was to be seen in the pubs and cafés of Soho, wrapped summer and winter in the same blue melton overcoat buttoned to the chin and with the collar turned up, for he keenly felt the cold and in December slept every night in a Turkish bath (Subramaniam wrote a story in which Tambi died in one, having had too much to drink beforehand: he was convinced that this would one day be his actual fate).

Tambi's blue-black hair was bobbed like a woman's and curled up at the corners; his extraordinary hands, with fingers that bent right back, apparently boneless and like a lemur's only longer, flickered mesmerically as he talked in rapid tones with an accent that on the wireless sounded Welsh, white teeth and eyeballs flashing meantime in the dusk of his face.

It was really Tambimuttu who introduced me to Soho or, as he called it, Fitzrovia. One night, soon after I'd been discharged from the army and before I was signed-on at Strand, he came up in the Swiss pub which I'd already found, and asked if I'd a book for sale.

'I'm not a bookseller,' I said.

Tambi said: 'No no I mean a book you have written yourself. I am empowered by my principals to offer a one-hundred pounds advance.'

'Sorry,' I said.

Tambi said: 'One hundred and fifty.'

'Not possible,' I said.

He said: 'Two hundred. That is the top.'

I said: 'We're not in the bazaar.'

Tambi's prehensile pink tongue darted out like a chameleon's from between his purple puckered lips. 'I will have to consult Nick and Wat,' he said, 'before I can go higher.'

When I explained that I was already under contract to Cape, he said: 'A pity. My imprint would give an added lustre to your work.' He was very fond of this phrase, which he used as a sort of slogan, like 'It is impossible not to be thrilled by Edgar Wallace': though in those days he had not actually got a publishing firm of his own.

Then he said: 'So you have already had an advance? That is good, you must be rich, we will go on a pub crawl,' and at these words masses of his supporters gathered round, they seemed to grow up all at once from out of the floor.

'Well I thought of finishing some work tonight,' I said.

Tambimuttu said: 'Yes work is good but you are a writer, you must meet people and it is better you meet them under my aegis. That is so isn't it?' and the supporters raised a sullen murmur of agreement like a lynching mob getting ready to string someone up at the behest of a rabble rouser.

'Only beware of Fitzrovia,' Tambi said quelling the mob with a flicker of his amazing fingers. 'It's a dangerous place, you must be careful.'

'Fights with knives?'

'No, a worse danger. You might get Sohoitis you know.'

'No I don't. What is it?'

'If you get Sohoitis,' Tambi said very seriously, 'you will stay there always day and night and get no work done ever. You have been warned.'

138

'Is this Fitzrovia?'

'No, Old Compton Street, Soho. You are safer here.'

'Why won't I get Sohoitis in Soho? Or is Fitzrovia in Soho too?'

'Fitzrovia's really a part of Bloomsbury,' said a supporter called Steven. 'But the borough is St Pancras.'

'Sounds complicated,' I said, whereupon he asked me if I came from Streatham.

'No he doesn't come from Streatham,' Tambi said sharply before I could reply. 'And Steven if you are rude you must buy beer for us all.'

Steven retired hastily to the back of the crowd like a boy who's been rebuked in class, and Tambi said: 'Now we will go to the Black Horse, the Burglar's Rest, the Marquess of Granby, The Wheatsheaf, then the Beer House and after 10.30 back to the Highlander which closes later at eleven and after this eat curries in St Giles' High or steak at the Coffee An'.'

'Steak,' Steven echoed his eyes snapping. 'Be quiet Steven,' Tambi told him and we set off up Dean Street outside.

'Where are all these pubs?' I asked him.

'In Fitzrovia. The other side of Oxford Street.'

I said: 'I know the Fitzroy of course.'

Tambi said: 'Ah that was in the Thirties, now they go other places. Wait and you will see.'

He loped along beside me in the soft late summer evening which was still light, and the supporters formed a rearguard, Steven often lurching out into the roadway then back on to the sidewalk with movements apparently un-coordinated, while Tambi pointed out a pub on the right-hand side where only Negro GIs went, as the other publicans had put up the colour bar: now in consequence the Negroes had established their own bridgehead which none of us might pass. A huge one standing in the open door, tunic unbuttoned, pint glass in hand, ready to repel invaders, shouted 'No white folks allowed in here,' in a Southern accent as we straggled by.

'And here,' Tambi indicated ground-glass windows on our left, 'is the Highlander but we don't drink there until half-past ten. This way round Soho Square,' then on the corner before reaching the post office he suddenly halted. 'Do you have a bank account?'

'Yes,' I said.

'Where?'

'Barclay's, Piccadilly.'

Tambi said: 'You should bank here. Martin's Bank,' pointing to it. 'It's one of the Big Five,' he added encouragingly, 'You should transfer your account here, I bank with Martin's myself.'

'At this branch?'

'No no, in Baker Street near my office, but this branch is better for you, near the pubs and you can come quickly down to cash a cheque if you are short or any of us needs money. And when the bank is shut, landlords will more quickly cash one for you if the branch is near.'

The supporters chorused agreement, I determined to disregard their advice and across Oxford Street, up Rathbone Place, the first step of our pilgrimage the Black Horse was reached.

We visited that night all the places Tambi had promised we should visit, these I will describe elsewhere, then the Highlander at closing time with a cellar-restaurant to follow; and I remember Steven being ripped untimely from his steak by a powerful Greek waiter who'd had enough of him, and holding it still impaled upon his fork he was hurled into the outer darkness.

I remember also getting back to my room determined to finish the work which I'd neglected, and waking fully dressed on my bed with the room full of smoke from a cigarette which had burned away a whole corner of a new leather brief case which I'd just been given: I was lucky not to have been burnt to death as Bill Makins was said to have been.

It was the first night of my many in Fitzrovia and perhaps Tambi had been right in warning me against Sohoitis although he was himself a demonstration case of the disease to which, however, we neither of us succumbed in the end.

A long time later he said to me: 'You know, Julian, some-body showed me a story of yours the other day, I don't read much prose, only poetic prose you know, but I read this right through and you know it was very good? I was surprised you wrote so well.'

'D'you mean you'd never read anything of mine before?' I asked astonished. 'Why, you offered me two hundred advance on a book, remember?'

'Did I?' Tambi was only momentarily disconcerted. 'Ah but you see,' he said recovering, 'my instinct told me your work was good, and my instinct cannot fail.'

'There now!' Kitty exclaimed in triumph when I reported this conversation. 'He didn't have to read you, he *knew*. He *is* a great editor, I told you he had *flair*.'

But Tambi had decided to become a great publisher as well. After long deliberation Nicholson and Watson were prepared to issue a separate non-commercial line of books, both verse and prose (poetic prose of course) to be selected and edited entirely by Tambimuttu.

The general title that this series should have gave rise to much cogitation on Tambi's part, and everyone was called in to help. He originally wanted something very succinct, with the hint of a telegraphic address conveyed in the title of his quarterly, and the metropolitan emphasis was to be retained: in the Forties there was no nonsense about regionalism or Liverpool or Salford being the centre of the arts, London was the centre and that was bloody well that.

Tambi read out with dissatisfaction a list of alternatives written on the back of a beer mat: 'Tambimuttu London Books, Poetry London Library, Poetry London Editions, Poetry Editions London. What else?'

I said: 'How about Prince Tambimuttu Poetry London Books?'

'Too long. Also perhaps,' reluctantly, 'too undemocratic-sounding. You know?'

I then suggested Editions Poetry London, as if the books were French. To my surprise Tambi pounced on this with enthusiasm as if the suggestion had been his own, though without the French *accentaigu* which he couldn't pronounce; and the series eventually appeared under this name: most people, however, referring to them as PL Books, so we need not have taken so much trouble.

Tambi at once commanded a larger salary, and commandeered larger offices which were staffed and stormed by aspirant young poetesses who hoped to have their verse published by *Editions Poetry London* and, wearing mackintoshes and black leather, made the mode which the Sixties followed (then a mark of ineffectual arty bohemianism).

Tambi let them hope, the hopes were unfulfilled for he was not a fool; he in turn entertained concerning them hopes of another sort which frequently *were* fulfilled, for he was extremely fond of women sexually without caring for them much as a sex.

He had already been married and his former wife Jacqueline who now went around with the poet and journalist Charles Hamblett was a permanent feature of the pubs that we frequented. A docile sweet-faced girl with long silky yellow hair and a head which rose to a point at the top like the skull of a spaniel. They were either separated or divorced but still on friendly terms, and later Jackie died: I don't know of what cause.

Tambi in fact must have been married more than once, for he had a brother-in-law who didn't seem to be the brother of Jackie and was a regular Indian Army officer who together with the Great Victorian's great-grandson had supplied some of the initial *Poetry London* backing and then been booted-out by Tambi, disappearing afterwards to Burma with his regiment.

But Tambi if he could have afforded it would have had not only two wives but a harem. His attitude, to most things Europeanized, was to girls exclusively Oriental. I remember once we were with two suburban young women, new to Fitzrovia, whom he'd picked up in the Wheatsheaf and who were both uninteresting and interested only in being bought a meal in some newly-opened restaurant which they'd heard was good but which was off our usual beat. Tambi was becoming increasingly worried as we stumbled over cobble stones further and further from the territory that he had made his own; he glanced longingly at strips of light visible through the black-outs of pubs where the girls refused to stop.

'Nearly ten o'clock,' he muttered. 'In an hour they'll be closing and this restaurant has perhaps no licence,' and suddenly he caught up the girls who were walking ahead arm-in-arm, giggling and whispering together, convinced that they'd achieved their objective in finding a pair of suckers who would foot the bill.

'Listen you must tell us please, my friend and I wish to know, do you do it or not?'

'Do it?' they chorused. 'Do what?'

'You know. Sex.'

There was a pause for shock to register then outraged gasps of 'Oh how dare you,' came in unison.

'You mean you don't?' Tambi asked.

'Certainly not. The idea!'

'Then be off!' Tambi shouted, banishing them with a gesture into the black-out: 'You are wasting our valuable drinking time,' and we retraced our steps to Rathbone Place.

I said: 'I could have told you those girls were NBG.'

'How did you know?'

'Well they were nurses or something weren't they?'

'Don't nurses do sex?'

'Yes but only with doctors whom they hope to marry after.'

'Only doctors? Is that all?' Tambi was silent for a moment then asked: 'Only medical doctors? A doctor of literature would not be any good?'

'Are you a doctor of literature?'

'Not yet. But I could have a degree conferred, Honorary you know. From Oxford, I know many professors there, and then I could fuck with all these nurses. What do you think?'

Actually I would not have been surprised if some university had awarded him an honorary degree but he lost interest later in the idea of using his contacts to get him one, as there weren't really, he explained, so many attractive nurses about just then.

This was in 1943-44, at the height of my intimacy with Tambimuttu, when with Subramaniam we ate curries almost every night in one of the Indian restaurants roundabout. After this, intimacy declined but he had great plans for me round about that time.

He thought it would be good for my career to marry a girl called Diana Gardner, whose excellent collection of short stories *Half-Way Down the Cliff* he later published in PL Books. She too had made a big stir in *Horizon* with a documentary piece *The Land Girl* and her first story *Crossing the Atlantic* had a harsh impersonal cynicism seldom found in feminine fiction at this period. Tambi felt that as presumably kindred souls we should make it a *Horizon* wedding, with Cyril Connolly to give away the bride and famous contributors outside the church to hold copies of the magazine over us when we emerged, as Guardees form an arch with their swords over a newly-wedded comrade and his wife. The fact that I wasn't yet divorced was held to be a minor detail, but actually I never even met Diana Gardner who had the good sense to not come round the pubs.

Another big plan Tambi had was that I should edit the PL Book of French Short Stories; he himself knew no French so he could hardly edit it himself, as he admitted with disarming candour; and at least £200 was offered as a fee for taking on the job, more if I did the translation work as well. This was just what I needed to replenish my bank account: somewhat depleted since my introduction to Fitzrovia, though not transferred to Martin's Bank in Soho Square.

Tambi assured me that this was certain to come off: an added publishing inducement being that authors included in the anthology would not have to be paid just yet, as France was still in the hands of the Germans; and one day I was actually summoned to Nick and Wat Headquarters for discussion of the project with his principals.

I saw a Mr Roberts. He said little but stood behind Tambi's chair as befitted a power behind the throne, scratching his ear with dark Welsh wisdom, then looked shrewd as money began to be mentioned, finally when it came to the question of some being paid out in advance he smiled indulgently as one who listens to the fantasies of a child and quietly left the office, closing the door as if it were a nursery.

To say that I was displeased is to put it mildly, but Tambi said that was only Mr Roberts' way and could be got round later, now he'd take me to lunch on expenses at a good restaurant nearby. Nicholas Moore joined us, perhaps some joint-venture with Grey Walls Press where Nick worked with Charles Wrey Gardiner was in the wind, I don't remember; but after the meal it turned out that Tambi as usual was without cash despite his increased salary, and we had to pay each for our own, splitting the price of Tambi's lunch between us; then he asked us for the receipted bills as these could be added to his expense sheet under Entertainment to Authors, and the French Anthology was never spoken-of in my presence: besides, with the liberation of France it became uneconomic, as the authors would all have to be paid.

Tambi had about him something of the snake-charmer to which I was impervious, and after this incident I could never be persuaded to join him in any business scheme. I've always been proof against anything of the hypnotic order; on the other hand Stewart Scott, who'd had political differences with the army and been repatriated from Burma, had implicit faith in the poet-publisher's occult force.

He told me that once he and Tambi were eating a curry at an Indian café where East-Indian sailors were also served; Tambi for some reason loathed and despised Lascars who, though all mankind was his country, did not to him belong to mankind, and it was not long before trouble arose.

All went outside to settle matters, Stewart Scott a dauntless fellow of only apparently frail physique took on several Lascars who luckily hadn't knives, but Tambi like President Wilson was too proud to fight: he stood by with folded arms and mesmeric stare fixed upon the fray, calling to Scott as his tongue flicked in and out: 'Don't sully yourself Stewart by fighting with this scum. Let me look at them with my eyes, and they will flee abashed,' and Scott telling me the story added: 'And they would have, too, if Tambi could have only got his eyes on them.'

Which didn't prevent Scott from being thoroughly done-up and having to have stitches in where his head had been thumped against some railings. But he bore no grudge either for this or for being thrown-out of the original PL set-up; and now that he was back in circulation became one of Tambi's most loyal supporters.

Yet despite the episode of the Lascars Tambi had plenty of physical courage: it was simply that he shared Scott's belief in his power to subdue the enemy by the naked eye alone. This was all part of his Holy Fakir of Poetry side for which I personally had no use. In a different kind of dangerous situation he showed great *sang-froid*, as I will tell later: also of his kindness and generosity in the case of Gerald Wilde the painter whom he did, against all odds, attempt to help.

I remember too one night when after closing time I was showing to a group of his supporters, in the light of someone's torch, the bullet which had struck my steel helmet in the butts and which I carried always as a good luck charm in my hip pocket. As it was being examined, the twisted shard of metal, shaped like the business end of a scorpion, slipped from my hand and fell through the grating of a drain beside the kerb. Horror struck I called on everybody to help me recover it; the torch was shone upon the grating below which the spent bullet could just be seen glinting, caught up by some obstruction at the side, though all attempts to salvage it with the ferrule of my cane completely failed.

The other fellows got fed-up after a while and were for moving on, but Tambi detained them crying: 'No no, you don't understand. It's his bullet, his talisman, while he carries this he cannot die, we must help him get it,' and on his instructions the grating was levered up and one of the supporters (surely it was Steven?), removing his jacket and rolling up his shirt sleeve, lay flat on the kerb, thrusting his arm down into the drain until his fingers reached the bullet, but unfortunately it was dislodged by his touch and vanished into water with a final plop: now beyond recall short of a descent into the St Pancras sewers.

Tambi mourned the loss as I did myself, but 'Never mind,' he said later, 'you will not die Julian, your work will make you immortal,' and recovering fell heartily to eating a horsemeat curry: all the same he did understand the way I felt.

Meanwhile *Poetry London* had ceased to come out quarterly, indeed to appear at all, and items announced on the *Editions Poetry London* were also overdue pending. Tambi pleaded all the standard wartime publishing excuses: paper shortage, trouble with printers, the binding bottleneck, but none the less rebellion was in the air.

John Banting, who afterwards did very striking jackets for two of my books and whose own *Little Book of Fishes* had been held up for eighteen months, cornered Tambi in the Swiss one evening and, clenching a large turpentine-stained fist under his nose, demanded a definite date or else.

Ignoring the fist, Tambi simply said: 'We will do our best, John. But you see I haven't a European conception of time.'

This pleased Banting so much that he was pacified, and Tambi signed to one of the supporters to buy him a pint of bitter, his sovereign cure for all ills. But not withstanding *Banting's Little Book of Fishes* remained among forthcoming publications. In the end even some of the supporters, who'd not yet received advances for books or payment for poems accepted but not printed, began to cut up rough.

To keep them quiet Tambi brought out an enormous omnibus volume of *Poetry London*, costing the earth to buy and known to us as *Chums*. I nearly got into it myself. While drinking around Soho with Keidrych Rhys and Dylan Thomas who'd mislaid his hat, I'd made up a bit of verse which epitomized the situation and also, we'd drunkenly decided, the poetic climate of the time. Tambi hearing that I'd composed a poem asked me to recite it. I declaimed:

Oh pisspot brimful to overflowing
with milk of Keidrych-curdled kindness;
My hat's in the Highlander
crying with Wheatsheaf voice
oh time gentlemen Police
bearing Tambi
   downwards
     Muttu
       to Tube.

'Marvellous,' Tambi cried. 'I didn't know you were a poet, repeat this please,' and only the repetition of his own name, betraying the send-up, prevented its inclusion in the monster volume. All the supporters were represented however; but when Antony Brown a young poet now turned television newsreader, who had several unpaid-for poems and poetic-prose pieces in *Chums*, was unable to pay his electric light bill and the supply was to be cut off in consequence, I urged him to approach Tambi and insist on some cash down.

From across the Wheatsheaf I watched Tambi's tongue and fingers flickering as he talked and Tony listened, but no wallet was produced or cheque made out: instead a brimming pint not unlike that in my poem appeared on the counter and Tony, returning to me with this clutched in his hand, explained that the expenses of production precluded any payment of fees at present.

Other contributors remembered a colossal banquet given by Tambi about a year before, where many beakers of his special cocktail had been drunk, the guests after receiving separate bills: later collected by the host and pinned to his entertainment account like those settled by Nicholas Moore and myself; and rumours began to circulate that this function had been to celebrate the sum given him by Nick and Wat to pay for poems printed in the omnibus PL. Tambi threatened to sue for slander, lost many supporters in the process, and then a setback occurred which would have knocked a less resilient man flat out.

Nicholson and Watson went bust. They however were responsible for any debts incurred, royalties to authors, etcetera, which must have made Mr Roberts smile less and look more Welshly wise; while *Poetry London* and its Editions were registered under a separate title in the name of Tambimuttu.

In no time a new patron was found, with money believed to come from coal and prepared to put up backing. This was a young man named Harold Musson, big, tall, broad-shouldered, heavy-faced and gentle, also with the reputation of a wit. Unlike other Wheatsheaf wits he did in fact once say something funny. When asked where he'd been for the last week or so, he replied: 'Farming. You know, Chalk Farm. The agricultural life.'

Brand-new supporters, secretaries and poetesses collected round Tambi, his salary went up again though he seemed to have less on him than ever, if that were possible; and he discovered a work of genius, both neo-surrealist and extentialist in tone, entitled *Bymus*. I never read this book but gather it was about a man with three legs who came to London and had a long talk about semantics with a policeman in Piccadilly. Musson was reputed to have paid out at least two hundred and fifty to secure the rights, some even said five hundred: although years later the author, a small bearded Beat whom I encountered in a club, told me that twenty-five was all he'd had from Tambi.

But suddenly a terrible thing happened. Musson decided to become a Buddhist monk. For some time, apparently, he'd been brooding over Hiroshima and not even Tambi could dissuade him from this course.

My second wife, whom I knew by sight but didn't meet until ten years later, saw a lot of them during the period of attempted discussion. Tambi had some forlorn hope that her mother being Leonard Woolf's sister might succeed Musson as a backer, and there was a night at the Imperial Hotel when

Diane suffered some un-monastic behaviour on the part of Musson, who seemed reluctant to relinquish his secular privileges until the last moment; however, being herself six feet high though only seventeen, she managed successfully to repulse him.

After this he took vows, had his head shaved and left for a lamasery in Tibet with a schoolfriend equally tall who used to drink with us also but had never been known to speak. I remember being shown newspaper photographs of them both : they were sitting cross-legged in their robes among other neophytes, and Musson's name was given as something like Brother O-Kai-Lung.

For a time Tambi didn't know where to turn. He even considered returning to Ceylon and showed me a letter from his father urging him to do so and offering money for the fare. The letter was written in impeccable almost Biblical English and a beautiful copperplate hand : it spoke of the Prodigal Son, was extremely moving and the writing paper did not bear any family crest or reproduction of the ancestral home (Subramaniam told me that Tambi's father, like his own, was a retired High Court Judge although of course he may have been a Prince as well). Tambi however managed to hold out until yet another backer took over his firm in more ways than one.

Richard March had been, perhaps still was, in the Diplomatic Service and had written two rather good books, a collection of allegorical stories a little in the fashion of Rex Warner and a novel about a Upas Tree, both published by the Fortune Press. In looks he faintly resembled Tambi's original patron, the Great Victorian's great-grandson, with regular features and distinguished diplomatist's greying hair, but though quiet in manner soon showed signs of wanting to take a more active part in the PL administration than his predecessors had ever done : especially Harold Musson to whom the word of Tambi had been, if not law, at any rate to be instantly complied with.

A dispute was not long in breaking out, many of Tambi's

secretaries, poetesses and supporters went over to the other side: it was then revealed by a firm of lawyers that he had signed some papers without reading them and that *Poetry London*, Editions and all, belonged lock, stock and barrel to Richard March.[1]

Tambi was out. He tried to organize a rally, a protest march with banners inscribed 'UNFAIR TO TAMBIMUTTU!' but by now there were no supporters left to carry them.

The climate of poetry too was changing. Already from the academic desert of the Fifties a dry cold wind was blowing, the red brick Doctors were drumming in the distance and talk of Consolidation and the Critic as Poet could be heard. Tambi fought hard, he slept on studio floors, twice spending the fare sent him by his father in efforts to regain his former position as Prince of Poetry Pundits, but he had to give up at last.

Back to Ceylon he went but not, it seems, for long. I recently heard from Stewart Scott, who'd just come over from the States, that he's now firmly established in Greenwich Village, with fresh patrons, poetesses, and a new poetry review at his disposal.

Good luck to him.

I remember on the last occasion we met standing him a hamburger and chips in some Charlotte Street café just before his departure; and he said then to my girlfriend that, being a Prince in his own country, he would arrange for us a truly royal reception, should we ever decide to visit his part of Ceylon.

'A feast,' he said, 'and the food will be served on plates of gold.' His tongue flicked out to absorb a last morsel of hamburger clinging to the corner of his mouth. 'Gold dust will be smeared upon the meat.'

'And can we have a castle to live in?' she asked, accommodation in London not being easy to obtain at that time.

'A magnificent castle,' Tambi replied.

[1] March died unexpectedly soon after, and the title to *Poetry London* presumably expired with him, for it never reappeared.

'With servants?'

'Certainly with servants. To do your every bidding.'

'And elephants?' she went on. 'Can we have elephants as well?'

'If you insist,' Tambi agreed but with, this time, perhaps a touch of restraint in his tone. Then he added: 'That is Nancy Cunard who has just come in. You know Nancy Cunard?'

We knew Nancy Cunard and Tambi, having finished his meal, hastened over to greet her: failing to return, subsequently, to our table. Asking for the elephants had evidently been too much.

# Fitzrovian Nights

*Pubs of Rathbone Place*

A former proprietor of the Black Horse in Rathbone Place had, so the story went, drunk himself literally to death.

The Black Horse was a sombre Victorian pub, as befitted the suggestion of plumed hearses implied by its name, with a narrow tiled passage leading to the various bars divided by partitions of scrolled and embossed glass, including a Ladies' Bar (no gents admitted) where old dears in dusty black toasted departed husbands with port and lemon from black leather settles. The funereal atmosphere had so affected the late proprietor that he had set out deliberately to commit suicide by drinking solidly for three days and nights behind closed doors, and when these were eventually battered down by police his dead body was found surrounded by empty bottles on the saloon bar floor. The exact amount consumed was never stated in the story, nor exactly what kind of alcohol the bottles had contained.

The Horse was the first pub to be reached, though usually the last to be visited, entering Rathbone Place from Oxford Street. Next on the right, round the cobbled curve of Gresse Street, stood the Bricklayers Arms, better known as the Burglars Rest because a gang of burglars had once broken into it and afterwards slept the night on the premises, leaving behind them as evidence even more empties than the dead landlord of the Horse; but the burglars did not die and, incidentally, were never caught.

The Burglars was a quiet house, useful for a business talk or to take a young woman whom one did not know well, unlike the Marquess of Granby at the foot of Rathbone Place where at that time the most fights broke out despite the efforts of the landlord, an ex-policeman, to keep order and put down disorderly conduct. Gigantic guardsmen went there in search of homosexuals to beat up and rob and, finding none, fought instead each other: one summer evening, in broad daylight, a man was savagely killed by several others in a brawl outside while a crowd gathered on the pavement to watch and was dispersed only by the arrival of a squad from Goodge Street Police Station nearby, by which time the killers had made their getaway in someone else's car. (Entering the Wheatsheaf shortly after this incident, I was surprised to find it empty except for a local tart known as Sister Ann, who told me equably: 'Oh, they've all gone to see the bloke being kicked to death outside the Marquess dear,' and added that the sound of the thumps was somethink awful.)

The Wheatsheaf was the last pub on the right of Rathbone Place, next to the cosmopolitan newsagent on the corner of Percy Street; and branching off diagonally past the Marquess was a roofed-in passage known to us as Jekyll and Hyde Alley because it was the sort of place through which Mr Hyde flourishing his stick rushes low-angle on the screen: this passage contained a pub called the Beerhouse because spirits were not served there, and behind it, to the left, was a ware-house yard piled with cardboard boxes into which one some-times guided girls in order to become better acquainted.

Along Rathbone Street, past the passage, was yet another pub named the Duke of York, much patronized in the middle Forties by the more Bohemian types among whom beards and fringes abounded and who would now be called Beatniks whereas they were then called, more correctly, Bums. The proprietor of the Duke announced himself, on a large placard hung behind him in the bar, as:

### MAJOR 'ALF' KLEIN
### THE PRINCE OF GOOD FELLOWS

but the Prince (or the Major) did not particularly care for me, and in the end would not allow me to be served in his pub, about which I can therefore say little.

Running parallel were the restaurants and cafés of Charlotte Street which made up the district of Fitzrovia and comprised also the Fitzroy Tavern from which at an earlier period the district had derived its name. But fashions, and rendezvous for writers and artists, change; and the Wheatsheaf of all the pubs in Rathbone Place and its environs had become in the Forties the most popular.

It was a Younger's Scotch Ale house and the door to the saloon bar was down an alleyway dominated from above by a perspective of tall tenement buildings with steel outside staircases in the Tottenham Court Road beyond, and often blocked by motor milk vans owned by two stout Italian brothers who ran a small creamery business round the corner of the alley.

When the milk-vans were parked too high up and customers had difficulty in squeezing past to enter the bar, the Wheatsheaf landlord would fling wide the door, and slapping the sides of the vans, shout with flailing arms at the Italian brothers who grinning good humouredly would shift their vans further down. The name of the brothers was Forte.

*The Wheatsheaf and Mrs Stewart*
The Wheatsheaf landlord was known as Red, not because he had red hair (in fact his hair was grey) but because his christian name was Redvers. Also he was not the landlord but the manager appointed by Messrs Younger, though it was his unmarried sister Mona who actually held the licence and whose name as licensee was lettered small on the lintel of the public bar door in Rathbone Place itself. Mona, short, plump and meekly-dressed with her hair drawn back in a bun, helped behind the bar with Red's wife Frances, who was tall, lean and in appearance strict, wearing rimless pince-nez and a tweed coat and skirt, while her husband supervised them both: portly and as a rule in shirt sleeves and braces except on Sundays when he wore a snuff-coloured suit. None the less it was Mona who got rid of awkward customers by simply ordering them to leave with a quite astonishing display of authority; and once barred by Mona you never got in again, whereas Red and even Frances were inclined to be much less inflexible.

The saloon bar of the Wheatsheaf was not large but cheerful, warm in winter, and always brightly lit, good black-out boards fitting tightly over the windows of armorial glass and the floor spread with scarlet linoleum. It had mock-Tudor

F

panelling and, inset round the walls, squares of tartan belonging to various Scottish clans. An important feature was the large china swan, hollowed out inside and sometimes used by vandals as an extra ashtray, which stood in the big bow-window above the long settee at the bottom of the bar and was frequently smuggled out, on very busy evenings, for bets: it was always however returned next day, as the bar would not have been the same without it.

As Tambimuttu had told me, everyone or almost everyone came sooner or later to the Wheatsheaf, even the very eminent paid a passing after-dinner call for the posh restaurants of Percy Street, where rationing was less rigorous, were only round the corner; also it must be remembered that as bottles of drink became in wartime and after more and more difficult to buy, and wine well-nigh impossible, fewer and fewer parties could be thrown and social life for most people began to revolve round the pubs at night.

Curtain-up on the evening was signalled by the arrival on the dot of six of Mrs Stewart, who lived on her old-age pension in one of the tenements at the foot of the alley and was collected by her married daughter towards closing time or when the pub became too noisy. Mrs Stewart was a very small elderly lady dressed in black silk with yellow-white hair and she arrived always carrying two evening papers in which to do the crossword and an alarm-clock to time herself by. She always drank bottled Guinness and having assembled her alarm clock, evening papers, spectacle case, purse, and other properties on the table, sat in front of them on a leather-covered bench which ran along the right-hand wall by the corner of the bar.

It was in this corner, propped up against the wooden partition of the seat, that I stood for many years (though not, as has been said, underneath my own tartan), having displaced from this strategic position a Central European sports writer on a daily picture paper by the simple expedient of arriving each evening earlier than he was able to.

The sports writer was furious and hated me virulently

because of this, since for years before my arrival on the scene he'd been able to lean there, wearing a brown porkpie hat and camel hair coat of inferior quality, speaking to few but hoping always that tourists would say: 'Who is that interesting-looking foreign man over there?' as he struck a Napoleonic pose and stared superciliously ahead with his pouched eyes through the smoke of a nonchalantly puffed-at cigarette.

Having permanently dislodged him however (for if prevented by business from getting there in time, I would have someone else to hold the corner), it became my duty in turn to keep Mrs Stewart's place, to pass over the Guinnesses in exchange for the exact money produced from her purse, and to see that well-intentioned idiots did not try to help her with the crosswords, a thing she hated above all. Great care had to be exercised in offering her a drink, it could only be done by split-second timing when her nightly ration was running low, but she was very proud and from certain people who plonked down heartily before her an open bottle, with the words 'Have that one on me Ma,' she would not accept anything at all.

She was spiky and occasionally irascible. Happily she approved of me, but Dylan Thomas and the poetess Anna Wickham she could not stand at any price. Red and Frances shared, originally, her dislike of Dylan, Mona to a lesser extent (luckily, or he wouldn't have been allowed in), but later when he had begun to broadcast they chanced to hear him on the radio and from then on nothing was too good. Mrs Stewart either didn't own a set or was perhaps too deaf, for her opinion of Dylan remained unchanged, despite the attempts of Red and Frances to win her over to what was now their side.

And yet she was no stranger to people of this sort. In Paris as a young woman she had lived in Montparnasse where she'd known Pascin, Hemingway and Joyce, also Denis Corrigan who'd once been my uncle's partner on the Côte and later hanged himself with his necktie in a prison cell awaiting trial (a paperback thriller called *Hangman's Tie* was found lying below the bench from which he'd kicked off).

Corrigan Mrs Stewart had met mainly on the racecourse, but her encounters with the painters and writers had been in the Paris cafés and her stories about them always ended with her saying: 'And there they were, my dear, staggering about just like you and the rest of the young fellows are doing today.'

She was unlike other old ladies in that she never spoke of the past from a personal angle, so nobody was told what she herself had been doing in Paris at this period. Nina Hamnett, who was better at painting old people than she was with the young, did a superb portrait of her, which for some time after she died hung above the spot where for so long she'd sat, though I don't know what happened to it in the end.

The death of Mrs Stewart—in the late Forties or early Fifties—marked, as writers of memoirs are fond of saying, the passing of an epoch, and it might have pleased her to know that she'd become a symbolic figure to a whole generation now no longer young: for there are few former Wheatsheaf habitués whose eyes fail to light up in memory of her name.

*Regulars, Wits and Bums*

Alan Ross, then a junior naval officer on leave, used to come round, among others, about this time. As a promising young poet he had been discovered by John Lehmann, whom he was later to succeed as editor of *The London Magazine*, and Lehmann had also printed in *New Writing and Daylight* portions of a novel which alternated brilliantly scenes of civilian and naval life but was never completed.

Ross in the navy had served with the triple murderer Ronald Chesney but he did not know that yet, since Chesney so far had murdered only once: his own mother, for which he'd been tried and acquitted at the age of 17 under his real name of John Donald Merrett.

Ross was very young and ingenuous in manner: clean shaven in those days with a dark complexion and black sleek hair which showed up handsomely against his blue and gold uniform, and he had brown eyes which peered with un-abashed interest at everybody and everything and took in a very great deal: as was revealed when he recreated from memory, with remarkable precision except for the high nasal voice allotted to me, the complete Wheatsheaf scene in a *London Magazine* editorial last year.

He described of course an evening on which absolutely everyone was there but the point was, as he said to me recently, that such an evening *could* and indeed sometimes did, take place.

But there were other figures whom he did not mention and possibly did not notice, without whom the Wheatsheaf wouldn't really have been complete: they made up the background and the unsung chorus and occasionally, on an off-night, the entire cast.

These fell roughly into three categories: Regulars, Wits and Bums.

Regulars, of whom Mrs Stewart was the doyenne, included the old Home Guard who though extremely old wore on his tunic medal ribbons of more campaigns than even he could possibly have served in: it was thought that the tunic or the ribbons had been handed down to him by his grandfather, and I was using him as a model for the old sweat in the Home Guard film which Dylan and myself were then still writing. Then there was the Central European sports writer, now relegated to the middle of the counter from which it was not so easy to get a drink; the orange-faced woman (so called because of the many layers of make-up which she wore and which made it impossible to assess her age), whose presence in the pub made it sound like the parrot house in the zoo and who was reputed to have green silk sheets on her bed (though no man was brave enough to investigate the rumour); and Sister Ann, the tart who was more respectable than many other female customers: she mostly moved in a no-man's land between public and saloon bars and patronized both as it suited her.

Sister Ann was short and wholesome-looking and always wore russet-brown tweeds and a round russet-brown hat in shape like a schoolgirl's. She used no make-up except for two round red spots on her round apple cheeks, for she was no common brass and her chosen clientèle wanted nothing loud or flashy, consisting as it did of middle-aged or elderly business men from up North who liked the sort of girl that might have been a sister to them (she was shocked when I suggested this relationship was incestuous and said she was surprised to hear a man of my education using nasty dirty words like that to a woman, and she certainly never did anything of *that* sort, thank you dear).

When later I started going to the little afternoon clubs in Wardour Street, I often saw Ann having a quiet talk with one of her clients before or after, it was hard to say which. She never drank anything except brown bottled ale.

Ann's beat was under the Guinness clock in Tottenham Court Road: 'You catch them going into the tube or coming out for a day up in London dear, and maybe they're lost and don't know where to go or they don't want to catch a train home just yet awhile, either way they're glad to spend an hour or two with a girl they can talk to quiet like, poor blokes.'

Wits came in various shapes and sizes, but could be distinguished by the fact that none was ever heard to say anything witty: indeed one elderly Irishman, who wore a grey wideawake hat and was supposed when young to have written a very witty book, never said anything at all. Sometimes however he gave vent to a very loud laugh addressed to no one in particular, so possibly some pearl of wit too precious to cast before swine had passed through his hoary head beneath the wideawake brim.

He was a lone wolf whose laughter was sufficient unto himself; but on the whole wits tended to assemble in groups in order to laugh at the witticisms of other members as well as their own. The leader of the main group was a scenic artist who described himself as a painter, and his wit was exercised at the expense of the film producers who employed him and whom he would not have dared to criticize face to face for fear of causing offence. He was a baby elephant character, big and burly with grey hair ruffled up into a crest at the back and dangling over his fleshy nose as he lurched unsteadily about, one arm semaphoring the air, the other pointing to the ground, while his high piping voice re-enacted some scene that had taken place at the studios that day, in which according to himself he had shown the stupid bastards where to get off. When drunk he was aggressively and grossly rude, when sober extremely timid, the high piping voice was seldom heard, and if attacked in this rare condition by victims of his previous rudeness, he would flee the pub altogether, no witticism apparently coming to his aid. I only heard one sample of his wit myself, and that was repeated to me years later by an admirer who had been part of the group, now of course long disbanded. Apparently he had been taken to a pub outside his usual orbit, the name of which he didn't know; and when told this was the Adam-and-Eve, he cracked back—quick as a flash !— 'Ah, I thought I saw an old bloke just going out with a halo and a long beard.'

Members of the group led by the scenic artist were always making ineffective passes at women with the object of afterwards humorously proclaiming their sexual frustration: some had literary aspirations and these passed round proudly newspaper cuttings relating to their arrests for being drunk and disorderly; it was the only chance they had of seeing their names in print, and once when the entire group was run in while searching in a cemetery, after closing time, for Hazlitt's grave, there was as much excitement as if they had won, collectively, the Nobel Prize.

Bums (some of whom under their new designation as Beats are still about), were of two kinds: (1) young men and women just down from provincial universities and wrapped in college scarves which after going several times round the necks were still long enough to hang down behind: these were known to us as the Slithy Toves since members of both sexes resembled facially the curious corkscrew-like creatures depicted by Tenniel in his illustrations to *Alice*, and (2) a number of shaggy bearded types who had managed to dodge the Services and lived communally in the cellar of a blitzed building, where they made lampshades and toy animals out of pipe cleaners while dealing in the black market on the side for a living. Their leader was known, for obvious reasons, as Robinson Crusoe and they called themselves the Young Anarchist Movement. None of them had any political convictions.

# The Metamorphosis of Peter Brooke

He can't have been more than twenty-five when I first saw him, but even at that age he seemed sublimely unconscious of anyone except himself.

It was during the summer of 1931, at the Salle Mercier in Nice. This was a dance hall for hire, situated behind the boulevard Tsarevitch in the Russian Quarter, not far from the Orthodox Church. Unorthodox activities, however, not infrequently took place at the Salle when younger members of the Russian Colony held a dance there, and on that particular evening, just before Brooke appeared, I was wondering how to get out of the place alive.

The cabinet gramophone with its amplifying horn was temporarily silent, the dance floor had been cleared for an interval, and on either side of the empty space two rival Russian factions were drawn up making ready for civil war. Into this electric atmosphere strode Peter Brooke, entering the line of fire much as in later life he was wont to cross the barrack square bang in the middle of a battalion parade.

Irina Petrovna, by whose invitation I had come and who was also apparently unaware of the tension at present building up, exclaimed: 'Oh here is that other Englishman, Brooke. You must meet him, he too is writing a book. He has just come all the way from Spain on a bike.'

Attire as always on Russian occasions was fairly formal, a grande tenue was not *de rigueur* but all the girls at any rate wore evening frocks. Brooke had on rope-soled canvas shoes, tarpaulin trousers stained with axle-grease and a white open-necked shirt the sleeve of which had been partly ripped away, showing the blade of a broad shoulder burnt almost black. He had a rugged face the colour of dark tan Kiwi shoe polish and his rough straight hair, falling in bangs over the forehead, was absolutely black. He advanced upon us with deep-set dancing eyes and a smile of enormous geniality.

'Did you say bike or hike?' I asked Irina.

'Bike,' she said and Brooke bowed over her hand.

He wasted no time on me but immediately drew himself up very tall and with head flung back began, smiling inexorably, to survey the young women nearby in a manner that betokened business.

At this moment the gramophone burst forth with the Stein Song and the prospective combatants reluctantly claimed partners without ceasing to exchange belligerent stares over their heads, while the amplified disc bellowed of undying campus comradeship, exhorting all to sing until the rafters ring. Brooke's glance had lit upon a placid pretty girl sitting with blonde hair braided round her head and eyes cast demurely down. It was not true, as he afterwards wrote, that I was ever his rival for this girl, whom I knew to be heavily engaged. Marousya would not in any case have been my type. On the other hand she was very much Brooke's; and after circling the floor a few times he steered her away through the open French windows towards the fairy lights of the garden beyond.

This gave me an idea. Taking Irina Petrovna in my arms and explaining the situation in a rapid undertone, I propelled her in the direction of the door, reaching it just as the Stein Song stopped abruptly and the fight broke loose. We made our getaway on the running board of somebody's car, and I often wondered what Brooke's reaction had been when, returning after his romantic interlude, he found the furniture reduced to matchwood, blood and broken bottles on the parquet floor, and the police in possession.

Long afterwards he told me that he'd always imagined I was in some way responsible. He described me as very pale, watchful and withdrawn; I wore an orchid in my buttonhole, another sinister trait according to the movies of the time, and moreover was smoking a Turkish cigarette through a long holder, the mark of at least a gang-leader if not a master criminal.

164

But next time I saw him he was himself smoking through a holder, and even flourishing it elegantly about on the stage at the Casino de la Méditerranée. He had somehow acquired a lounge suit and was playing Algy in *The Importance of Being Earnest*, produced by a woman with three names who ran something called the Anglo-American Repertory Company. A friend of mine had been slated to report the matinée for *The Monte Carlo News*, a weekly paper printed in English for British residents. He had no literary or journalistic aptitudes, it was his father who'd got him on to the staff, and I had offered to do the review for him, thus it came about that the first notice of Peter Brooke ever to appear in print was written by me.

It was also the first time Brooke had ever acted professionally, but he put up a rousing show. Great panache and aplomb, and his voice carried easily to every corner of the theatre, while the actor playing Ernest was barely audible over the footlights. There was only one thing out of place: Brooke had forgotten to shave. He also dozed off at times during Ernest's long explanation of his predicament, but awoke always in the nick of time, rising to come in on cue with a tremendous shout.

'Is that chap tight?' asked my friend. 'What d'you suppose he'll be like by tonight?' and I wish we had attended the evening performance instead; for, as I was told by those who did, Peter Brooke, delivering an epigram with a careless wave of his hand, stepped backward off the stage and was buried up to the neck in the jazz drum which in the orchestra pit awaited the negro musicians booked to appear on the following night.

After this I saw him no more for thirteen years, nor did the blonde Marousya ever mention his name to me.

At the Café Madrid, corner of Dean and Old Compton Streets, good strong cups of black French coffee could be had in 1944, not like the frothy Italian mud that's served up now. Outside was winter, inside was warm, and Philip Toynbee often came there to write part of a novel or Paul Potts to read a book of verse. Neither of these was present on the afternoon I met Peter Brooke again.

This time he was dressed as a corporal and wore an army greatcoat buttoned to the neck. His tan had faded slightly, his rough lamp-black hair comprised already streaks of grey, but the deep-set eyes still danced beneath brows that had grown bushier with every year that passed and the smile of set geniality remained. He was not a figure one forgets, and I said: 'So they dug you out of that jazz drum in the end?'

This greeting startled Brooke, who went through a quick routine denoting the double-take, passing a hand over his face, rubbing a finger across the nose and pushing the hair back from his forehead. Then he shouted: 'Why good God. You're that fellow who smashed up the Russian dance hall in Nice.'

By the time this was straightened out and several rounds of coffee had been swallowed, I'd found out a good deal concerning Brooke: never reluctant in any case to talk about himself. His father was a Bavarian Count born in England and a British subject, who had changed his family name and ended up as a film actor in Hollywood, and there was an elder brother who'd written several novels, including one about the private life of Jack the Ripper. I had often seen the father as an eccentric millionaire or mad scientist on the screen, and used to play Parc Impérial tennis with the brother, a fashionable type who hobnobbed with the King of Sweden, so I was in a sense a sort of family friend and when we reached the Swiss pub across the way, where sloe gin or arak could be drunk instead of coffee, Brooke had adopted me as such.

'Would you say I'm like my brother?' he asked, choosing arak because he'd lived in Tangier where Kif was smoked and after Ramadan orgies of sex ensued.

'To look at, d'you mean? It never occurred to me you were related.'

'Well I don't think I look like him either, but a funny thing happened. Right here. In this very bar.' He pointed to the bar where the man had come up to him. The man had said:

'Brooke?' 'Yes.' 'Your name *is* Brooke?' 'Certainly,' Brooke replied and with that the man had socked him in the face.

Brooke drove a fist into his palm to illustrate the blow, which it turned out was intended for his brother. 'Silly sod had got the two of us mixed up. I asked what my brother had done to him but he simply wouldn't say. Finally I got fed up and grabbed hold of him to make him talk, so they told us both to go, and in the black-out the bastard got away. I've never set eyes on him since. Most extraordinary, though. No one's ever taken me for my brother before. And he couldn't have ever seen my brother or he wouldn't have made the mistake, so how could he have been injured by a man he never saw.'

It was an insoluble mystery, but things like this were always happening to Brooke: his future career was to be founded on the fact that he was dogged by misadventure. He himself had written a novel but of course its publication coincided with the outbreak of war, which effectively killed any sales there may have been. He enumerated with a shout of contemptuous laughter the kind of Resistance novel on which public interest had centred at the time: *'The Moon is Down, The Night is Ending, Fucking Dawn Broke,'* and I heartily agreed that this type of book had long outlived its day.

Brooke's own novel, which I'd read but not connected with the young man I'd so briefly met in Nice, had been far better. It was extremely accomplished and original: a macabre fantasy with cosmopolitan backgrounds, about the Aztec wife of a famous French aviator converted from childhood to vampirism, and the pages as one turned them had the authentic dry rustle of leathery wings. At the same time extravagantly comic passages belied the gruesome theme, and the technical structure of the book alone merited much more critical attention than it got.

Brooke told me about the original of his character, with whom he'd once been in love. She was also the wife of a famous French aviator and claimed to be of Aztec origin though not a vampire. As in the novel, she actually came from Mexico.

167

'Of course you've been to Mexico?' I said, but he said no, that part was all imagination: apart from Tangier he'd been to America, Australia, New Zealand, France, Italy and Spain, several of these continents he had crossed on foot, but he had never got to Mexico. He'd joined the army hoping to go abroad again but although he spoke three languages at least, would the bastards send him overseas? Not a bloody chance, and now he was being shunted round the bugger like a lost truck: a phrase he'd used as opening sentence of a story which no editor would print. Eventually his company commander, a man who looked like a shark, had compromised by transferring him to Intelligence, so here he was, with six more days of pending-posting leave to go.

At this prospect his eyes began again to dance: the effect, I realized, was due to the way his high cheekbones seemed to make them slant, also to short sight, so extreme that he would have often to peer closely into several peoples' faces before he could identify a friend. The eyes themselves were yellow.

Brooke would have none of this, however. According to him, his sight was equalled only by that of a hawk; and when the colour of his eyes was commented on, and this was done frequently by girls: 'I have *golden* eyes,' he would correct them sternly.

Arak had by now run out and was succeeded by rum, sloe gin being also in short supply. Together we sang the Stein Song which had been playing at the Salle Mercier on the night we first met. We sang until the rafters rang, and having no steins clinked our glasses of rum as the song required when undying friendship was being pledged. The glasses were not really up to these repeated shocks and when they broke the barman, who'd probably been on duty when Brooke was mistaken for his brother, said rum had run out as well. So we sang the Stein Song stumbling along the blacked-out streets until a couple of red caps suddenly flashed a torch on Brooke and asked to see his paybook. He then cursed all the way to Rathbone Place, with occasional indignant shouts of 'Fighting for Freedom, my *God*!' or 'Might as well have the bloody

Nazis here,' but on entering the Wheatsheaf, where strong ale and even whisky were plentiful and girls also quite abundant, his geniality returned.

He made several dates which next day he did not keep, when the pubs closed it turned out he'd nowhere to stay, and soon he was tucked up on the couch in my upstairs sitting room, after having eaten half a pot of jam out of the jar with a spoon. His greatcoat was spread over him and he started to snore before I switched off the light.

A few seconds after, or so it seemed, the light was switched on in my bedroom and Brooke stood over me stark naked, shouting: 'Wakey, wakey, rise and shine. It's past four in the afternoon and I could eat a horse. I could eat fried cat.'

I said, perhaps a little crossly: 'Better ring up the Ritz and find out if they've any,' and Brooke forthwith seized the phone: 'That the Ritz? Put me onto the restaurant please. Restaurant? This is Colonel Sebastian Moran speaking. Have you any fried cat on the menu for tonight? What, no fried cat? Damn it sir what's England coming to I'd like to know. No *fried cat* indeed.'

So we ate spaghetti at the Scala Restaurant, and at the close of another evening in the pubs Brooke told me about his current love affair, which was going far from well. I tried to concentrate sympathetically but, after two heavy nights of drinking plus the fact that I'd been working late for weeks, a cloud of fatigue descended halfway through. I would drift into a semi-doze as Brooke had done while playing Algy, then abruptly start awake to the sound of his voice declaring that the air, whenever he saw his love, was like a perfumed thunderstorm. I managed to assimilate the really important bits, such as the salient facts about the husband, but these only strengthened my conviction that he should pack it in as hopeless; and eighteen years later he wrote that I'd been profoundly shocked by his recital, not being myself interested in sex and unmoved by any sort of beauty.

Brooke did nothing by halves. Love to him was either a Florentine tragedy or an affair of ineffable enchantment.

Night club hostesses, unscreened starlets, suburban typists were transmuted by his powerful imagination into nymphs, goddesses and legendary queens, apt to revert overnight to their true selves when the light of reality was shed upon them, as Dracula could be dispersed by a single ray of sunshine. His more mundane appetites were prodigious. Great gallons of beer, large measures of spirit, were poured upon mountains of whatever food was available, with the action of one trying to put out a fire. He could also smoke with apparent enjoyment any kind of tobacco, even the sinister nameless wartime brands or fags for the Forces made from sweepings off the Naafi floor.

He was not perhaps the perfect guest. He woke noisily, with yawning, coughing and stretching that shook the house, sang flamenco while shaving and splashed water, soap and lather in all directions: the bathroom after he'd used it was always awash as if a brontosaurus had wallowed in the tub. For the last weekend of his leave I took him down to the house of my current girlfriend's parents who lived near Windsor. On the morning after we arrived he stayed in bed until after eleven because his sinuses were playing him up, then rose suddenly and, draped in my dressing gown that had Chinese dragons on it, strode through to the dining room where he consumed at one go all the bacon, eggs, butter and marmalade rations for the week, finally throwing down his napkin and exclaiming to the hostess: 'What a wonderful breakfast. Really pre-war standard, one so rarely gets enough to eat these days. Pity I couldn't taste any of it with this confounded sinus trouble of mine, but you're not to blame for that.'

After dinner he imitated for us the fever bird of Whakarewarewa, NZ, drank several pots of coffee and half a bottle of the host's scotch, and read aloud two acts of *Hamlet*, playing all the parts himself with stupendous verve and brio.

Next day there was nothing much left for breakfast, so he didn't get up until it was time to assemble his kit, find his forage cap and gloves which had been mysteriously mislaid, and get him not without difficulty onto a train bound for the

Graham Greene

Dylan Thomas (right)

Stephen Spender

Woodrow Wyatt

Cyril Connolly

Anthony Carson

Jonathan Cape

Philip Toynbee

Stevie Smith

Arthur Calder-Marshall

Intelligence Corps Depot, where he was promptly clapped under close arrest.

It seemed that all his papers had not been sent on and the Intelligence people, having discovered he was a Dual National, decided to play safe.

'Your dad was a Jerry, that makes you a Jerry, mate,' a stalwart sergeant said, locking Brooke in a guardroom cell. 'Chances are you'll be interned under 18B, less of course you're a Nazzy spy, when you'll be bleeding well shot.'

Brooke's papers did not arrive for several days, in the meantime he was interrogated by security officers, then they let him out and apologized, but said the experience would be useful to him on the course where he had to learn the technique of querying prisoners and suspects. Halfway through the course, however, they said he really shouldn't be in Intelligence, not with a German father he shouldn't: paradoxically another point against him was that he couldn't speak German, so he was returned to his unit where the shark-like OC again sent him on leave pending another posting.

'Perhaps they'll boot you out of the army altogether,' I said when he turned up in the back bar of the Café Royal, this time wearing civvy clothes: at first I thought he had been discharged. 'You'd be much more use in a Ministry, or writing documentary films,' but it turned out Brooke had already been in documentary films, and Donald Taylor said later that he would have to overcome a certain amount of opposition before getting a job in the industry again.

I was between jobs myself, it was just before Donald's new company started up, and money was short, to put it mildly.

'Look at my paybook,' Brooke said, thrusting this into my hand when the situation was explained to him.

'Why should I want to look at your paybook?'

'Feel underneath it you fool,' Brooke whispered, and thus a fiver changed hands. John Collinses came up, soon Brooke was engaged in a contest of insults with one of the back bar regulars, and acquitted himself more than well; for he had studied rudeness under the Master in Paris, having shared a flat with Brian Howard on the boulevard St Germain. He had also adopted many of the Master's mannerisms, the sidling approach, one shoulder slightly hunched, which I was to recognize several years after I met Howard himself in the Mandrake Club.

'No more spirits, sorry,' Frank the barman called out when Brooke's antagonist reeled away, routed by a parting volley of invective, and Brooke said, eyes still dancing with the light of battle: 'Let's go and look for the Pebble Man.'

One of his favourite fantasies centred round the personality of this Pebble Man, a perhaps semi-mythological character whom I certainly never saw. With his double lensed pebble glasses, his loud hectoring voice, authoritarian opinions and obvious position of power, he epitomized everything that Brooke had a hatred for, though apparently they had never spoken. Brooke had once heard him in a Soho café, bullying the waitress and laying down the law to a group of subdued satellites, and longed ever since to teach him a lesson.

He had an idea that the Pebble Man belonged to the film world, was perhaps a leading producer or distributor, so we tried the Wardour Street pubs and then the Highlander, where I pointed enquiringly at a large man wearing a sort of Stetson and spectacles, the look of whom I personally disliked. But Brooke, having sidled up to and peered closely at my candidate, said: 'No, no, nothing like him at all,' and the search was resumed without success, even though we had a meal in the café where the Pebble Man had first been seen.

Brooke's blood, however, seemed still up the following morning and, straightening his bow tie before the looking glass in my flat, he said: 'Now we'll go and find someone to persecute.'

In the tube train he threw back his head and looked round for victims rather as he had surveyed the girls at the Salle Mercier. The person he picked on now was a dark suited prim faced clerkly man, carrying a briefcase, perhaps a low grade civil servant. Brooke, nodding slowly as if in satisfaction, said to me in accented English: 'It is he, Karl,' and took a seat farther down the compartment but facing the man, at whom he stared fixedly, while whispering audibly to me in what sounded like a foreign language. The clerkly man fidgeted, first in embarrassment then with increasing nervousness, and Brooke said in a louder tone, as if I'd disagreed with him: 'I tell you Karl. That *is* the man. I have here the description that they gave me, the papers are there in his portfolio, soon will come the moment, not yet.'

The clerkly man clutched his briefcase in mounting agitation; at Oxford Circus he made a bolt for the doors, but Brooke marched stiffly, like a Prussian officer in mufti, down the platform on his tail. The quarry dived through an arch and on to the escalator, we followed close behind; at the top the clerkly man, glancing about in desperation, trotted towards a policeman standing by the entrance, whereupon we stepped on to the escalator going down and boarded a train for the Tottenham Court Road.

'That put the wind up the little bastard,' Brooke said at the other end. 'I cant bear these stinking pin striped mice,' and he broke off to pour derision and abuse on a tube wall poster, which showed a squeezed lemon grinning wryly and got up as an aircraftman, to advertise a brand of squash.

'They've even got to put the bloody lemons in uniform,' he shouted angrily. 'It's making fun of the Forces,' then outside the station stopped short at sight of a big Ministry safety precaution placard which said: 'GOING OUT? LOOK OUT —BLACK OUT!'

Brooke at once became a foreigner again, but this time a timid refugee baffled by alien customs and this cryptic pronouncement in particular. The aid of passers-by was enlisted to explain it to him: 'Pliz to tell me sir, what is meanink this?'; he became more and more excitable: Goink out lookink out blackink out? But is not yet the blackink-out, is sun shining now!' then indignant: 'Black—out! Not Negroes then allowed? Is Britain not democracy?' etc. until a small crowd had collected and the Guinness clock announced 11.30. Then he said in his normal voice: 'Come on Julian, they'll be open now,' and we quickly crossed the road to avoid being lynched by the crowd, which seemed not to enjoy the joke.

In the Horseshoe he asked: 'How are we now for cash? Less than a quid? Not much use that, drink up and we'll see what the Charing Cross Road has to offer.'

My opinion was that in the way of money it had nothing to offer, unless you'd some books to sell, but Brooke saying: 'Wait here,' strode through the doorway of a music publishing shop. I stared at song sheets and piano accordions in the window, wondering whether he could be already tight, when out he came with ten pounds flourished in his hand. Apparently, years before, he'd written the lyrics for a pop song about a gypsy and the ten pounds represented accumulated royalties.

Song writing was one of the ways by which he planned to make a living when discharged from the army, another was writing trailers for films: often the most exciting part of the programme, as he very truly said. He devised many trailers during the days that followed, also a complete documentary of the 'This is My Job' type then in vogue, which featured the occupation of a Lavatory Man called Dan. It was to end with Dan patriotically foiling a Nazi agent whose code messages were disguised as graffiti on the walls. In the struggle the gallant latrine-wallah was to die for his country and the last shots showed a monument being unveiled to his memory, a giant lavatory pan inscribed with the legend: 'WE ALL HAVE TO GO SOMETIMES.'

'In Latin, of course,' Brooke said emptying his pint with a shout of laughter in which the whole of the Wheatsheaf joined, and he was invited to write the script forthwith by a man who could get the backing if Brooke himself put up a hundred on the spot.

Another, more serious proposition he received was from Charles Wrey Gardiner of the Grey Walls Press, who was present when Brooke outlined a projected fantasy novel called *The Monastery of Information*. The basic elements included an astrally projected Tibetan lamasery, controlled from the forbidden city itself and invisible to all except those in a state of ecstasy: drunks, lovers, etc.; there was also a London bank which financed the nefarious operations of the Tibetan fifth-column with phantom money and was manned by cashiers stuffed with straw. Murders of people who knew too much were committed by a band of trained commando midgets, and the conspiracy's total aim was world domination, narrowly averted.

Wrey Gardiner, impressed by what he called a poetic variation on thriller themes, actually offered to advance something on a synopsis if I collaborated on the writing of the book; and, as the music publishers' tenner was running out faster than the spirits in the pubs, we got down to work that night, but Brooke fell asleep over the table just as we reached the first murder by midget.

Next day deafening shrieks both male and female, and the sound of feet scampering downstairs, awoke me. The front door banged and Brooke gave another wild yell from the sitting room above, which I reached just in time to restrain him from throwing himself bodily through the window.

I'd forgotten to warn him that the woman who came in once a fortnight to clean the flat was a kind of pixie-dwarf. Brooke had woken up to find, staring at him from the doorway, what seemed to be one of his own murderous midgets come to life. She on the other hand had assumed from his posture that he was dead. Both started simultaneously to scream, Brooke's panic-stricken roar causing the cleaning woman to decamp so quickly that he thought he'd imagined her in a fit of lunacy or the DTs, hence his attempt to end it all.

The shock to his nerves was such that he was quite unfit to continue work on the synopsis, and later that morning a loud knock on the downstairs door further unmanned him. It was a telegram recalling him to his unit for posting, so *The Monastery of Information* remains unwritten to this day, although Wrey Gardiner still talks about it at times.

A long Brookeless lull ensued. He never wrote letters, and I began to fear he'd been drafted overseas and fallen during the

Normandy landings.

Then one late autumn day I was passing a Charing Cross Road bookshop and heard a voice raised angrily within. It came from a tall smart subaltern, with polished Sam Browne and one brass pip on each shoulder strap of his service dress. He was swishing his swagger cane and standing over the short blonde young woman who worked in the shop and was very efficient, impersonal and self-possessed.

Her close-lipped Mona Lisa smile seemed to infuriate the subaltern. He sidled nearer with one shoulder hunched and said: 'Of course, if you want to play cheap chess with me . . .'

Though his back was turned, the voice was unmistakable. 'Mr Brooke!' I snapped out in a tone of command. The subaltern wheeled round startled, snatched from his pocket a pair of horn rimmed spectacles, and inspected me through them as though they were a lorgnette. Then his eyes began to dance like yellow dervishes beneath the bushy black brows and the peak of his service dress cap, and he strode forward to embrace me.

'You old bastard,' he said. 'I thought for a moment you were my colonel. One never knows what voice you'll put on next.'

I said: 'So they fitted you out with specs at last. As well as all this,' indicating his officer's uniform.

'Yes I had to have my eyes tested before going to OCTU. We were on an exercise with live ammo and I led my chaps into a minefield by mistake. Signs all round saying DANGER, apparently. Curious thing, always thought I'd perfect sight, but the eye specialist didn't agree. Anyhow I can hardly see through the damn things he gave me, and they won't fit behind my ears.'

During this speech the short blonde young bookshop woman, who had not ceased to smile close-lipped, started unhurriedly for the stockroom below.

'My wife,' Brooke explained, nodding towards the wooden steps down which she'd disappeared.

'I didn't know you were married.'

Brooke said shortly: 'Been separated years,' and in the street outside: 'We met today to talk about the future of our son.'

'I never thought of you as a family man.'

'Neither did I,' he replied with his shout of laughter, and that was the only time we mentioned his marriage, except when much later he told me they were divorced.

Being commissioned, he said, made no difference to him except that he was now able to cash cheques at Coutts' Bank and could no longer be stopped with impunity by red caps in the street. All the same he was different, much more debonair: the awkward squad corporal had given place to the dashing young officer, a new rôle which his protean personality automatically absorbed.

His grand passion seemed to have burnt itself out, and the latest girl was a small brunette dressed in black with lace collar and cuffs, who did part-time typing and whom he used to take out to tea. I began to believe he must like them small, Marousya had been short and his estranged wife was exceptionally so: both these too were of outwardly placid temperaments and the brunette hardly spoke. But then she vanished abruptly from the scene and was replaced by a strapping turbulent wench who had a mad husband hidden somewhere, like Rochester in reverse, so I was apparently wrong about Brooke on both counts: the only link remaining was that Marousya, the wife and the strapping one were all of them blonde, and the brunette hadn't stayed the course.

I too had meanwhile acquired a new girlfriend and a new, much smaller flat, but later on Brooke settled down without comment on the new sitting room couch, and in the Wheatsheaf greeted the new girl with as much warmth as if she'd been the old. It's doubtful indeed if he knew the difference, since happily for our relationship we didn't share the same taste in women. But he was less boisterous on this leave and perhaps found the new couch not so comfortable, for soon he sloped off to the country with the hulking blonde, whose husband I believe was left locked up in the cellar.

Again a long interval elapsed.

I'd changed my address again to a one room Mayfair flatlet,

and one night came home to find a figure huddled, apparently asleep or drunk, upon my doorstep. The figure scrambled upright as I drew level and, gripping me firmly by the shoulder, said: 'Sorry but I've my duty to perform. As an officer of His Majesty's Army I'm arresting you for subversive activities as per War Office instructions and my advice is don't resist.'

'Come in Peter,' I said, fitting latchkey into lock.

Brooke was tighter than I'd ever seen him. He didn't say where he'd got the skinful or how he'd found out where I lived. He slumped in the armchair which was the only bed I had to offer him, looking baffled and bull-like: his hair had begun to go grey at the temples though his eyebrows remained very black. He now had two pips up and had been put in charge of a camp for Italian prisoners, a duty he detested. He cursed women, fate, war and the army for a while, then shouted: 'Sartre! A man writing an enormous newspaper!' and snatching up a copy of *John O'London's Weekly* started scornfully to read aloud an article on Existentialism, but subsided halfway through and lay snoring on the floor.

Even the steady thunder of bomber planes on the way to Germany overhead failed to wake him, but just before dawn he had a fight with himself in his sleep. I watched from my ringside seat: himself seemed about to win but just in time he knocked himself out. I counted ten but he lay stiff and silent, not even snoring now; and in the morning we were roused by the ringing telephone. It was my girlfriend to say that Germany had surrendered, which places this meeting in early May 1945.

Brooke was once more recalled to his camp and discharged not too long after the war ended with the rank of full lieutenant. A War Office letter told him that he was quite entitled to style himself Lieutenant Brooke in civilian life, which as he said was a fat lot of good, since you couldn't even get a job as secretary of a golf club unless you were at least a captain.

He decided to become an actor instead. With his gratuity he bought new clothes and appeared among us in a very elegant navy blue suit, wearing a carnation in his buttonhole. With his greying temples he looked immensely distinguished and actorish; he had several photographs taken and acquired an agent who was a wonderful person.

But all this came to nothing, because in the course of making theatrical contacts he encountered a mid-European composer who persuaded him to collaborate on a musical which would make a fortune for them both. The composer was a wonderful person too and their future was assured. Brooke sang flamenco often in the streets at closing time—the musical was set in Seville—and it was months before the composer became a bastard who had done him down, the agent was also consigned to the ranks of the enemy and Brooke ceased altogether to be able to buy a drink.

When it came to his round he would take out all his money, usually adding up to three-and-six, squint closely at it in the palm of his hand with head cocked to one side, then replace it in his pocket, humming a phrase from perhaps *La Traviata*, as if completely dissociated from the proceedings in the bar. All but a few understood, but it was a dark period of disillusion during which civvy street seemed to lead only to the Labour Exchange and the pawnshop, into which Brooke's elegant suit eventually vanished.

One winter's day, wrapped in his army officer's greatcoat with the badges of rank removed, and having said that Neville George Heath was England's most representative post-war citizen, he told me he'd decided to turn short story writer.

'I've just been reading a couple of your collections. That's clever, the way you present yourself as an innocent shrinking chap who just blundered into these absurd situations through no fault of his own. It gave me an idea. No reason why I shouldn't do the same, I could easily turn out that sort of thing, a series of autobiographical adventures, after all we're both incident prone,' so he bought several dark blue duplicate order books and sat writing in them every afternoon over a cup of Turkish coffee at the Scala Restaurant.

The restaurant cat had recently given birth, and while writing he was festooned with tiny kittens swinging from his shoulders and clinging round his neck. When one of them dug in its claws too hard, he would reach up and remove it gently without lifting his eyes from ball point pen and paper; and the kitten, placed upon the floor, would start once more to clamber up his leg. The horn rimmed spectacles, which had finally been adjusted to fit and which he wore for work, lent him the scholarly look of an eminent eccentric don. He never referred to the kittens as kittens, but always as little cats.

The stories he wrote were fast moving, economical and extremely funny. He'd long ago shed the strapping blonde and now had another typist in tow, who wore flowers round her hat and when off duty typed the MSS which I did my best to place with magazines on Brooke's behalf. Editors however had relapsed into their pre-war habit of taking ages to decide; the public too had largely given up reading now that there was no blackout and its members were again able to dash about in motor cars, and new writers were no longer being eagerly looked for as in the early Forties.

Unprompted by me, Brooke embarked on a round of personal visits to ginger the editors up. I began to get telephone calls beginning 'Look here old chap, that fellow what's his name whose story you sent me,' and the stories themselves came back en bloc.

Brooke didn't connect these multiple rejections with his appearance at the editorial offices; he believed that they were due to some confusion about his name. It seemed there was another Peter Brook, who wrote long sagas called *Arden Vales* and had already protested by letter about his near namesake's first novel, pointing out, in a paraphrase of Cassius during the quarrel scene, that he was an older writer if not a better and that he considered the name as his copyright however differently it might be spelt.

Brooke in turn felt much the same about the stage director Peter Brook, at that time more than a coming man, and he frequently dilated on what he would do to this new, upstart namesake if ever they should meet, and very soon they did.

I'd known Peter Brook when he'd just come down from University, having made a film version of Sterne's *Sentimental*

*Journey* which attracted a lot of comment from the critics. Short, chubby faced, with a schoolboy crest of hair, he was often to be encountered at the flat of Marcella Salzar, an actress who afterwards married the poet Clifford Dyment, and whose advice Brook used to ask about the course that his career should take: he was at this period undecided whether to continue in pictures or direct plays upon the stage.

One evening I was with Brooke at the Scala, having vainly tried to cheer him up by joining in another fruitless search for the Pebble Man, when Peter Brook appeared suddenly before us, perhaps after a visit to Marcella who lived not far away.

Peter Brook said to me: 'Patrick Hamilton has a new novel out called *The Slaves of Solitude*. It's bound to be a flop, no novel with an alliterative title has ever been successful.'

Peter Brooke, not knowing who this was, nonetheless fired back: '*Sense and Sensibility, Pride and Prejudice, The Pickwick Papers, Nicholas Nickleby, Anthony Adverse?*'

'*Mrs Miniver?*' I added, and Brook was about to retire in defeat when I quickly introduced them, getting ready for retreat myself should hostilities break out.

A truce however was immediately declared, Turkish coffee drunk by all; and Brook, detecting in Brooke some affinity with Nöel Coward, ended by urging him to write a play.

This more than ever decided Brooke to send out his stuff under a pseudonym in future. He'd just been given a journalistic assignment about which he was annoyingly mysterious, and when he reverted to the question of a choice of name for about the hundredth time, I said: 'What about your real name? Foreign books are all the rage just now, and there can't be anyone else writing called von Bohr.'

To my surprise this provoked a sudden denunciation: 'That's a bloody bright idea, when we've just finished fighting the bloody Germans. Exactly the sort of cheap flippant crack that I'd expect from you, anything to be clever at your friends' expense, unless as I suspect you'd really like to sabotage my work,' and with that he stormed out, for the next few weeks remaining absent altogether from our usual haunts.

Then one lunchtime my girlfriend rang me on the Wheatsheaf telephone. 'Have you seen this week's *Leader*?'[1]

'Of course not.'

'There's an article in it about Soho pubs and so on, attacking all of us as wasters. Somebody we know must have written it.'

'Nobody we know would write for the *Leader*,' I said loyally.

She said: 'You are described as a pistol packing Oscar Wilde.'

I said: 'The article's not signed?'

'It's obviously pseudonymous, but if I didn't know better I'd say it was by Peter Brooke.'

'Brooke!' I exclaimed, realizing she'd hit upon the truth. 'What name's it written under?'

'Anthony Carson,' she replied.

[1]A popular weekly, then of low literary standard, now defunct.

# Painters

*John Minton*

One of my last memories of Minton was connected also with a poet, W. S. Graham. It is not the most pleasant memory I have of him, but before this happened I had already found that Graham in some way contrived to promote unpleasantness around him. Unpleasant things tended to happen in his vicinity.

Graham himself was not unpleasant, just inordinately prickly. If one entered a club or pub where he happened to be and acknowledged him simply with a nod or a smile, he would call out 'You didn't say good-afternoon to me,' making out of this an issue which could, unless ruthlessly cut short at the start, last for what was left of the day. If on the other hand you greeted him by saying 'Good afternoon,' he would morosely reply 'What's good about it,' making you feel that you had tactlessly interrupted his meditations on some unfortunate mishap that had overtaken him a few moments earlier.

Or else you had omitted to add his name to the salutation, another terrible offence (if this were done he would affect to believe you were addressing someone else, and glance all round in search of this non-existent other person), or alternatively you had added his surname instead of calling him Sydney as his friends did, thus publicly proclaiming that you'd no wish to be considered a friend of his.

Even if the difficult hurdle of the initial greeting were successfully surmounted, any chance remark could give rise to a fancied slight, and endless argument would ensue or reproaches if not actual abuse would be heaped upon your head.

Graham was of sturdy build, dressed as a rule in blue-grey tweeds and had light brown curly hair, a snub nose and protuberant grey-blue eyes. My first introduction to his work

183

came through Kitty of Bloomsbury who had a great belief in it and gave me his second volume of verse with the prophecy that he would become another Dylan Thomas; and I see that the above description of him sounds as if he physically resembled Dylan, which was not the case. The total effect was quite other, being predominantly Scottish: his lips moreover were a very different shape, always twisted or prehensilely thrust out to accommodate themselves to his accent which was also Scots to a degree.

His expression was that of one stolidly bearing up under constant injustice or undeserved misfortune, and an atmosphere of brooding perpetually surrounded him. He sat over his beer as though reviewing every insult he had ever received with the purpose of devising effectual retorts for the future. In fact nobody insulted him at all and most people had a great respect for his poems.

Sydney Graham was quite the most competitive poet I have ever met: and this in a profession where competitiveness and rivalry by far surpasses any existing among writers of prose. Prose-writers in England, until lately, did not form themselves into groups; consequently among them there was far less deification and hero worship, and, since few idols were built, less chance existed of their turning out to have feet of clay: a flaw of course always discovered eventually by disciples who have decided to take over in turn as Master.

In the Forties internecine strife between individual poets and, on a larger scale, the various schools to which they belonged was at its height and Hemingway's warning never to praise one general to another, given apropos Gertrude Stein and James Joyce, more than applied to the world of poetry at that period. (Those poets encountered in pubs today—Kensington and Fulham are now the areas in which to encounter them, or else the BBC—seem to concentrate exclusively on who has won or is likely to win something called the Guinness Award, when not discussing some incident—usually detrimental to another poet or showing him in a ridiculous light—which occurred at the last prize-giving party: they themselves at the same time drinking Guinness, presumably to boost sales of the product from which the prize derives, though not all of them Irish.)

But Dylan Thomas might well have had W. S. Graham in mind when declaring that poetry was not a competition. I remember mentioning, on the particular occasion which I'm about to describe, that Charles Causley (a poet whom I never knew but whose work I have always liked) had in correspondence given me leave to use part of a Ballad of his as epigraph for a future novel of mine, and not only this: he had actually given me the lines in question as a sort of present.

Graham was immediately aroused, his glaucous eyes glowed with the light of battle and he asked me to quote the lines concerned, saying after I'd done so: 'I will write you a better poem than that right now, and if you agree you can keep it for your very own.'

This was a Saturday morning in winter, we were in a pub in Fulham: already the poetic area was moving South-West. Above us on the wall hung a full-length portrait of John Macadam the sports columnist who presumably before his death had been a regular customer, across the table sat John Davenport whom I'd specially sought out as a companion most likely to soothe and help me cure an hysterical hangover brought on by drinking all the previous day and night; and beside him was Graham's wife, whom I was meeting for the first time and who seemed to me also soothing and a thoroughly nice person whose presence until now had prevented her husband's prickles from rising in hostility or dispute of any kind.

Now, as Graham pulled out pencil and paper and was about to settle to his self-appointed task, John Minton waved and grinned at us from the centre of a group at the other end of the bar.

I'd known Minton since the early Forties when he was a young promising painter who had, I think, some kind of art-teaching job, and I'd always found him exceptionally pleasant. He did not then have the tormented El Greco expression which Alan Ross effectively hit-off in a *London Magazine* editorial, but looked more like a Modigliani or the archetypal young man whose portrait Nina Hamnett always painted irrespective of the actual subject. Tall, bony and attenuate, his face swarthy and elongated, he had protruding white front teeth which caused the mouth to remain open in a slightly awkward oval.

There was a Spanish quality about him, had he been an actor he'd have been a natural for the rôle of Don Quixote, and that face could equally have topped the ruff of a young hidalgo at the Court of Philip II or scanned the ocean for sight of undiscovered land at the time of Pizarro: a more modern maritime association being brought to mind by the blue reefer jersey which he usually wore.

In those early days he was boyishly diffident, yet affable and very ready to talk, always genuinely gay and smiling, full of energy and go without the febrility animating his movements in later years, when he would dance a sort of fandango in the streets or stand clicking fingers and tapping his feet before a bar counter, seldom still and the gaiety only simulated.

I remember one party of John Lehmann's when he stood alone by the chimney-piece, looking acutely embarrassed but self-consciously ignoring his complete isolation. This was before the days of lionization and promising young painters at that party were two for tuppence. I was as glad to come to his rescue as he seemed that I had done so, since it enabled me to escape from a South American delegate who spoke no English and whom the host had mischievously inflicted on me.

Minton did occasional book jackets and one of them, for a novel called *The Soldier Room* published by Rupert Hart-Davis, depicts the central figure in a pose which in my second wife's words resembled me in a Vincent Price-like mood and the features not unlike either. He had said more than once that he'd like to do a jacket for a book of mine, and therefore when a new one was due I got my publishers to write to him, adding a personal request for good measure.

We heard nothing for some time, until it became imperative to get another artist, then one afternoon I came down into the Mandrake Club, almost empty just after opening time, and Minton sitting alone over a drink on a settee jumped up and coming over explained that he'd been abroad and had not received the letters until his return, therefore had not been able to fulfil the commission as he would have liked. He was very bronzed and healthy looking and said he'd got a lot of painting done under the influence of his new surroundings on the trip.

It was soon after this that the exotic canvases which made him generally known were exhibited, and from then on it was rarely that he was seen alone. The raffish crowd that encompassed him made communication scarcely possible, though he remained unspoilt by success in his overall attitude.

A creative person (horrible phrase but how else to put it?) must however be armoured against the supporters who at successful periods immediately accrete like barnacles on the bottom of a ship, unimportant in themselves but capable of causing erosion if not from time to time scraped off. Minton was incapable of scraping anybody off and the sight of him latterly brought another image to my mind: recalling the story, told to me by a man who had served in the Chindits, of a comrade who'd been torn to pieces by tiny marmosets which, descending suddenly from the trees, swarmed all over him and pulled him down by sheer weight of numbers. When they were dispersed by small arms fire, nothing of the unfortunate soldier could be found except a few shreds of flesh and khaki drill.

Only once, in the late Forties or early Fifties, did I come across Johhny Minton without a colossal cohort in attendance: Christmas was in the air, plans for parties being made, and down Dean Street towards the Colony Club he danced, his long loose jointed figure in a sort of petty officer's pea jacket skipping ahead on the cold bare winter pavement, with bony fingers snapping like castanets and gaunt hollow face alight in the neon glow. He seemed in a state of euphoria rather than drunk, though he'd been drinking more heavily than I'd known him do before.

Since then I'd not seen him until that Saturday morning in the Fulham pub. Sydney Graham, seeing him also, forgot for the moment about writing the poem which would outdo Causley's Ballad and crossed the saloon bar to swell his group. I'd seen them often together in the Wheatsheaf and Minton's equable temper was probably proof against any quarrel engendered by Graham's touchiness.

Mrs Graham then told of her husband's secret desire to make a friend of me, until now frustrated by his Scottish pride and certainly hitherto admirably concealed: the gift of the poem was a gesture intended to consolidate this new relationship. Davenport talked about Norman Douglas; closing time approached and I'd begun to propose going round the Soho clubs, when Graham reappeared at our table saying that Minton was giving a party at his studio right away and we were all to come.

He'd gone ahead to prepare for the party, Graham said, nor were we to bring any drink as there'd be plenty on the premises; and in the taxi on the way he handed me a sealed envelope containing the poem which he'd apparently written after all and which he asked me not to open until we were actually in the studio: then, if I liked it better than Causley's lines as Graham confidently expected, I should read it aloud to the assembly.

At this point we dropped off Davenport near his flat in Flood Street, Chelsea, he was to rejoin us at the party later, and for the rest of the journey Graham's Scottish pride seemed overcome to the extent of allowing him to be amicable and relaxed for the first time since I had known him.

I myself began however to have doubts about crashing a party to which I'd not been directly asked; and when the taxi stopped facing the studio, which I remember as a sort of small pavilion and was certainly the last house in a short cul-de-sac somewhere behind Battersea or Albert Bridge, I refused to go in at all unless invited by Minton personally.

188

But after a moment both Grahams emerged from the house and told me I'd be more than welcome, Johnny was downstairs getting something ready but he'd said to come right in. So I paid off the cab and entered a little lobby where other guests, not known to me but obviously just arrived, were standing rather respectable in overcoats: the lobby being, in my memory, white painted and done up with brass like a ship's cabin, but I may have got it wrong.

There was a steep flight of steps like a companion way, leading down on the left, and up these at top speed, leaping two at a time in haste (I thought) to welcome me, came Minton. My hand was outstretched and I'd got out a few words of congratulation on some recent work of his when advancing quickly from the head of the steps he shouted: 'Maclaren-Ross you're interfering with my sex life. Get out at once, d'you hear.'

I was dumbfounded, I could feel my mouth hanging open like a half-wit's, but promptly turned about and stretched my hand towards the latch of the door. Nobody else said anything and I hadn't time to see the expression on the Grahams' faces though they were standing by.

For Minton had followed close behind and shooting out a long arm to turn back the latch with which I was fumbling, he tore open the door with one hand and, catching my shoulder in a hard bony grip with the other, he thrust me through the opening with all his strength.

My back had been turned to him, I'd not expected any such move, and I staggered off balance and almost fell. Then, recovering, I turned just as the front door was slammed to in my face. By now in a murderous fury I thumped the door first with my fist, then with the knob of my heavy malacca cane, shouting for Minton to come forth; but not a sound could be heard from inside, it was as if they'd all been struck dumb and rigid there, and I succeeded only in denting my stick's silver top, though some damage was inflicted on the door as well.

I stumbled furiously away and was soon on the Chelsea

embankment with a nightmare stream of enormous trucks clanking by like dinosaurs and not a cab in sight. My hangover returned in force, I took nearly an hour getting a taxi, when inside it found I was out of fags: having moreover paid everybody's fare to Minton's on top of the astronomically expensive night before plus that morning in the pub, I'd barely enough silver left to settle up when we got to Meard Street, Soho, and in the Mandrake had with difficulty to cash a cheque from the *Times* which I luckily had on me.

My rage had not, in consequence, abated when John Davenport showed up later in the afternoon.

It was tempered only by astonishment since I'd never known Minton be violent or pugnacious nor seen him lay a hand on anyone. Why had he chosen to make me an exception? There could be no question of a grudge being harboured since we'd not met for a year or more and had on the last occasion parted on friendly, even affectionate, terms. And how could I have been interfering with his sex life when he was homosexual and sailors were not my cup of tea?

Also why had he told the Grahams to fetch me in when he meant bodily to fling me out? Or had the Grahams deliberately retailed a wrong message with the object of seeing me humiliated in front of a pack of strangers? And if sex or some kind of orgy were taking place below, why were guests invited? Those I'd seen did not look at all like people who'd relish being involved in this type of situation or enjoy seeing an all male exhibition staged.

All these queries I put to Davenport who sat impassive as a Buddha but was unable to supply the answers. His sole comment was: 'You fared better than I, I didn't get in at all, knocked and knocked, no one opened, so I thought you'd all have come on here.'

We sat there grimly waiting for Minton to appear and give an explanation, but of course he did not. I'd unfortunately torn up in my fury and scattered from the taxi window the envelope handed me by Graham, which might have afforded some clue such as a message inside reading: 'SOLD AGAIN!

HA HA!' but he didn't seem the kind of chap to play such jokes and it might after all have contained a poem surpassing that given me by Causley. I wouldn't know because I've never since set eyes on him in London or any other place.

I did, however, see Minton twice more, both times in the Mandrake Club.

The first time he was standing dead sober by the cash desk very late one night, and once more alone: the supporters with their rat-like nose for impending disaster seemed all to have fled as from a sinking ship.

Emerging from the closed bar I came on him abruptly and at once asked what the hell he'd meant by behaving as he had. Minton drooped dejected, had simply no excuse, a sudden brainstorm or else too much drink; he agreed that I could not have interfered with his sex life for reasons I've already stated, also that throwing me out of his house had been unpardonable: nevertheless he hoped I would forgive him, shake hands and have a drink.

I shook hands but refused the drink because I'd a young woman outside getting her coat from the doorman whom I was anxious as quickly as possible to take home, and to join him in a drink just then would be interfering with *my* sex life.

Minton laughed though not heartily, and next time I saw him he was not dead sober but almost the reverse, alone again and late at night, swigging red wine out of a bottle in front of the closed bar grille. He urged me despairingly to help him out, pointing to another bottle opened on the counter and saying he couldn't get through all that alone; but again I'd to refuse or lose my last train to Oxford where I was staying at the time.

A few days later I heard of his death by suicide or accident, and wished I'd had that final drink with him.

*Gerald Wilde*
There's no truth in the assertion, sometimes made, that Wilde is the original of Joyce Cary's Gully Jimson in *The Horse's Mouth*.

At the same time certain aspects of his work and attitude to life have Jimson-like attributes, though one cannot imagine him painting a large biblical subject crowded with human figures nor has he served a sentence in gaol.

*The Horse's Mouth* appeared in August 1944, some years before Joyce Cary in Oxford met Gerald Wilde who was staying there and had already read and enjoyed the novel. Some people, while admitting Gully is not meant for Wilde, claim to have heard Cary declare that, had he not previously invented his eccentric painter, Gerald might well have served as a model; but I personally never heard him say anything of the sort when Wilde was under discussion, and Cary's characters were not constructed that way in any case.

Cary, however, could not fail to find Wilde entertaining, admired his work; and, being a kind and generous man, helped him out financially by buying some of the canvases he painted during his stay in Oxford. He also wrote an article on Gerald published in a 1956 issue of the excellent but short lived review *Nimbus* which contained reproductions of Wilde's work and other appreciations of it. If I remember right the Jimson connection is specifically denied in this article, though I haven't a copy by me and cannot check.

I have seen pictures by Wilde at Cary's house in Parks Road; behind the bar of the Victoria pub in Walton Street (one of Gerald's drinking haunts down there) hung an arrangement of orange and black stripes giving the effect of a cage beyond the bars of which an imprisoned tiger prowls; and a drawing of a magnificent toad could be seen, too, on the panelled wall of Professor Ronald Syme's college rooms: toads playing the same rôle in Gerald's life as owls do in the work of Francis Rose.

At my request Gerald once drew a toad on the Wheatsheaf counter, first with his finger dipped in beer, then with a stub of crayon on a crumpled scrap of paper which he gave to me but which was unfortunately lost during subsequent confusion: usually attendant on any of his appearances in the Wheatsheaf, which is where I first met him.

Entering the pub one October evening in 1943 I was immediately confronted with Tambimuttu who, thrusting towards me someone else's hat upturned, exclaimed: 'Ah Julian, just in time to contribute to the cause. I am getting up a fund for Gerald Wilde the Mad Artist, he's starving and with no money, you know?'

I'd never until then heard of Gerald Wilde the Mad Artist, but I put something in the hat and was then introduced to the Mad Artist himself: sitting at a table guarded by Tambi's supporters, with only a glass of mineral water before him and seeming not noticeably insane: just pale, dispirited and sad.

He sat motionless, without speaking, until Tambi had been all round the pub collecting; then stretched out wordlessly a hand, trembling no doubt with hunger, towards the hat which jingled by now with coins and silver. Tambi slapped the hand reprovingly, as one who corrects a too-presumptuous or greedy child, and Gerald Wilde relapsed remonstrating in a rapid inaudible mutter, this incipient mutiny being quelled at once by a glance from Tambi's celebrated eyes.

'Gerald's on the wagon, you know?' he told me. 'It's not good for him to drink and he has work to do. Gerald!' he like a lion tamer shouted and Wilde shrank back cowed: 'Gerald go back to the flat and paint. Steven you go too, lock him in, bring back the key. I will return later Gerald with some food.' He pointed with a prehensile finger fiercely to the door and Wilde obediently rose and shuffled out, the tails of a grey overcoat too long for him trailing far below his calves.

Steven followed and Tambi watched the pub door close behind them, his pose gradually relaxing as might that of a tamer whose lion has gone successfully through the flaming hoop.

'Lock him in?' I said incredulously.

'Yes, you must be severe with Gerald, a firm hand you know,' Tambi told me. 'If you give him money he buys drink with it, then he's drunk and does not work,' buying a round himself with money taken from the hat. 'But I am keeping him a prisoner now, locked in my flat, he can't get out to drink so he is painting much.'

'Hasn't he a studio of his own?'

'No no, he has no place not even to sleep, so I am putting him up, he has brushes, paint and canvas there, all he needs to work.'

'Is he really any good?'

'Good? He is a genius, Kenneth Clark says so, you know who is Kenneth Clark? Well a White Hope he says, you know? But soon we will hold a Gerald Wilde exhibition, then you'll see,' and soon, too, the hat was empty and Tambi once more reverted to his regal state of not having money on his person.

It was closing time by then and Steven had returned with the flat key, reporting that Gerald Wilde was safely locked in after two attempts to escape into pubs on the way and obtain credit therein.

Tambi said: 'Let us go to the Coffee An' and there eat steak,' Steven's eyes lit up and at the Coffee An' Tambi insisted that all of us scrape a portion off our plates into a paper bag which he pulled from his overcoat pocket, scattering several MS poems from contributors in the process; then he toured the cellar as he had earlier the pub, proffering the bag instead of the hat and demanding: 'A donation of food, please, for Gerald Wilde the Mad Artist who is starving you know?'

The idea of a Mad Artist, and starving what's more, appealed strongly to the tourists who in those days flocked to the Coffee An', and the bag was speedily filled to bursting: the response indeed being so big that Tambi was emboldened to go round for a silver collection with yet another hat, the contents of which paid the bill for steaks eaten by himself and his supporters (I dont know if either of the owners ever got their hats back).

But outside the Coffee An' Tambi lost his temper suddenly and flung the bag of food at the head of one of the supporters who'd been slow off the mark in executing some command: however, enough steak and chips was recovered from the pavement to assuage the appetite of Wilde, by now presumably paint stained and ravenous locked in Tambi's flat.

Tambi was ceaseless in his vigilance at this time, reporting to us regularly the progress of his protégé and the increasing number of paintings that had got done; and a show was being arranged—when, alas, all came to naught.

One Friday Tambi went away for the weekend, leaving Gerald locked in as usual. Unfortunately it proved to be a long weekend (perhaps the one when he stayed at Whitstable with Jaeger's patrons, which I'll tell about), anyhow on the following Tuesday he returned to find the flat door open and askew upon its hinges, a chair lying shattered on the floor nearby, and all his books gone from the shelves. Nor, needless to say, was Gerald Wilde inside: also all his paintings and painting gear had gone.

What had happened was this. Gerald, feeling hungry after four days without food (Tambi on his own admission having forgotten to lay any provisions in) got tired of painting: the creative impulse needed a re-fuel so first he collected Tambi's books in a kitbag which some PL contributor from the Forces had left behind in the flat, then he gathered together canvases and painting gear, then smashed in the lock having telephoned for a taxi, and descended to the waiting cab, which he directed to Subra's bookshop.

When Subra had bought the books, Gerald got back into the cab and was next seen eating and drinking in cafés and pubs belonging to a different area.

Subra had to give back all the books (as happened with someone's Gauguin souvenirs sold by Manolo the Spanish sculptor on a similar occasion described by Alice B. Toklas, which is doubtless where Wilde got the idea), but both he and Tambi forgave Gerald freely ('You know how it is,' they said, 'when you're with no money') and Tambi even went on trying to help him whenever possible with commissions for book jackets etcetera (I think, though I wouldn't be certain, that Gerald was responsible for the cover design of *Chums*, the omnibus *Poetry London*).

But the prospective show had to be abandoned, for **Gerald** had either sold the paintings in order to prolong the bender that he'd embarked on or simply given them away to strangers in the pub because he was sick of carting them around. He himself could not remember, and that particular relationship with Tambi came to an end: Tambi couldn't in any case continue to lock him in because the door was never repaired: and the shattered chair, left lying on the floor of the flat like the relic of a crime reconstructed in a museum, was seen there by many visitors and caused Gerald to acquire a quite undeserved reputation for violence, adding to the legend of his madness already blazoned forth by Tambi.

It may be for these reasons that his overcoats were always so long: perhaps they were given to him by very big men met round the pubs; it's inconceivable to imagine Gerald actually buying an overcoat of his own and, owing to the stories that were current, only outsize men would have had the courage to invite him home where they had overcoats to spare. Since I've known him he has had three overcoats, one grey tweed, one black (with a large rent just below the collar) and one dark brown, which is the one I last saw him wearing though he wore the black one with the rent for a very long time. All three overcoats had cuffs coming down over the knuckles though his arms were long. I have also seen him wearing a pink shirt and he never appeared without a bootlace tie, usually black and turned partly inside out.

He was not tall, had sloping shoulders and a long neck, his spade-shaped face was also long and his head flat at the back. There used to be a portrait of him by Wayland Dobson in the window of Subra's bookshop, showing Gerald with a scarlet face and one eye about to burst from its socket, to symbolize the feeling of something frustrated, shut in, but about to break out which is present in his own work: arrangements of bold colour patterns in the depths of which some form, not necessarily human, can be dimly discerned attempting to emerge. Dobson's portrait therefore was a better likeness than one more representational would have been, though in fact

196

Gerald's skin was extremely pallid and he showed signs when I first knew him of once having had ginger hair.

His hair now was brownish, carefully brushed back but often growing long on the nape though with a tonsure on top, his lips, eyelashes and eyebrows were almost colourless and his eyes also pale, large and salient, one of them indeed protruding outwards and not quite in alignment. He spoke when sober in a subdued gentle voice, not easy to hear unless one knew him well, and when drunk in a loud slurred inarticulate shout.

Gerald was not a drunkard nor anything approaching it, but alcohol, especially spirits, affected him with extraordinary speed and after a glass or two of Scotch he would begin to whirl his arms with a curious clockwork motion as if drink wound up some mechanism inside him. His speech became incoherent and his movements jerky but rapid like those of a lizard. He never lost the use of his legs. Later would come the stage of staggering and clutching painfully at people's arms while shouting imaginary grievances into their faces, if he could reach up far enough or they were sitting down.

He developed a persecution complex, not apparent when he wasn't drinking, part of which centred round policemen who, he was convinced, were out to insult if not actually to molest him. In fact they behaved good humouredly when he got into their hands and in Oxford, where he speedily got to know the whole of the Force, would indeed lead him back to where he was staying after a cup of tea at the Station, instead of shutting him in a cell or beating him up as he dared them to.

After he got to the shouting and staggering stage few landlords would have him in, and I have seen him many times burst through one door of a double entrance pub and promptly be ejected, then immediately reappear in the second doorway, same result: a performance he could keep up, scuttling from door to door, for hours, not getting a drink in consequence and ending the evening almost sober.

This happened only when he sold a picture and had, as he would put it, the wherewithal. At other times he was a quiet charming companion with beautiful manners, fond of reading and the cinema: I remember him telling me once of seeing at some Film Society an unexpurgated version of Pabst's *The Love of Jeanne Ney* which showed, during the orgiastic sequence, a close-up of a Tsarist officer's prick. Gerald was very disappointed since, this being such an unusual sight on the screen, he had not recognized what it was until told by the man sitting next him, by which time the prick had been flashed-off.

He was capable of working for long hours with immense concentration whenever he had somewhere to paint in and sometimes talked of holding an exhibition, not as any painter might but as if consciously indulging a fantasy or recounting a day-dream. For he knew that, when enough work was done, he would again sell the canvases for nugatory sums when drunk or simply give them to any bystander who showed appreciation, which he once said gave him a feeling of being liberated.

The sense of imprisonment conveyed by his painting was certainly very strong and perhaps of psychological origin since Gerald found the greatest difficulty in understanding the sources of his confusion and was not a ready talker. Perhaps it was the vision of his own interior chaos that was struggling to break through the cryptic coloured patterns that enclosed it, as he had broken out of Tambi's flat.

Impossible to tell, for Gerald never discussed the problems of his painting though often willing to discuss the problems of how to get it done without a place to live. This problem was never solved except for short periods, since Gerald's talent for self-organization was non-existent.

One apparent solution was found when somebody got him a job designing scarves for one of the biggest textile firms. The salary was enormous and Gerald's designs were the most beautiful and original I have ever seen on any woven fabric of this type, but in the end it didn't work out, supplementary or bread-and-butter jobs being for second-rate artists only: since having less to give they put only half of themselves into any activity they are engaged in, leaving plenty over for other purposes, which is why they're second rate.

Although the textile designing could be done quickly and easily, Gerald like all first rate talents put as much into it as he would have into his painting and was left too exhausted and emptied out to embark on anything else in his leisure time of which he had plenty.

So despite the salary he quit and went back to the nomad life which to him was normal; then came one night in the late Forties when he'd nowhere to stay and asked me for a bed which living in a single hotel room I could not supply. Standing nearby was Dan Davin the New Zealand novelist, by then an executive at the Clarendon Press. He said: 'Why not come and stay with us in Oxford, Gerald. And down there you'll meet Joyce Cary.'

*Robert Colquhoun and Robert Macbryde*

I once asked Fred Urquhart the short story writer, a friend of both painters and of course a fellow Scot, if he ever meant to write anything about Colquhoun and Macbryde. I thought he was perhaps the only writer who could do them justice because he had in an early short story a line of dialogue reading 'Wha quair clae they farriners hae,' which interpreted[1] is a let down but which epitomized to me the way the Roberts talked: Macbryde perhaps more than Colquhoun.

Fred Urquhart frowned and pursed his lips with head on one side, then said in his soft cooing and not so broad Scots accent: 'Ah well, you know Julian it's not so simple to do Colquhoun and Macbryde. They may look easy but they're difficult to do.'

I agree with Fred but all the same I'm going to try, only since I hate using phonetics myself their accents are beyond my power to reproduce and readers will just have to imagine these for themselves.

Actually, the first time I met Robert Colquhoun, in 1943, I was pulled up sharply about my own accent.

[1] 'What queer clothes these foreigners have.'

He was sitting on a bar stool in the Highlander, darkly glooming with a pint of bitter in his hand, and his words were these: 'If you're who you say you are, why've you no a proper Scots accent like a man?'

I answered: 'Possibly because I was brought up in England and France.'

I had come up to congratulate him on a show of his pictures which I'd visited that afternoon, but now wished I hadn't done so.

Colquhoun made a hissing contemptuous sound between his teeth, his expression that of one about to spit. 'England and France eh?' he said. 'And you call yourself a Scotsman?'

'I never said I did.'

A short pause ensued, during which Colquhoun took a swallow of beer, then he asked: 'Are you sure you're not just some phoney trying to show off? You look like a bloody phoney anyhow,' at which I gave up, not yet having learned to reply in kind to this type of thing with the ease I was shortly to acquire.

Dylan Thomas told me he'd much the same experience sharing a taxi with Colquhoun and Macbryde on the way to a party: they'd upbraided him thoroughly for not talking like a Welshman and he too as a result had been declared a phoney.

Before this I'd already met Robert Macbryde without realising his connection with Colquhoun. It was in the Coffee An', Macbryde was wearing a fringe and a kilt, and when we were introduced he'd said to the cellar at large: 'I don't doubt he's as scared of me as I am of him.' Again I had no answer, such remarks were new to me in any case; and after a silence during which Macbryde continued quizzically to smile, I excused myself and moved away.

In those days both Roberts, round about their early thirties (they never seemed afterwards to age), were fervent Scottish Nationalists, sported kilts, and felt strongly about the accents Celts should speak with. They were then accompanied everywhere by a third, huge blond-headed smiling Scot called

Shawn, who'd been a blacksmith, also sported a kilt, and seemed a permanent fixture, though he later got married and dropped out altogether, returning to the village forge from which he'd come.

Later, too, the Roberts ceased to be Nationalists or to wear kilts and, as they gradually lost the need to defend their origins and the feeling of inferiority which had to be concealed under an outward sporran of racial pride, they became more bearable and even at times quite human. They retained however their accents, though Macbryde told me once that when they went back to Glasgow they were often accused of having become bloody English and people were not always able to understand what they said.

Macbryde was the more friendly and sociable, Colquhoun the wolfishly lean and sullen one, who conspicuously didn't run with the pack. Like Macbryde he'd a swarthy skin but his sombre face was hollow cheeked and lantern jawed, with regular features and curling brown hair that became ringlets at the back of his head and neck. In his appearance there was something of the handsome hell-fire Calvinist preacher, as if he might at any moment call down the wrath of the Lord on the Sodom and Gomorrah that surrounded him. Spinsterish girls nearly swooned at sight of his ascetic mouth so masterful and clamped determinedly tight, as one of them described it longingly to me.

Colquhoun was the taller of the two and indisputably the leader; when they loosely loped along the street, always in single file and wearing pullovers (Colquhoun's a tawny red, Macbryde's thicker, dark blue, and naval looking) Macbryde devotedly followed. Once, when asked what he'd do if he came suddenly into a lot of money, he replied first that this was 'no likely,' then that he'd give it all to Colquhoun to further the cause of his painting.

Macbryde had a round blue chinned smiling face, thick straight black brows that crinkled wryly, a fag wobbling Dylan-like between his lips, and as a rule a cowlick of hair on the forehead instead of the fringe he'd worn when I first saw him. He had the reputation of being a wit and, though this was scarcely deserved, was certainly wittier when being rude than Colquhoun. He could also talk eloquently about the height of rhododendrons in his native land, but like his confrère and so many other denizens of Soho and Fitzrovia he was rude and eloquent only when full of beer, and at sober moments silent, subdued and even polite.

One day I said to him as he leaned his elbows silently on the bar counter beside me: 'What d'you think about when you're sober, Macbryde? Do you prepare apologies for the people you've been rude to the night before?'

Macbryde after a pause replied: 'Maybe I'm thinking up a new lot of rude things to say next time I'm drunk,' by which he scored a point.

Colquhoun also had a sense of humour of the grim, gallows type; but he was at all times morose of mien, though after a lot of scotch he would occasionally throw back his head and give vent to a strident savage contemptuous laugh, directed apparently at the world in general, and gnashing his teeth in a manner that had possibly endeared him in the first place to Wyndham Lewis, who approved of him both as a painter and a person, and many of whose more sympathetic characters were given to teeth gnashing and laughter of precisely this sort. At a later stage Colquhoun's laugh became more savage until it was merely a snarl and the nearest person who would stand for it (and it was amazing how many would) was turned upon and torn verbally to pieces.

The Roberts did command devotion. There was a constant stream of young women yearning to cook, clean, sew, look-after and generally make them comfortable, though in fact they were perfectly capable of doing all these things just as efficiently themselves.

Both were excellent impromptu cooks and I've seen them clean and tidy from top to bottom a flat in which they'd passed out cold the night before, taking over two hours to do so and also making all the beds although the host had gone off to work and no obligation was laid on them to clean up at all.

Nonetheless the devoted ladies persisted: the most zealous of them, and the one who lasted the longest because more resolute than the rest, being Cedra Osborne, secretary to Annigoni about whom she wrote a long article in a woman's magazine, besides translating Maupassant.

The Roberts had actually lodged for some time in her house, but even after they left she continued to be concerned about their welfare and to look after them all she could. Cedra was a striking young woman with dull gold hair and earnest intense ultramarine eyes, built generally along the lines of Caitlin Thomas but with a straight instead of an aquiline nose and even better looking.

I fancied her myself, but whenever we had a date she would talk earnestly about psychiatry and the electra complex, as though she were a head shrinker's secretary instead of a portrait painter's; then she'd start to wonder how the Roberts were getting along, could we just look in and see as otherwise she'd worry all evening, but once we arrived at the pub or club, Macbryde, usually by that time singing or stamping in a Scottish reel if not reeling tight, would without a word reach an arm round Cedra's shoulders, sweep her into their circle, and that was all for me that night. I don't know how Cedra reconciled her daily duties and undoubted loyalty to her employer with the very different artistic tenets propounded by Colquhoun and Macbryde.

But throughout all this the relationship of the Roberts to each other never altered. They had come from Glasgow together and they stuck together, whatever young women came and went around them. It was truly a case of David and Jonathan and perhaps this was what attracted the girls of Soho, always subconsciously eager to break something up. But if that were so, they were doomed to disappointment.

Colquhoun and Macbryde quarrelled occasionally of course, and I have seen them fight: careering in a clinch the whole curve of a long bar, with all the club members skipping out of their path, until they reached the doorman at his desk, who then toppled them, still gripped together, into the street.

Perhaps this incident was symbolic, since basically nothing could separate Colquhoun and Macbryde except what finally did: against which not even they were proof.

A period which promised to be particularly fruitful as regards their work was when they shared a studio in the Notting Hill area: a period written about by Wyndham Lewis in his satirical but affectionate sketch of them in the volume of stories *Rotting Hill*. (Though Lewis implies here that they never read anything and Macbryde is shown regarding books with fascinated horror, this was certainly the reverse of true where Colquhoun was concerned. When drunk, for instance, he could quote long passages of Shakespeare by heart, not only from the familiar plays but from *Timon of Athens* and *Pericles*, and he always quoted accurately.)

Colquhoun and Macbryde were going through a sober, industrious phase, one hardly saw them about, they'd got a lot of work done and a measure of security at last seemed within their grasp. Then came a black stroke of bad luck, from which they were not to recover for years.

While they were out of London on a well-earned holiday, teenagers or local yobs broke into their studio, wrecked everything, mutilated and defiled the pictures, and on top of that the Council decreed that the property should in any case be demolished. Colquhoun and Macbryde were evicted with nowhere to go and no means of earning a living since all their work for months, maybe years, had been destroyed.

The obituary writers who so smugly stated that Colquhoun had not developed much as a painter during his last few years were not apparently aware that for some of them he was virtually homeless, or else did not realize that it's difficult to develop or even paint at all without a studio to do it in. The rich dilettantes and art-fanciers who claimed to admire his work so greatly when it was too late could have shown their appreciation better by putting a place to live at his disposal, though I believe that this was finally done.

I'll not forget the day on which I heard the news. It was an afternoon in September 1962 and I was engaged in hurrying towards the Bayswater tube a lady who was for private reasons not at all keen to be observed in my company at that time or in that district. As we glanced round guiltily before the station entrance, another young woman known to both of us and one of the Roberts' closest friends emerged from it, almost colliding with me though obviously too upset to notice what was going on around her.

As if sleepwalking she handed me a copy of the evening paper she was carrying, open at a news-item which announced that Robert Colquhoun had that day dropped dead.

# Topolski and Picasso

*The Anglo-French Art Centre*
I spoke to Picasso only once and very briefly, and that was
due to Feliks Topolski whom I met one summer in the mid-
Forties through the agency of a strange Continental man,
the secretary of something called the Anglo-French Art
Centre at that time.

This man approached me one afternoon in the lounge of
the hotel where I was then living and introduced himself with
a faint click of the heels, saying simply: 'Green.'

'I don't quite follow.'

'Green. It is my name. Like all your English writers.'

'Writers?' I said, perplexed.

'Julien Green, Graham Greene, Henry Green, F. L. Green,
G. F. Green,' this new addition to the clan reeled off. 'All of
these are English writers, no?'

'Not Julien Green, I said. 'He's an American who writes
in French. Are you an English writer?'

'I have not this honour,' Green said, 'but I am devoted to
the service of Art. Pictorial Art also Anglo-French relations.
May I sit please and explain to you?'

'Go ahead.'

While he was explaining, I observed him closely but
without coming to any conclusion as to his country of origin.
He was thin, tall, sallow, spectacled: he had receding dark
hair, his spectacles dark rims, and he wore a thin black
moustache, but despite his pigmentation he was not, I'm
certain, a Latin and certainly not French. He wore a check
tweed suit not tailored over here and reminded me, though
not physically, of a fellow who in the Twenties started up a
school for English boys in Nice and was supposed to be a
Dutchman, though soon all the English boys whom he'd
managed to enrol were singing lustily *Der Tannenbaum*. This
man had attempted to enrol me too and produced a prospectus

of his school, but when addressed by my father in German bowed himself out with no further parley. Green had a prospectus on him too but was not a German, at least not judging by his accent, which was impossible to identify. He was an enigma that I never solved.

The prospectus he brought out was of the Anglo-French Art Centre, a gallery mainly intended for exchange between painters of these allied nationalities though other important international figures would, Green assured me, have their work displayed as well. There were plans for an Anglo-French library of books and periodicals, and he displayed an impressive list of patrons and supporters, the name of Feliks Topolski prominent among them. He'd in some semi-official capacity roped in also Rayner Heppenstall, always dead keen on anything French, who'd put him on to me.

What Green wanted was a translation of a sort of blurb for the catalogue advertising their first show: of whose paintings I've forgotten but French and abstract if I remember right. The blurb was written in an aphoristic post-surrealist French prose, a kind of corruption of Cocteau but lacking all his clarity, and not easy to translate because the meaning was itself obscure. Green wanted to print a double column, French one side, English on the other, and could I translate as soon as possible for the show was going to open and the printers were standing by.

Some valid reason was given why Rayner couldn't do the job: Green's excuse was that a celebrated British literary name should be appended to the English version of the blurb, though I believe he didn't attempt it himself because he didn't know French awfully well: I tried to get him to speak it to me but each time failed.

The Cause seemed worthy enough, though I'm not an addict to causes of any kind; but of course, Green said, he was a business man besides being a devotee of art and Anglo-French relations, and a substantial fee would be payable on completion of the commission (this turned out to be two guineas), also I would be made an honorary member of the

Centre and be invited to the opening do.

I managed the translation within the deadline, and had it snatched from my hand by Green, who'd taken to dropping in too often to see how the work was getting on. He did not however put a cheque or any money in my hand in exchange; and after that we heard from him no more, until a copy of the catalogue, incorporating my translation, arrived: also a card of invitation to the opening, on both of which my celebrated British literary name was misspelt. No cheque was enclosed with either.

I was late getting to the Centre as my taxi driver did not know the street, the fare was prohibitive and the exact house hard to find. To my surprise no party was under way and the guests of both sexes were standing about in a bare lobby beyond which behind closed glass doors the gallery could be seen, empty of any human presence but with paintings on the walls and some sort of refreshment table in the middle.

The guests were kept from entering by a crimson velvet rope looped across the lobby as in the aisle of a cinema, and a sort of turnstile like that of a public lavatory which further barred the way. There was no sign of Green or anyone in charge.

I looked in vain for a familiar face but knew none of the guests: they did not seem particularly artistic, literary or ultra-international, though I heard a few phrases of French being spoken around me, such as 'Mais alors, qu'est-ce qu'il se passe içi?' or 'Quoi donc, est-ce qu'ils se fichent de nous?' etcetera.

Suddenly through the glass I saw the figure of Rayner Heppenstall appear inside the gallery. He stood by the refreshments table with his head bent, not eating or drinking anything and looking neither at the pictures within nor the guests outside. I called out and waved, he raised his head but did not otherwise move, except to shrug helplessly in the direction of the doors and make the motion of a key turning as if he were a prisoner, himself, inside.

The sight of him was shut out by a middle-aged English

woman who came through a side entrance and told us to queue up before the turnstile like a sergeant calling his platoon to attention on parade.

When I approached her asking for Mr Green I expected her to shout 'Markers—stead-y!'; instead she said: 'The Secretary is busy now. Get in the queue please.'

'I'd like to speak to Mr Heppenstall then.'

'Who did you say?'

'Rayner Heppenstall. There he is. Look, in the gallery,' but at that moment he moved out of sight and the woman said: 'The gallery is locked and not open to the public yet. Take your place please in the queue.'

'I want to speak to Mr Green about this catalogue.'

'I don't think I have your name.'

'You can see it here. On this translation.'

The woman said: 'The Secretary is *very* busy but an opportunity may perhaps be made for you to speak to him later on.'

'Will you kindly fetch Mr Green at once.'

A quiet-looking medium-sized man in a dark suit, standing in the forefront of the queue, backed me up with unexpected force. 'This gentleman is right. I am on the Committee and the Secretary should be here to welcome and admit us. We're guests invited to the opening of this Centre, not people queueing for a cinema.'

'Bravo!' I cried, seconding him in my turn.

There was some clapping at the back. Many guests took up the cry for Mr Green and mutiny seemed imminent. A few of the French faction began to chant and stamp as they do in a theatre when the curtain is slow going up. The English woman left by the side entrance and did not return.

The dark-suited man, who proved to be Feliks Topolski, called after her: 'I will raise the matter of this treatment when we sit on the Committee,' adding to me: 'If there's a Committee to sit on.'

'Who else is supposed to be on it?' I asked.

Topolski pointed to a list on the catalogue: 'All these. The patrons and supporters. Or so Green told me.'

'But none of these people are here tonight.'

'No and I seem to be the only painter present,' Topolski laughed. 'Do you think we'll ever get in there? To the champagne and caviar?'

'Is that what's on the menu?'

Topolski said: 'It had better be, after all this.'

The chanting and stamping broke out redoubled and he exclaimed 'Look there is Green. He's going to open up at last.'

Green with a key in his hand approached us down the gallery: sailing alongside were several large ladies apparently in mourning whose big black hats and trailing silk closed round him like a bodyguard directly he'd unlocked the doors and the turnstile had clicked to let us through.

I made a move in his direction but Topolski touched my arm: 'Come, let's see what there is,' indicating the refreshments table behind which two younger women in smocks now stood ready to serve.

Advancing upon them Topolski delivered a rapid commentary like a radio sports event: 'It's not champagne nor sherry either I don't see any caviar,' then suddenly recoiling from what I could see myself: 'This is tragic, it's terrible, no glasses on the table, only cups and cakes.'

I turned accusingly on Rayner Heppenstall, who again was standing with furrowed brow by the table, which seemed in some way to fascinate him.

'Rayner what have you let me in for.'

Rayner said disconsolately: 'It's all gone wrong. Some big bug was to open the show but he's not turned up. Everything's disrupted.'

'You might have seen to it there was something to drink.'

'There was to have been beer. Anyway I didn't organize this do. Green's the organizer.'

'Where's Green?' Topolski asked brightly looking round.

But Green was no longer present, and did not reappear even to bid the guests goodnight. The coffee had long strings of skin in it, white flecks floated on the surface and the rock cakes had been clearly bought at least a week before. They were the only evidence that the party had been in any way prepared-for.

'This is a bad show all round,' Topolski said as we met again after circling in opposite directions the paintings on the walls: there were not many, not a single one can I remember, and we completed the circuit in record time.

Topolski said: 'That bug who didn't turn up had got the right idea. Let's go, I know a pub nearby.'

We tried to persuade Rayner to join us but he muttered that he'd better stay behind and see it through. He avoided our eyes when we said goodbye and the gallery was emptying all around us as we left.

A few weeks later, Green bounced in on me again, bringing a much longer translation that he wanted done in a much shorter time. I suggested an immediate advance, cash down, also payment for the last lot or no dice.

Green was first astonished, then shocked, then aggrieved; at length passed over two crumpled one pound notes but said he would have to consult the Committee before disbursing any more. I asked him to make sure Feliks Topolski sat in on the meeting when this question was debated; and later came a phone call during which Green said he'd be unable to put any further translation work my way unless I became more realistic about the manner of remuneration. And this, he explained, would be my loss, since the opportunities for increment would be enormous as the Centre continued to expand.

After this he ceased to get in touch, except to send a demand for payment for my overdue subscription, signed formally THE SECRETARY.

The Centre did not expand, and I never discovered what country Green returned to when finally it folded. Nor, in the pub on the evening that it opened, had Topolski and I been able to decide his nationality, out of many possibilities not unnaturally excluding Polish.

I didn't see Topolski for several years, but evidently he'd

not forgotten our meeting, for one day out of the blue I received an invitation to a party he was giving in honour of (a) Pablo Picasso; (b) Vladimir Pudovkin, the Soviet director whose film *Mother* remains a classic of the Russian cinema.

## The Party for Picasso

I shortly afterwards used the exterior of Topolski's studio when describing the headquarters of Stevenson's Suicide Club in a film-script I'd been commissioned to do of *The New Arabian Nights* brought up to date.

Seen from outside the building was ideal for this purpose: big, ramshackle, and dark, only small chinks of light showing as if blacked-out, and approached through a walled garden in which grass and weeds grew nearly to knee-level. It was somewhere behind Warwick Avenue and, Topolski told me later that evening, under threat of demolition by the local Council though he was fighting hard to retain it. Not far away lived Alan Pryce-Jones in quarters similarly menaced, and within the same area was my former flat where Peter Brooke had been scared almost to self-destruction by the midget char and which was under sentence of death, even when I lived there, owing to the Blitz that had shaken all these structures: rendered doubly unsafe by the explosions of the Paddington Gun and the Fly-Bombs that followed after.

Inside, the studio wouldn't have made a bad set for the Suicide Club-Room either. It was immense, indirectly lit and shadowy, high-ceilinged and with a huge skylight overhead. The walls which may have been painted with murals by Topolski were entirely in shadow, yet despite its size the studio was very warm in contrast to the cold clear winter night outside.

Neither of the guests of honour had arrived when we got there and Topolski, quiet smiling and friendly as he'd been before, at once issued us with a bottle of special Scotch which we were warned to keep behind a statue on a shelf when the invasion really started.

Adair whom I'd brought with me was a tall striking slender

girl, dressed tonight in scarlet, young, non-literary, but intelligent unaffected and gay. Some people preferred her to any girl I've produced before or since; and Arthur Calder-Marshall, whom I hadn't seen for years and who'd joined us where we stood over by the window, seemed of this number.

I'd been earlier on to a champagne party at John Lehmann's flat; but Adair, whom I'd picked up from our place on my way to Topolski's studio, hadn't had a drink all day, during which she'd been acting as secretary to a solicitor in Whitehall, and the whisky bottle didn't spend much time behind the statue.

We were atrociously hard-up at the time, ten shillings I remember was all the money we had between us: I'd not yet been commissioned to write the Suicide Club script (which incidentally never went on the floor), there were crises in the book-trade and film-world and Adair's secretarial salary just paid our weekly rent. We'd not been anywhere for weeks, and were all the more prepared to enjoy this party which bore every sign of being an outstandingly good one.

Calder-Marshall too seemed in great form. Ara his wife was not with him that night, and he'd been hot on the track of Aleister Crowley, then still alive, whom he'd never met but wanted to write a book about. I didn't know Crowley either, but I told Calder-Marshall what Joan Graham-Murray had recently recounted of his final, semi-respectable phase.

Joan, a friend of Louis Wilkinson alias Marlow, Crowley's literary executor who afterwards scattered his ashes on the wind, had gone to stay with Wilkinson in the country, taking with her a copy of my short story collection *The Nine Men of Soho*. Crowley, also there as a guest, had idly glanced through this, and saying he'd like to see what the young men were up to nowadays, asked Joan's permission to borrow it. When he returned the book she saw that the margins had been scribbled over with rather petulant old-world comments, such as: 'Yes yes, all very well, but why doesn't he tell us what the girl's *background* is?! Who are her people?!!' and so on.

He also asked Joan if she knew me, she said yes, and Crowley then said testily: 'Well next time you see him, tell him to be more precise about his characters' origins. He seems to ignore all the traditional social values that make up the fabric of our civilization,' which, since I'd always understood that Crowley's mission as Worst Man in the World was to tear this fabric down, amused me quite a lot. But then maybe all diabolists are conservative at heart, or where would be the fun?

Calder-Marshall, amused as well but slightly frowning since this didn't equate with his idea of Crowley either, asked me if I thought the story true. I answered that I'd seen the annotated copy for myself and had offered to give Joan another in exchange, to which she had replied with the best-known line of Shaw's Eliza.

Meanwhile there was a stir among the guests and at the door: Picasso had just arrived. He was instantly surrounded and too short to be seen from where we stood, though all of us were naturally intent. We caught just a glimpse of him, gesticulating gaily, before he was whisked away to the far corner of the studio facing us, where it was better lit though Picasso was hidden again from view by the same sort of statuesque black-clad women who'd formed a bodyguard for Green at the opening of the Centre, and who seemed to attend every function concerned with painting or painters.

Then abruptly these fell back as Topolski was hurrying towards us with Picasso himself in tow. Their objective was the window by which we stood, the only one on that side of the studio and Topolski excusing himself to us tugged at it and with the aid of Calder-Marshall finally flung it open.

Picasso, close on his heels, small, square and nimble, wearing a thick rough suit of sack coloured tweed, was within touching distance; and as a cold blast of air rushed into the room he gave a sigh of relief, nodded vigorously and grinning at us fanned himself with both hands, blowing out his cheeks to show he'd been too hot: since he must have thought we understood no French. The female retinue had followed en bloc and waited with expressions of concern while Picasso took great gulps of air and grinned at all.

At that moment through the door Vladimir Pudovkin came, with a somewhat similar following, the few men having the air of attachés; and Topolski hastened forward to welcome him. Calder-Marshall went too, being as sold on Russia at this time as Rayner Heppenstall still is on France, besides he'd some job connected with Anglo-Soviet cinematic relations; and the stately ladies speedily bore Picasso back to their original corner.

Adair observed their departure with suddenly narrowed eyes. The scotch combined with the air blowing in from the open window was having its effect on her.

She said: 'Why don't *you* go and speak to Picasso? I'll bet you speak better French than any of those women. Come to that, I'll bet I do.'

This was quite possibly true. Her mother lived in Jersey and as a very young girl Adair had met Françoise Rosay who'd taken a liking to her and taught her French. Some years after she got a job with a London distributor of French films and was sent by her boss to Paris where she assisted at the shooting of a film by Jacques Tati: an experience which I envied her, but by that time we'd parted company.

'I dare you to go over there now.'

'Darling don't be silly. Later perhaps.'

'But you'd like to meet Picasso wouldn't you.'

'Of course.'

Adair said: 'Then I'll bring him over to you.'

'Are you out of your mind,' I said alarmed, but she was already in motion.

Too late to intervene I watched the swinging skirts of her scarlet frock scythe a way through the black silk and velvet of the female entourage, and perform a kind of pirouette before Picasso's startled stocky tweeded figure. It was a terrible moment.

Then at my elbow I heard the voice of Topolski: he'd come to present me to Pudovkin, who was now established on a divan at the opposite side of the studio. On a semi-circle of chairs in front sat his followers, including Calder-Marshall; the men with the air of attachés stood stiffly up and I had to reach over the seated women in order to shake hands.

It was clear immediately that Pudovkin spoke no English, and the only Russian I knew had been learned from exiled noblemen in Nice: how, for instance, to invite a girl to accompany me for a moonlight walk along the Promenade des Anglais, which did not seem appropriate to this occasion.

Topolski had been called away to welcome a fresh influx of guests, including some whom I'd seen at the Lehmann party but not, surprisingly, Lehmann himself; and I stood irresolute, holding a glass which I'd been handed, and wondering whether to try French. Then I noticed Calder-Marshall motioning me to look round.

I turned and saw Picasso and Adair heading straight towards me. She had hold of his arm and stood taller than he by more than half a head. Both were smiling and Picasso seemed delighted. Behind, from the corner they'd vacated, the white faces of the black-clad women glared rigid with shock and outrage.

I swallowed at a gulp what was in my glass, vodka scorched my throat, and as I went forward with outstretched hand various topics of conversation, none suitable, shot through my head, then the word Cubism; and before my inner vision appeared the walls of Tube platforms, plastered at this period with inferior imitation Cubist advertisements perhaps hastily put together to commemorate Picasso's visit. I'd been commenting on their repulsiveness only the day before.

Adair was by now performing the introduction in her best Françoise Rosay French, but I realized with horror that she'd got it the wrong way round: was introducing Picasso to me.

Hastily I interrupted to say that I was greatly honoured, addressing him as Cher Maître and remembering too late that he was known to hate this.

We both bowed, Picasso continuing to smile with steel grey hair smoothly brushed across his forehead and a face the colour of Spanish earth, oddly unlined for a Spaniard and a man his age. In his rough sack coloured sack he looked like a well barbered version of Harpo Marx, perhaps owing to the intensity of his stare.

I said: 'Do you remember, monsieur, saying once to Gertrude Stein . . .'

Picasso nodded encouragingly, and I waited for him to say 'Gertrude' with the simple affection and confidence which according to Alice B. Toklas always characterizes his pronunciation of the name; but he did not.

Instead he said: 'Oui, oui, Mademoiselle Stein,' his bright prominent sloe brown eyes fixed unblinking on mine; and I continued: 'You told her, did you not, that when you make a thing, it is so complicated making it that it is bound to be ugly, but those that do it after you they don't have to worry about making it, and they can make it pretty, and so everybody can like it when the others make it?'

I was by no means sure if I'd got this quotation right or had translated it properly, it was some time since I'd spoken French; but Picasso said instantly: 'Oui monsieur, I did indeed once say something of the sort,' and I went on: 'Then, monsieur, have you as yet descended, travelled by, the Tube, our English metro?'

'Non monsieur,' Picasso replied, 'I've not so far had that pleasure,' and I noted that after all those years in France he still retained his Spanish accent.

'Then when you do, monsieur,' I said, and he nodded several times emphatically to indicate that he couldn't wait to get down the Underground: his eyes were still fixed on mine and he must have been wondering what the hell, if anything, I was getting at.

'Then,' I said, 'you will realize, from the crude imitation Cubist advertisements on the platform walls, the truth in reverse of your so brilliant axiom. For, in seeking to exploit your discovery for vulgar commercial purposes, they have succeeded only in making the beautiful ugly.'

I bowed, taking a step back to do so: sweat was standing on me as I ended, more or less as I'd begun, by saying it'd been a great honour.

'That, monsieur, is reciprocal,' Picasso said, bowing in his turn; at which Adair whose arm all this while had been hooked in his turned him about and led him away, completely bemused by now, to his corner where she left him among the indignant clucking women: while I hurried back to the whisky bottle behind its statue.

At the time I thought I'd carried it off rather well, only later did I feel embarrassment and shame, and later still in self defence began to think of it as funny.

Nonetheless, when beset by celebrity snobs, I can truthfully say that I've talked about painting to the greatest living painter: moreover Picasso made a special point of turning to smile and bow in my direction. Perhaps he really did believe he had met somebody important: on the other hand, his politeness being almost oriental in its inscrutability, he may have been dying inwardly of laughter.

*Worse than Aleister Crowley*

Picasso and Pudovkin had gone. At the end of the evening there was only a small group left, we were over by the door with Adair animatedly talking to our host who was standing, as I recall, with either a grand piano or a giant easel for a background.

He'd brought out more scotch as the original bottle was empty, and with us was Calder-Marshall also Tom Driberg, the initial William Hickey whose column Jaeger in *Munich Year* used to read so avidly over breakfast before going down the Labour.

Driberg, very tall and broad in a brown suit, had springy dark hair and a pleasant tough impassive face like a highly intelligent rugger blue. I remember questioning him eagerly about the hands of Weidmann the mass murderer, whose trial he had covered for *The Express*, and he stuck now to what he'd written at the time, namely that 'Weidmann seemed a nice quiet chap.'

I remember Topolski asking me, as he gave us a hand with

our coats in the hall: 'Do you ever think of Mr Green? And the coffee? And the cakes?' and my uncontrollable fit of laughter, which also infected Adair though she'd never heard of the Mr Green Topolski meant.

I remember flagging a taxi into which we climbed with Calder-Marshall. I remember saying that Feliks Topolski was one of the finest hosts and nicest men I'd ever met: an opinion which I've no reason to retract.

I remember developing as well a sudden great affection for Calder-Marshall: Good Old Arthur, whom it was so wonderful to see again after all this time, Dear Old Arthur who must come home with us and have a last one for the road.

No denials were brooked, and when the flat door was unlocked Rashomon our white cat, who'd come in from the balcony at sound of the taxi stopping, fled again at sight of a stranger. Because of the window left open to let him in and out, the living room felt like the inside of a fridge. I remember all this, then comes a tiny gap.

I was kneeling down trying to light our gas fire that had an air lock in the pipe, when I became conscious of Calder-Marshall saying loudly: 'You mustn't speak to a woman like that.'

'Woman?' I said startled.

'Mustn't talk to her like that.' His Auden-like lock of hair was hanging forward and his face mushroom-pale with anger.

Afterwards Adair told me I'd said to her sharply: 'For Christ's sake shove over and let me do it,' after she'd spilt a match box at my feet attempting to get the fire lit. It was to this that Calder-Marshall had taken exception; and seeing Adair's eyes narrowing once more I said quickly, before she could tell him not give me orders in my own home: 'Oh balls Arthur, have a glass of wine.'

The bottle of white burgundy which we'd been saving to cure our morning hangovers stood open on the table. Calder-Marshall ignored this. He said heavily: 'You're a bad man Julian. A bad man.'

My affection for him was on the wane, but I didn't want to

**H**

end a good evening with a quarrel. I thrust another match into the hissing fire and said lightly: 'Like Aleister Crowley?'

'*Worse* than Aleister Crowley.'

At that the asbestos lit at last with a sound like a bomb going off; Adair gave a startled cry and I one of satisfaction: then I heard behind me the flat door bang and looked round to see Adair standing alone, as if the explosion had blown Calder-Marshall out of the room.

She cried: 'Arthur's just rushed off, go after him quick, he'll get away!'

On the stairs I heard his footsteps running down ahead of me then the front door slammed below, and when I reached the street he was heading full tilt for the main road beyond. I gave chase shouting: 'Arthur, Arthur come back!' and from behind came the clatter of Adair's high heels and her voice calling like a light echo of my own.

But Calder-Marshall had more than a head start; down the main road towards him came a taxi with FOR HIRE lit up in the front, a thing that usually happens only on the screen, and by the time I reached the corner he was already climbing in.

I said: 'Arthur don't be a fool, come on back,' but the taxi door banged, he leaned out of the lowered window to say loudly: 'A bad man. *Worse* than Crowley!' and the cab drove off just as Adair drew level with me on the pavement.

We watched its tail light turn the next corner out of sight, then Adair asked: 'What got into him? Who is Crowley? He can't have meant the one you were talking about at the party, the Worst Man in the World?'

'Never mind,' I said and we walked back arm-in-arm to where our cat mewed from the balcony and the wine waited to be drunk.

I didn't meet Calder-Marshall again until this year, when I chanced upon him drinking with the fiction editor of *The Times Literary Supplement* in a Great Portland Street pub. With his hair gone beautifully silver and the Auden lock combed back, I recognized him only when he spoke. He seemed quite affable and to have forgotten completely that I was worse than the Worst Man in the World.

I don't suppose I'll ever know what got into him that night of Topolski's party for Picasso.

# Second Lieutenant Lewis
## A Memoir

I'm no good at dates and I don't keep a diary; so it may have been spring or summer, 1942, I can't really remember.

I stepped into the hall of BHQ over two janker-wallahs on hands and knees scrubbing down the chequered tiles; a smell of yellow soap steamed up all around me; the door knob of Company office fell off with a clatter as the door itself opened. Corporal Dexter came out: shirt sleeves and a big grin, scratching his chest.

'Hey, Rossy, where'd you get to? There's an officer been round looking for you.'

'Let him look,' I said. 'I'm off duty.'

'Never 'eard of it. A soldier's on duty twenty-four hours a day.'

Dexter had a whole store of these idiotic army catch-phrases, which he repeated as though each were an epigram coined fresh by him that very moment. He was permanent orderly sergeant, Category C, and underneath his bluffness and easy going air he enjoyed the authority. In civvy street he had been a manufacturer of ladies' straw hats.

He said: 'Don't give a bullock what you do, meself. All I know is he said for you to report to him straightaway, soon's you come in.'

'The morning'll be soon enough,' I said. I took for granted it was one of our subalterns: the twenty-year-old school prefect type who was always asking me how to spell something, or perhaps Lieutenant Buckley who wanted some typing done in my spare time. I was on my way again when Dexter's voice arrested me.

'Ain't one of our mob. He's a Taff. One pip. Name of,' he looked at a pencilled scrap of paper in his hand, 'Lewis. Mr Lewis. Said you was to report down the road, their HQ. Asked for you very special, by name an' all.'

He broke off to bawl out the jankermen, who'd stopped

scrubbing and squatted back on their heels to enjoy our dialogue. I was intrigued. I knew of no Welsh one-pipper named Lewis, and it was curiosity, not obedience to an order, that drove me out into the evening sunshine along what had once been the marine parade, past the rusty hoops of Dannert wire cutting off the pebbly beach and the sea in which mines bobbed like buoys.

A guard on the gate of the Welsh Headquarters halted me. Mr Lewis'd be eating his dinner; Officers' Mess; third house on the left. I went in there; it seemed uninhabited: bare boards echoing to my boots, flakes of fallen plaster, wallpaper peeling off. I shouted. An orderly appeared from the kitchen with a mug of tea in his hand. He said he'd see. He disappeared up some stairs. In a few moments a young officer came running lightly down these. He wore one pip and service dress, but without his Sam Browne belt, as though he were awaiting trial by court martial. He had a Welsh face, dark, with eyes set deep.

I came smartly to attention and saluted. '6027033 Private Ross J. reporting for duty, sir.'

To my surprise the face of Mr Lewis flushed even darker at this. He turned his head away and muttered something in a voice so low that I couldn't catch the words: I said: 'I beg your pardon, sir?'

He muttered, but more audibly this time: 'I'm Alun Lewis.' He held out his hand. In a second we were shaking hands heartily. I said: 'I'd no idea. They just said Mr Lewis and I was to report to you straight away.'

'The fools,' he said. 'My god, isn't that typical. When you saluted I thought you were making fun of me.' He smiled, a quick boyish grin. He spoke very quickly, too, and with a strong Welsh intonation which I found difficult at first to understand. Later this wore off and I discovered it was a mark of embarrassment. He was extraordinarily shy. He said: 'But come upstairs. There's only one fellow there, the others are all out. Gone to the dance.'

We started to climb the stairs and I said: 'How did you

226

know I was here?'

'Your padre told me. When he said your name was Ross and you were a writer, I thought you must be Hugh Ross Williamson.'

'I never thought you were Wyndham Lewis,' I said.

That set us back again; his face flushed up and he muttered something I couldn't catch. I soon learnt not to make wisecracks of that sort; they only upset him. We reached the door of the Mess and it was my turn to be embarrassed. How should a private behave when invited into the Officers' Mess? I decided it must be a social occasion and removed my cap, as if going up before the MO. This obviated the need for saluting the other subaltern whom Alun Lewis now introduced me to, and as the table was between us we didn't have to shake hands. His eyes nearly fell out of his head when Lewis asked me to sit They'd finished dinner and the orderly was clearing away. down and have some coffee. When this was served we were all at a loss. Lewis jumped up and looked out of the window. It faced on to the sea. A ship could be seen way out. We looked at this through field glasses. But at last even the ship was exhausted as a topic of conversation and we sat down again. Cigarettes were handed round and then the other subaltern excused himself: he had to do his tour as duty officer.

Once he'd gone, Lewis said: 'You see, I wanted to talk to you, because I thought you could tell me about India. I'm being posted there any day now. Or is that a military secret?' He smiled.

'Not to me,' I said. 'Everyone knows your mob's bound for India. But why I should be able to tell you about it I can't imagine.'

Lewis stared at me astounded. He said: 'But surely you know India well?'

'Never been there in my life.' Then, too late, I realized. At that time I'd only had two stories printed, and both of them dealt with India—or, to be precise, Madras. I now had to explain how I had acquired my material. This story is always

a let down, and leaves people with a feeling that they oughtn't
to meet writers whose stories they have read.

Lewis was no exception. He was disappointed. He said:
'I've just read another story of yours. In *Fortune Anthology*.
It's not about India.'

'No,' I said. It wasn't. It was about a man of thirty seducing
a girl of sixteen in a seaside hotel.

Lewis's face had begun to flush and his Welsh accent came
on again. 'I've got to review the *Anthology* for *Tribune*. I
wonder if you'll mind,' here he coughed and looked into his
coffee, 'if I don't mention your story?'

'Not at all. Do you think it's so bad?'

'No, no. But you see it's about sex. I couldn't possibly say
anything about it.'

'Because I don't treat sex seriously?'

He nodded. That sent me off into a denunciation. I particularly hate the idea of sex treated as a solemn fetish. I couldn't
understand this attitude, which seemed to me puritanical, in
a writer who had produced a fine sensual story like *The
Wanderers*. It seemed like hypocrisy. It was not that, as I
understood later, and Alun Lewis was not a puritan. But his
deep love and respect for women, the fact that his wife was
expecting a child at a time when they were about, any
moment, to be separated, made him inimical to anything that
savoured of a sophisticated approach to sex. We argued for a
while but Lewis remained unconvinced. He coughed and
kicked the table leg doggedly. The talk switched from sex to
technical problems in writing. He had a great admiration for
the stories of Flying Officer X, and asked me if I knew who
this was. He said he himself was writing some stories about
the army and we went to his room to look at the MSS.

His room was a tiny cubby hole with a window looking out
on to a wall: no bigger and no better—except for the camp
bed and the small table piled with army pamphlets—than my
own bunk at BHQ. Lewis sat down on the bed, ran his fingers
through his dark hair which had just been cut: his OC had
talked about curling pins and violins. Some of the pamphlets

228

slipped off the table and lay scattered on the floor; ABCA, WAR, Battle and Weapon Training, War Office Memoranda: Lewis looked at them with despair.

'I've got to swot all these up somehow,' he said. He'd just come back from a battle course. It'd been hell and yet he'd enjoyed it. This was what he hated: the paper work, swotting up pamphlets, reports to prepare, red tape and routine, always something to remember that had slipped the mind; he voiced the eternal hope of the soldier. 'It'll be different out there,' and then: 'But it's a long way to go.'

He showed me two stories called that; with a third one, as yet unfinished, they were to form a trilogy. He showed me one called Flick and gave me a bundle of MSS, to take away and read. At this moment a knock came on the door. I thought it would be Lewis's Officer Commanding, come to give him a bollock for fraternizing with a private soldier. It wasn't. Instead it was our C. of E. Chaplain, who had been instrumental in bringing us together.

This padre asked me as a favour not to write anything about him. I have already broken my promise, so will not say any more, except that he was one of the most intelligent and understanding men whom I ever came across during my service in the army.

The padre did not stay long, but before he knocked out his pipe and went, the constraint remaining between Lewis and myself was completely gone. We agreed to go and have one in the pub. When we got outside Lewis had to rush back in for his Sam Browne: 'I'm always forgetting the damn thing.' He walked along the street beside me buckling on the belt. My RSM was passing on the other side of the parade. He gave Lewis an eyes-right and his stiff jerky salute, imitated behind his back through the battalion. Lewis attempted to return the salute and the belt fell to the ground. He stopped to retrieve it while the RSM passed on stiffly disapproving in his rubber soled shoes.

'I made a mess of that,' Lewis said ruefully, getting the Sam Browne round him at last. 'An RSM, too.'

'That's my RSM,' I said. 'Used to be a milkman.'

'Nothing against him,' Lewis said. 'That's class distinction.'

I said: 'It's something against him when he uses his war time authority to work off the past grievances and an inferiority complex. He's more class conscious than either of us. I bet you he votes Conservative.'

Lewis couldn't see my point, although he admitted to having had some pretty bloody sergeant-majors in his time.

Comparing notes about the sergeant-majors brought us to the pub. This was jammed to the doors. It took ages to get a drink, and then they'd only mild. We had to shout to make ourselves heard. Soldiers from Lewis's regiment kept on coming up to greet him and to offer him drinks. Eventually they shouted 'Time' and we left. Corporal Dexter, hanging on the gate chatting with the curious woman who gave us haircuts, turned and saluted. This time Lewis managed to return the compliment without dropping his stick or his service dress cap falling off. Dexter stared after him open mouthed. Neither of us had the army knack of surface smartness, and by military standards we must have seemed, officer and private, a pretty scruffy pair.

'Did you ever put in for a commission?' Lewis asked me.

'Failed the WOSBE test,' I told him. 'Returned unsuitable.'

'I'm not certain I shouldn't have stayed in the ranks,' Lewis said. 'I thought that as an officer I'd be able to do something for the men. But one's more helpless than ever.'

The sense of helplessness and the thought of the pamphlets that remained to be swotted up in the small airless room, while the poems, the stories, stayed unwritten: these were the things that oppressed him. Had it not been for his wife, the idea of India—the jungle, the Japs, something doing at last—would have seemed a welcome opportunity: one that I myself, being without ties, certainly envied him.

I asked how his brother officers treated the idea of his being a poet. At first they'd regarded it as rather rum, made contemptuous little jokes about Shakespeare and asked him to make up smutty limericks, but then a photograph of him was found in an old copy of *Lilliput* and the Mess was impressed. Fame could reach no higher: unless, of course, the photograph had appeared in *Men Only*. Now his writing was regarded as a harmless pastime, so long as it didn't interfere with his efficiency as an officer. It was generally hoped, however, that India would knock all that nonsense out of him.

We arrived at the door of the Mess and Lewis sighed—the pamphlets awaited him inexorably upstairs. He said: 'You must show me your stories too.'

As we were in the street I raised my hand to salute. Lewis said: 'For Christ's sake don't do that,' seized my hand and shook it. Then he doubled inside and I could hear him running up the stairs. But my RSM had observed our parting handshake from the door of BHQ where he was giving the Picquet Commander a dressing down.

'Ah, Ross,' he said as I came up, showing in a crafty smile his greenish teeth under the clipped white moustache. 'Going up in the world, aren't you?'

'Sir?' I said.

'Consorting with officers. Who was that? Your brother?'

'A brother writer, sir,' I said.

'Ah, that explains it; I thought something of the sort. I observed him putting on his Sam Browne belt in the street.' The RSM shook his head. 'These civilians—writers and such-like—you can't make soldiers out of 'em.'

'Sir,' I said stiffly—I was standing to attention—'I didn't know that it came within your province to comment on the dress of commissioned officers belonging to another regiment.'

The RSM opened his mouth. He gasped, and looked round to make sure the Picquet Commander was out of hearing. His eyes narrowed but he knew I had him knackered, as the saying goes. He said: 'One of these fine days you'll go a bit too far, Private Ross, and I'm warning you.'

'Yes, sir,' I said, and went on upstairs to my office. I had meant to write a short story that evening, but I sat down and read Lewis's instead. I started with *Private Jones* and ended with *The Prisoners*. This is not a work of literary criticism and the stories have now all been published and can speak for themselves. I will say only this: that after reading them, the army stories which I myself was trying to write seemed by contrast a joke in rather bad taste. This feeling had worn off by the next morning, but I went to bed profoundly dissatisfied with myself and my work.

I sent my stories back to Lewis next day by an orderly who happened to be taking a message to the Welsh HQ. He returned with an odd story. He had accosted a fatigue party who were coal heaving outside—why, at that time of year, I can't imagine. He asked where Mr Lewis could be found. One of the fatigue party, in shirt sleeves and covered with coal dust, had turned and said: 'Here I am.' This had so shaken the orderly that he'd delivered the packet of MSS without remembering to salute. I don't suppose that Lewis minded.

## II

I saw him several times after that. We ate steak and chips together in a café along the sea front, full of snobbish Wrens talking at the tops of their voices about the RAF officers who'd taken them out. I didn't show Lewis any of my stories except one which again dealt with sex, and part of a novel that I was writing. I think that to a great extent he disapproved of what I wrote. I remember him speaking once of the enormous responsibility which a writer should feel towards his characters having once called them into being. He spoke of this almost with awe.

I do not think that in civilian life we could have been friends. We were too different. Where he was genuinely humble and modest, I am arrogant and didactic. Where he felt sympathy and love, I feel anger and contempt. I have only a film gangster's kindness towards small things—animals, children—Lewis had a deep tenderness towards life itself: a nostalgic yearning for his Welsh village, his wife, whereas I have no roots and regard family life with fascinated horror. That doesn't mean to say I am ascribing all the virtues to Lewis, to myself all the faults. I don't necessarily consider them faults or virtues in either case. We were simply of different temperaments: even our aims as writers were violently opposed. But in the army, where the strangest friendships are struck up, it was natural for us to draw together and to talk of intimate ambitions which in civvy street—in a Soho pub or the Café Royal—we might never have discussed.

Our friendship excited much hostile comment in our respective regiments, owing to the differences in rank. Lewis, being an officer, got the worst of it. He had several open rows, whereas I only had to put up with Corporal Dexter talking about my officer pal and the RSM's innuendoes.

One night we were drinking in the saloon bar of a posh hotel. Officers were staggering about with blondies and popsies in all directions. Suddenly Lewis's Officer Commanding walked in. He gave us a terrible yellow stare and said: 'Lewis, I'll see you in the Mess later.'

Lewis flushed. He was furious. Outside in the street he cursed. Later he got a blowing up, and after that we were driven out into back streets where the OC was unlikely to see us. We used to walk aimlessly about or dodge into furtive pubs.

On the night before Lewis's mob was due to move, we sat on a rusty abandoned roller in a field of long grass. Lewis didn't talk much. He was depressed. Once he said: 'I'm not sure that I want to go really,' and later: 'But there'll be something to get to grips with out there.'

I said 'Write to me.' We shook hands and he walked on down the road to see if they'd got his gear ready. He had his Sam Browne belt slung wrong again.

That's the last time I saw him.

'Your officer pal's gone then, Rossy,' Corporal Dexter said with relish next morning. 'See the Taffys've moved.'

'Yes,' I said. 'He's gone.'

He never wrote to me, or if he did I never got the letter.

In March, 1943, I was travelling to hospital under escort, for I was at the time awaiting court martial: as the RSM predicted, I had gone a little bit too far at last. On a station bookstall I saw *The Last Inspection and Other Stories*, by Alun Lewis, and bought the book. I wondered how he was getting on; but not for long, as I had my own troubles and plenty of them. Much later, when I was a civilian again, I heard he'd been killed in action.

Kiedrych Rhys heard the news first and rang up the War Office. They didn't know what he was talking about.

'This is the War Office.'

'I am inquiring about Second Lieutenant Lewis, believed killed in action.'

'Oh, I *see*. At first you said a poet or something. Why didn't you say he was an officer?'

234

# Some Stories

# Y List

It started with a pain in my side. I didn't know I had pneumonia; nobody told me. We were out on the square, first period, 06.55 hours. Arms drill. The CSM himself was taking us. He looked browned off: I don't believe he liked it any more than we did. Drilling before breakfast's a bugger, believe me.

That morning I just couldn't do anything right. I felt sick and also I had this pain. It caught me every time I breathed: you know, like when you've been running and you get a stitch. Only worse than that, of course. At last I couldn't stand it any longer. I thought I was going to be sick over the man in front of me, so I committed a terrible crime: I broke the ranks.

The CSM was outraged. At first he couldn't speak at all when he saw me walking across the square towards him. He went scarlet and his face swelled up. Then he found his voice and shouted: 'Go back! Fall in! What the hell you think you're doing?'

'I'm sick, sir,' I said. 'I feel sick.'

'I'll have you in the guard-room,' the CSM shouted. 'Sergeant Smithson, get hold of that man. Take him to hell out of here!'

'To the guard-room, sir?'

'No, back to his hut. Anywhere. But get him off the bloody square. Out of my sight.'

'Very good, sir. Come on, you! Quick march!'

But once off the square Sergeant Smithson said: 'You don't need to look so scared, lad. He won't stick you in the guard-room. He don't mean nothing, not really.'

'I'm not scared Sergeant,' I said. 'I'm sick. 'I've got a pain.' I could hardly stand up.

'Where's it get you? In the guts?'

'No, not in the guts. In the side.'

'Take off your belt and lie down, then. If you don't feel no better after breakfast you better go sick.'

I lay down on the bed, and lying down the pain didn't seem so bad. In fact I thought it'd gone, till I tried to sit up. Then I found out my mistake. So I lay down again.

The other blokes came tumbling in; they'd been dismissed. The corporal said: 'Dodging the column again, eh? You ought to be under arrest by rights, you ought, breaking the ranks like that. I reckon you got off bleeding lucky meself.'

Then they all went off to breakfast, rattling their mess tins. I didn't feel like eating anything, so I didn't go. I just lay there until they came back again.

'Ain't you eaten nothing?' the corporal said. 'Cor, you *must* be sick.'

'He *looks* sick,' the other blokes said, examining me. 'He don't arf look yellow.'

I didn't care if I looked green, I only wanted to be left alone. The corporal got concerned and put his hand on my forehead.

'You got a temperacher all right. You better go sick.'

'Oh, f— off,' I said, 'for Christ's sake.'

'Who're you talking to?'

'You,' I said. 'Anyone. F— off and leave me in peace.'

'He's sick all right,' the corporal said. 'Better ring up the Reception Station.'

'Get an ambulance.'

'Get the MO.'

I didn't mind who they got, it was all one to me. A runner went off to the Reception Station and the others all stood round the bed talking in hushed voices, as though I were already dead.

Presently an ambulance arrived. Two orderlies came in; one shoved a thermometer in my mouth. Then he took it out and looked at the result. The other orderly looked at it and said 'Cor.' He was impressed. They both shook their heads.

'You in any pain, mate?' the first orderly asked.

'Yes,' I said.

The orderly nodded; he'd expected that. 'Appendix,' he

muttered to himself. 'Obvious case.'

The other orderly thought not. He favoured ptomaine poisoning. 'We'd fish for tea last night, remember,' he said. An argument ensued. I could have stopped it by telling them that I'd had my appendix out long ago and that I hadn't eaten any fish the night before, but I didn't feel like a lot of talk.

The corporal said: 'Well, what I want to know is he for the sick bay or not?'

'Yes, he's for the sick bay all right.' they said.

'Right. Get his small kit together, someone.'

The orderlies lifted me on to a stretcher. The sky tilted round as they carried me down the steps of the hut. Someone threw a hastily packed haversack into the ambulance after me. Then there was the road running backwards behind us and the sky tilted again as they lifted me out at the Reception Station.

The medical officer looked down at me. 'Hullo, you again?' he said.

This medical officer didn't like me. I didn't like him either, come to that. It was a reciprocal dislike. He said: 'A pain in your side? Which side? H'm. We'd better keep you in. I'll examine you later. Can you walk upstairs, d'you think?'

'I can try, sir,' I said. I started to struggle up off the stretcher, but the pain caught me and I fell back.

'Carry him up to the sick bay,' the medical officer told them.

Upstairs in the sick bay the wireless was on and the patients were sitting up in bed. Other patients, wearing hospital blues, were sitting in armchairs round the stove. All looked round as I was carried in.

A nurse came up with some pyjamas. Screens were erected round a bed and behind these I managed to get undressed, holding myself upright by hanging on to the bedrail. It took me some time, but I managed to do it in the end. I was damned if I'd let anyone else undress me. Then I got into bed. I could hardly breathe at all by this time. When the sister brought me a glass of something to drink and I tried to say thank you, only a whisper came out. I thought I was dying for sure, and I should have been frightened, but I wasn't. I felt too weak and too tired to be frightened. I lay back in the cool sheets and went off to sleep almost at once.

I woke up to find the MO standing by my bed. I opened my mouth to speak and the sister thrust a thermometer into it. The thermometer was withdrawn just at the moment when I felt I must spit it out or choke and the MO said: 'Off with your jacket. Let's have a look at you.'

He put on his stethoscope and listened through it to my chest. 'Say ninety-nine.' 'Ninety-nine.' My voice sounded a little louder since I'd had a sleep. The MO said 'H'm.'

He applied the stethoscope to my back next. 'Take a deep breath.' I did. It hurt and made me cough, and coughing tore something inside me. I tried to cough as gently as possible, but still it hurt. The MO said 'H'm' again and commenced to tap my chest with his two fingers. I'll say this for him, I didn't like him, but he could get more sound out of my chest with his two fingers than any MO who's examined me before or since. He got a terrific sound out of it. Through the stethoscope it must have sounded deafening. He took the stethoscope off again and said 'All right.' Then he walked out of earshot with the Sister and started to give her some instructions. I hoped he wasn't telling her to have me chucked out. I didn't feel able to move.

I watched him walk out and then two nurses came up and started to raise me from the pillows. I thought I was going to be forcibly ejected, but I was wrong. A third nurse came and banked up a lot more pillows behind me. Between them they strapped me bolt upright to a wooden rest and put a bolster between my legs, like the Dutch wife you read about in books about the east.

'Is that comfortable?' they asked. I nodded. It wasn't comfortable, but I felt too weak to argue. I went to sleep again straightaway. Later I woke up in a sweat and the wireless was on. I'd been hearing it in my sleep; it was playing full blast. The patients were having tea, digging marmalade out of a tin. I didn't want any tea. I'd acquired a distaste for the thought of food and in particular for the thought of chocolate and Horlick's: formerly my staple diet at break-times. But they didn't seem to expect me to eat, so that was all right. I didn't feel like smoking either, which was a minor miracle, because ordinarily not a day passes but I smoke at least thirty cigarettes, excluding a few occasions when for some reason or other I've not had any cigarettes to smoke.

The man in the next bed to me was smoking, and the smoke from his cigarette, blowing across at me, smelt like cabbage soup, and I knew that if I lit one it'd taste like that, too, and I didn't mean to try it. I had a drink of barley water that the Sister brought me, and then they fixed a hot poultice on my chest, that smelt strongly of aniseed.

I went back to sleep, or rather I dozed and once I woke or dreamt that I woke, I don't know which. My eyes were open, I'm certain of that. I could see the patients in blue walking up and down, but they didn't seem to make any sound; it was as though I were not really there, but looking at a silent film of them or seeing them through glass. I wondered if perhaps I'd died without knowing it. I once read a book where a man died in a hospital ward and afterwards he could see the whole of the ward and the people moving about and bending over his own dead body. I wondered dimly if this had happened to me, but on the other hand the man who wrote the book had never died himself, so he couldn't really know how you felt afterwards. Anyhow, it was like that at first; I could see them in front of me, but they seemed simultaneously at a distance, and then bit by bit I could hear the wireless. It kept fading in and out as though someone was fooling with the set, but I could see it and nobody was anywhere near. It faded on and off, IN and OUT, IN and OUT, OUT and IN, and the people I was seeing began also to fade in and out with the sound, like watching a series of lap-dissolves, and then there was a final fade-out and I woke next in the middle of the night, everyone in the ward asleep and the lights turned low, and I couldn't remember where I was at first. I felt terrible.

I looked round and saw something sitting by my bed watching me, a shape with some kind of headdress on, and I knew at once that this was Death waiting patiently his chance. Or her chance: it seemed to be a woman. Well, why not? Somerset Maugham portrayed Death as a woman, and I couldn't see anything against it. I began to feel a bit frightened then, but I thought perhaps it didn't really matter because if I died then I shouldn't presumably feel so terrible.

By the time I thought that, my eyes had got accustomed to the dark and I saw it wasn't in fact Death watching me, but the Night Sister.

'Can't you sleep?' she whispered to me.

'No,' I said. 'I feel awful.'

'Sick?'

'Yes.' I didn't have to keep my voice down as she was doing; it was a natural whisper.

'I've got some tablets for you to take,' she said. With her arm around me I managed to sit up and take the tablets; they were washed down with barley water. She turned the pillows and bunched them up again behind me, but I still couldn't sleep. It was a terrible feeling of nausea that I had, but it wasn't really like wanting to vomit; I can't describe what it was like. Later I began to shiver, although I wasn't cold. I just shivered and I had a cold sweat on me. The Night Sister kept smoothing the hair from my forehead, which she couldn't have liked doing because it was damp and clammy and horrible.

'You're awfully good to me,' I whispered when finally I stopped shivering.

She said, 'It's nothing.' She smiled and I could see her teeth gleam white against her face in the dark. I still couldn't sleep, and then I could, and when I woke the eight o'clock news was on and they were all having breakfast.

The feeling of nausea had subsided and also the pain, but later when I sat up they were there again and I started to retch. I tried to hold it back because it hurt, but I couldn't and the nurse fetched me a bowl. What I brought up felt like blood, and I looked in the bowl and it was. It was mostly dark, almost black, but there were some bright scarlet threads mixed with it as well, and it was blood all right.

When I saw the blood I got a little scared, but the nurse said there was no need. 'It's quite usual in cases like yours,' she said. I was relieved by that; I'd have hated to do anything irregular. I was so relieved I coughed up quite a blob more blood without minding at all.

The coughing hurt and exhausted me, but I felt much better afterwards. Then the two nurses sponged my face and hands; they wouldn't let me do a thing myself. They even combed my hair for me. 'You mustn't exert yourself,' they said.

'What about shaving?' I said.

They said: 'You'll have to grow a beard.'

Then the MO came round. He looked at the blood in my sputum bowl without much interest and asked me a string of questions. Had I ever had chest trouble before? Was there any chest trouble in my family? Did I feel any better today? The answer to all these questions was No. I felt too exhausted to add Sir, but the MO didn't seem to mind. Perhaps he wasn't really so bad after all.

When he'd gone they put another poultice on me; it was very hot and seemed to bring the pain out through my back. They gave me two more tablets; I went to sleep. I woke and felt sick again. It was like that all day.

During the afternoon Brailowsky came round. He was a Russian boy naturalized British, but not related, so far as I know, to the pianist called that. I liked him, and we used to argue about the way Russian slang should be translated into English and also, because he was Russian, about the soul. But that afternoon when he came I didn't feel like arguing about the soul. I had one of my lap-dissolve periods on and the face of Brailowsky, seen as if through glass, seemed to recede and advance, dissolving and re-forming, in and out, in and out, out and in. I couldn't talk; he sat by the bed awhile then tip-toed away. I slept.

Next morning I felt better. The news was all about Hess and how he'd landed by parachute and all the patients were talking about Hess, and how the bust-up in Germany was coming for sure and the war'd be over by Christmas, you mark my words.

There were too many patients for me to sort them all out, but I noticed that one of them had his face painted a bright orange. I'd noticed this before, but thought it was part of my delirium. Now I saw it was real; he had some spots on his face and the stuff they put on turned him this peculiar colour. He looked extraordinary; he was a New Zealander someone told me.

Well, there they were, talking about Hess, and after this the wireless continued to be Hess, and it was also a little Roosevelt and dance tunes, 'Falling Leaves' and 'There I Go' and 'Yes, My Darling Daughter', and when I hear these tunes again I shall remember the Reception Station and the poultice drawing out the pain gradually, the orange-faced New Zealander and the tablets that were known as M. and B.

They always made me feel sick and the days were divided up by the times I took them and there were also poultice-changing, temperature-taking, barley water and broth. Then there was sweating and sleeping and coughing, less and less blood by degrees, and the tablets made me feel less sick as time went on.

The nights, when I began sleeping better, were my best time because then the Night Sister was on duty. I knew all the sisters by now: the fair, wispy one who was engaged to a subaltern in the eighth, the spectacled talkative one, the tall, thin, dark one, and the two nurses: the short dour Scotch one and the grey elderly tired one. They were all very sweet and kind to me, but best of all I liked the Night Sister.

She was not beautiful; there's a temptation to think of her as beautiful because I was sick and she nursed me, but I like to remain a realist, and she was not beautiful, no. She was a big dark girl with a cloud of dark hair under her coif and she had very white teeth. In the night I sometimes woke and I was frightened. I'd not been frightened at first because I was too weak, but later I was, and seeing her sitting by the bed used to stop me being frightened at once. She had also to wake me during the night to give me two of the tablets and she always did this by stroking my forehead.

'Why do you stroke my forehead to wake me?' I asked her once.

'I want you to think you're at home and wake up happy,' she said.

'No one wakes me like that at home,' I told her.

'Not your girl?'

'No, I haven't a girl.'

'Surely you must have a girl.'

'No, I haven't.'

'You're a poor lonely boy,' she said.

'No,' I said. 'I'm poor, but I'm not lonely. I'm hardly ever lonely.'

'Ssh,' she said. 'We're talking too loud. We'll wake the others.'

Then I'd take the tablets and go off to sleep quite happily. The nights were like that, and in the morning she was gone and there was Bing Crosby and the Morning Star on the radio and afterwards Hess.

Now I was better; I no longer coughed up blood, and one day the Sister showed me the thermometer and it was down to normal. I used to lie there and sometimes read, and I used to think of all the sick leave I'd get when I got out of hospital.

I knew now I'd got pneumonia; at first I didn't care what I'd got, but later I became curious and got the orange-faced man to turn round the chart that hung on the end of my bed and this said PLEURISY AND PNEUMONIA. I remembered the company clerk who'd gone down with German measles and how they gave him seven days, and if you got given seven days for measles what'd you get for pneumonia? My mind soared to dizzy heights of sick leave. Twenty-eight days? Two months? The camp with its dust and heat and the CSM shouting seemed agreeably remote—almost a thing of the past. A month anyway, I thought. They can't give me less than a month. I felt so bucked at the thought of a month that I even felt hungry for the first time and ate a piece of chicken cut up into tiny little squares. Hess was having chicken, too, we heard.

Then one morning I'd been asleep and I woke and there was the colour-sergeant rattling a bag of coins and grinning at me; the company commander was with him. It was Friday; I'd been ill for almost a week.

'Here's a quid for you,' the colour-sergeant said. 'Better take it while you can. They'll only pay you eight and six when you shift to the hospital proper.'

So I took the quid and they went round the ward rattling the bag of money. Everyone woke up when they heard it, even the man who'd been carried in nearly dying of something the day before woke up, and all got paid out.

That afternoon Brailowsky came again. He had some news for me.

'D'you remember Collins? In No. 7 Platoon?'

'The one with glasses?' I remembered Collins; he was a country lad and not too good on drill—he just couldn't seem to grasp it somehow.

'A terrible thing happened this morning,' Brailowsky said. 'He had his eye put out; he was blinded. We were on bayonets and a scabbard slipped. It was the corporal's actually, Corporal Evans. It struck Collins and broke his glasses into his eye. It was awful.'

'I should think it was,' I said. 'Poor devil.'

'If only he hadn't worn glasses he'd have been all right. It was the glass breaking that did it really.'

'How awful,' I said. 'Did he faint?'

'No, he was conscious all the time. The Corporal's awfully cut up about it.'

'Where is Collins now?'

'At the town hospital. He's to have an operation.'

'Well, there's one thing,' I said, 'he'll get his ticket.'

'Oh, yes, they'll give him that, I should think. And you d'you think you'll get yours?'

'No such luck.'

Then we talked about the soul. Tolstoy was mentioned and Dostoievsky. We both got a little exalted and in the end Brailowsky was asked to leave by the sister in charge. He said he'd be back. I felt a little less exalted when he'd gone and I thought a bit about Collins; I thought principally poor bastard. Anyway, he'd be out of the army, that was one good thing, but was it worth losing an eye for? I decided not.

On the Sunday after that I was moved. There was no warning; the MO suddenly came round about midday and said I was to go to the town hospital that morning. Immediately I was carried out to the ambulance on a stretcher. It was lovely weather and the sun felt good on my face, but I was worried because I hadn't said good-bye to the Night Sister. Later, though, she came round to the town hospital, and I saw her there, and when I came out finally I went to look her up, but she'd been transferred and I never saw her again.

At the town hospital they had huts adjoining it for the military, and I was in one of these. When they carried me in there was lunch going on, and I was hungry. I asked for something to eat.

'Bread and milk,' the nurse told me. 'You can have some bread and milk if you like.'

'They're eating stew. Why can't I have some of that?'

'Not until the doctor's seen you.'

'But I'm eating normally now, nurse. I've had no lunch. I'm hungry.'

'Well, you can't have anything till the doctor comes.'

'When will that be?'

'About three o'clock.'

'Oh Christ.'

The nurse was a little shocked. She went away and I watched them eat the stew. Later the nurse returned with some junket. I didn't like junket; I told her so. She said I ought to be glad of anything I could get these days.

Then there was an altercation when she took down my particulars. She wanted my mother sent for. I said I didn't want her worried and it all ended in this nurse not liking me.

I was surprised at the difference in atmosphere. Of course, these were not VADs; they were trained nurses, and there's the difference between amateur and professional; it's something like that, and there were also more regulations and less food, as I found out later.

The doctor came round about half-past three, and it was a woman doctor. The first thing she did was to knock off the tablets. She said I was progressing satisfactorily. I said could I have something to eat; she said of course. So I ate bread and jam for tea and later stew.

The hut was a long one and stretched down a perspective of beds to long French windows leading on to a lawn. The end beds by the French windows were not filled except one that had a man who had fits in it. We were always waiting for him to have one, but he didn't; we thought he was a washout. Most of the patients were up and about; they used to get free passes to go to the cinema in the afternoons, but at meal times they always reappeared and there was a scramble to sit down at the long table that ran down the middle of the room, and the bed patients sat agitatedly up and made desperate signals to the nurses to make sure they didn't get overlooked.

Everyone was always hungry because, although the hospital took military patients, they still had civilian rations and food was scarce. One day we had a major who shouted at us that we were under military discipline and any man misbehaving himself'd damn soon find it out. But we were not interested in discipline; we were interested in food. The food remained unmilitary and we were hungry all the time.

The food we got was mainly vegetable stew with a few shreds of meat in it and beans abounding. The beans had an effect on us that was embarrassing when the matron came round at night; it was like crackers going off all the way down the ward. At each explosion the matron would give a little start as if stung. From the beds behind would come giggles smothered by blankets and a fresh salvo burst out in front, so the matron was caught between two fires, so to speak; it was

248

amusing but embarrassing for everybody.

That was in the evenings; in the mornings there was the wireless, which was now altogether Roosevelt and sometimes Bing Crosby; Hess had fizzled out. Roosevelt made a rousing speech; it was terrific, and the patients all said the war'd be over by October, but some still stuck to Christmas; they were pessimists. With the wireless went washing, and now that I was stronger, shaving, and there was also Yes or No.

At the Reception Station Yes or No had been considered a rhetorical question, but here the nurses began to ask it with increasing urgency, and one came round with potions and pills and various kinds of purges on a trolley. I took a yellow-coloured medicine and several pills without result and they began talking about dynamite.

When I did at last get going it was quite an adventure. The lavatory was just outside the ward, and to get to it you had to pass eight beds. My body felt as light as a blown feather and my legs as though the laws of gravity had altered. I had to look down to make sure that my feet were in fact touching terra-firma. I refused the offer of a stick and a nurse's arm. I set off to float down the ward on my own, the other patients cheering me on. As my head seemed also independent and a separate entity, it was an exhausting experience and tired me out for the rest of the day.

The afternoon was merely an interlude between dinner and tea, and during it there was a blanket bath, which I did myself, and rubbing methylated spirit on my body, which was done by a nurse. I was always embarrassed by this, especially since the nurse who did it was a good looking one. She was a well-set-up girl, and I used to watch her walking down the ward with detachment, and then one day it was no longer detachment, and I knew then that I was getting definitely better.

Every day after that I got steadily better, and now that the pain had entirely gone and the doctor said the lung was almost healed, I had great pleasure in breathing; every time I breathed my whole body seemed to expand, and it was very pleasant. I could feel my blood circulating freely and I felt very strong; it was always astonishing that when my feet touched the floor I felt dizzy and so weak I could hardly stand.

Sometimes I was allowed to get up and sit in a chair by the stove, which was not lit now as it was the middle of May and warm weather. I used to send out all the time for food; one of the up-patients got it for me. The colour sergeant's quid soon went, and I ate always with tremendous appetite.

The orange-faced man turned up, but now you couldn't see his face because the new treatment he had caused it to be swathed in bandages, and he looked like the Invisible Man in the film before he actually became invisible.

And then Collins turned up. He didn't see me at first, but I saw him; he had a black patch over his eye and looked really none the worse. I heard what was said when his doctor came round. We each had separate doctors, and his was a doctor who considered it his duty to demobolize the army, or at any rate such part of it as came under his care. I heard him tell Collins that he'd been recommended for discharge and Collins muttered something in his slow country voice, but he didn't seem pleased about it; he seemed just indifferent. Later he saw me and we had a talk.

'How'll you like getting your ticket?' I asked him.

'Oh, I dunno. I ain't so keen. I dunno as I want it really.'

'You don't want it!'

'I ain't all that keen. 'Course I wouldn't mind getting home for the harvest, but still.'

I was astounded. I knew that if I'd been blinded in the army I'd expect my ticket and probably a pension as well. I looked at him and thought he took it so calmly he must have more guts than I had. But then I knew it wasn't guts; it was just that he hadn't the imagination—if something happened to you and you didn't imagine it, it had not really happened: and even the tangible loss of an eye did not entirely happen until it'd been fully imagined. Well, in his case he was better off like that—and who wants imagination, anyway?

I looked at Collins standing there with his black patch and in his hospital blues that were rather too big for him; the sleeves hung down over his hands.

'Well,' I said, 'it looks as though you'll get your ticket whether you want it or not.'

'Ar,' he said. 'Well, I don't mind much either way.'

I watched him walk back to his bed, and later Corporal Evans came, the one who'd done it to him by accident, and I watched the corporal come walking down the ward with a look on his face as though he were going into action; he was Welsh and emotional, and you could see he was all worked up about it.

Collins was sitting on his bed and he stood up and slowly grinned.

'Hullo Corp,' he said.

I couldn't hear what Corporal Evans said, but I could see Collins wince at the grip his hand got; it must have nearly cracked the bones. Then they sat down and talked. Corporal Evans gesticulated a lot, and I could see Collins shaking his head slowly from time to time. They talked for quite a while, and when Corporal Evans got up to go he seemed tremendously relieved. He left the ward with a shout of laughter and at the door he turned back to wave at Collins. 'So long, lad!'

'So long, Corp,' Collins said, and he sat there on the edge of his bed for some time afterwards smiling to himself, and I couldn't tell what he was thinking about; perhaps he wasn't really thinking at all.

That afternoon, too, Brailowsky came, but Collins was out by that time; he'd gone to the cinema; it was 'All This and Heaven Too'. Brailowsky said I'd been Y listed; it was on orders, twenty-one days in hospital; but as I wasn't an NCO it made no difference to me. I had no stripes for them to strip.

Brailowsky had brought a book by Turgenev, and he'd brought with him also the same book in Russian. He was showing me how the translation differed from the original

I

Russian when a sudden blood-curdling yell from the end of the ward made us both start round.

The yell proceeded from a bed occupied by an Irishman who had some kind of stomach trouble. I'd never spoken to him, but I'd never thought that he was really very ill. We looked round and he was sitting up in bed, gaunt and unshaven, with a wild look on his face.

'I want my wife!' he yelled out.

Two of the nurses came running in and immediately went to his bedside, but he waved them away.

'I don't want you; I want my wife. I'm a dying man. I want my wife.'

The nurses said something; he wouldn't listen. He started to beat on the bedrail with his hand and to shout over and over again, 'I want my wife, I want my wife, I want my wife.'

Brailowsky had turned pale. 'What's wrong with him?' he whispered. I said I didn't know. I was watching the Irishman. Everyone in the ward was watching him; the patients from their beds and some of the patients who'd got back from the cinema stood watching him and the nurses. The Irishman glared back at them with his eyes starting out of his head.

'I'm dying, I tell ye!' he howled. 'I'm dying, and ye can't tell me no different. I know it! I want my wife!'

Suddenly there was a commotion at the other end of the ward. It was the man who had fits; he was having one. The Irishman had evidently upset him. Now attention was divided; our heads kept turning from side to side, and all the nurses made in a body for the man with fits. Screens went up round his bed in no time, but the Irishman, on the other hand, feeling himself abandoned, began to shriek at the top of his voice; it wasn't pleasant.

'I'm dying I tell ye I'm dying I want my wife I'm dying I'm dying I want my wife I tell ye I'm dying I want my wife I'm dying I'm dying. The Mother of God have mercy I'm dying.'

Brailowsky stood up; he'd gone green in the face. You'd have thought that being Russian he'd have been used to this kind of thing, but evidently the naturalized part of his nature asserted itself suddenly and he couldn't take it. He muttered 'So long,' and left the ward promptly and with expedition.

The Irishman was on a new tack now. He pointed a furious finger at the patients who stood gaping round his bedside.

'Aye, ye can stare, all of ye, ye can stare. Take a good look; I ain't afraid to die. The Lord God strike ye where ye stand. May he strike all of ye dead!' He added: 'And may a dying man's curse be on ye all!'

More patients came in, attracted by the noise from another ward, and two more nurses; they all stood staring. The Irishman included all these newcomers in his malediction.

'Die, all of ye, die!' he shrieked. 'Ye're dead! Why don't ye die?'

He leant forward and waited for them to die. They didn't; they just stood there. The Irishman cast his eyes to heaven and again called on God to strike them dead.

The bed patients further up now began to call angrily down the ward.

'He's loopy! Lock him up!'

'Fetch a strait jacket!'

'Fetch a doctor!'

'Fetch a priest!' this evidently from a fellow Catholic, but delivered in a Scots accent.

The Irishman paid no attention to these exhortations. He was watching the group round his bedside, waiting for them to fall.

'Nothing happens,' he muttered after a moment. 'Nothing happens.' He said this hopelessly, his faith was shattered. He dropped his head in his hands and began to sob.

A doctor now rushed in with a stethoscope dangling round his neck and took instant command of the situation. Up went the screens, and from behind them we could hear the Irishman sobbing brokenly.

'Is he really dying?' I asked one of the nurses, who'd halted by my bed on her way down from the man with fits.

'No,' she said, 'of course not. He won't die.'

'What about his wife?'

'She's in Ireland. Besides, he's separated from her.'

The Irishman quietened down after a while, and later he apologized to all of us. It'd been a mistake, he said, the devil had entered into him. We accepted the apology and also the theory of demoniacal possession, but that night the Irishman had a relapse, and this time he kicked over the screens and hit someone, a sergeant, I think. In the morning when we woke he'd been removed, and I don't know what happened to him because shortly afterwards I was moved myself.

I went to a convalescent home, where I remained for three weeks. And I never got any sick leave after all. An AC1 had just come out saying that if you went to a convalescent home you couldn't have sick leave; the MO at the camp took great pleasure in explaining it to me.

I did get my seven days' privilege leave, which was, anyway, six weeks overdue, and they said I was lucky to get even that, because being on light duties I wasn't entitled to any kind of leave without the MO's okay.

When I came back to camp I saw Collins. He hadn't got his ticket; they'd graded him B2 and given him a job in the company stores. They gave him also a brand-new glass eye, which he's very proud of; he can even move it about in its socket. The boys all call him Nelson, but he doesn't mind that; he doesn't seem to mind anything at all.

# I had to go sick

I hadn't been in the army long at the time. About a week, not more. We were marching round the square one afternoon and I couldn't keep in step. The corporal kept calling out 'Left, left,' but it didn't do any good. In the end the corporal told me to fall out. The platoon sergeant came rushing up and said 'What the hell's wrong with you, man? Why can't you hold the step?'

I didn't know, I couldn't tell him. There was an officer on the square, and the sergeant-major and they were both watching us.

'Got anything wrong with your leg?' the sergeant said. 'Your left leg?'

'I've got a scar on it Sergeant,' I told him.

'Dekko,' the sergeant said.

So I rolled up my trouser leg and showed him the scar on my knee. The sergeant looked at it and shook his head. 'That don't look too good, lad,' he said. 'How'd you come to get it?'

'I was knocked down by a bike. Years ago.'

By this time the sergeant-major had come up and he looked at the scar too. 'What's your category, lad?' he asked me. 'A1?'

'Yes sir.'

'Well you go sick tomorrow morning and let the MO have a look at that leg. Meantime sit in that shed over there till it's time to fall out.'

There was a Bren Gun lesson going on in the shed when I got there. My arrival interrupted it. 'Who the hell are you?' the NCO taking the lesson asked me. 'What d'you want?'

'I've been sent over here to sit down Corporal.'

'To sit down?'

'Sergeant-major sent me.'

'Oh well if he sent you that's all right. But don't go opening your trap, see? Keep mum and don't say nothing.'

'Very good Corporal.'

'Not so much of it,' the corporal said.

The lesson went on. I listened but couldn't understand what it was all about. I'd never seen a Bren Gun before. And then the corporal's pronunciation didn't help matters. I sat there in the shed until everyone else had fallen out. Then the sergeant-major came over to me.

'Fall out,' he said. 'What're you waiting for. Parade's over for the day, you're dismissed. And don't forget—you go sick tomorrow morning,' he shouted after me.

'How do I go sick?' I asked the other fellows, back in the barrack-room.

They didn't know, none of them had ever been sick. 'Ask the Sarnt' they said.

But I couldn't find the sergeant, or the corporal either. They'd gone off to a dance in the town. So I went down to the cookhouse and there was an old sweat sitting on a bucket outside, peeling spuds. You could see he was an old sweat because he was in shirt sleeves and his arms were tattooed all over. So I asked him how to go sick and he said 'Ah, swinging the lead, eh? MO'll mark you down in red ink, likely.'

'What happens if he does that?'

'CB for a cert. Scrubbing, or mebbe a spot of spud bashing. You won't get less than seven days, anyhow.'

'What, seven days CB for going sick?'

'Sure, if you're swinging the lead. Stands to reason. There ain't nothing wrong with you now is there? A1, aintcher?'

'Yes.'

'There you are then. You'll get seven all right,' said the sweat. 'What d'you expect. All you lads are alike. Bleeding lead swingers the lot of you.'

He spat on the ground and went on peeling spuds. I could see he wasn't going to say any more so I walked on. Further along I stopped by another old sweat. This second sweat was even older and more tattooed than the first one. And he hadn't any teeth.

'Excuse me,' I said, 'Can you tell me how to go sick?'

'Go sick?' said this second, toothless sweat. 'You don't want to do that.'

'Why not?' I said.

'Well look at me. Went sick I did with a pain in the guts, and what's the MO do? Silly bleeder sent me down the Dental Centre and had them take all me teeth out. I ask you, do it make sense? Course it don't. You got the guts-ache and they pull out all your teeth. Bleeding silly. And they ain't given me no new teeth neither and here I been waiting six munce. No,' said the sweat, 'You don't want to go sick. Take my tip, lad: keep away from that there MO long as you can.'

'But I've got to go sick. I've been ordered to.'

'Who by?'

'Sergeant-major.'

'What's wrong with you?'

'My leg, so they say.'

'Your leg? Then mebbe they'll take your teeth out too. Ain't no knowing what they'll do once they start on you. I'm bleeding browned-off with the bleeding sick I am.'

'Well how do I go about it?'

'See your Orderly Sarnt. Down Company Office. He's the bloke you want.'

On the door of the orderly sergeant's bunk it said KNOCK AND WAIT. I did both and a voice shouted 'Come in, come in. Don't need to bash the bleeding door down.'

There was a corporal sitting at a table covered with a blanket writing laboriously on a sheet of paper.

'Yeh?' he said, looking up. 'What d'you want?'

'I was looking for the Orderly Sergeant,' I said.

'I'm the Orderly Sergeant,' said the corporal. 'State your business and be quick about it. I ain't got all night.'

'I want to go sick Sergeant. I mean Corporal.'

'Don't you go making no smart cracks here,' said the corporal. 'And stand properly to attention when you speak to an NCO.'

'Sorry Corporal.'

'Ain't no such word in the British army,' the corporal told me. 'Now what's your name? Age? Service? Religion? Medical Category? Okay, you parade outside here 8.30 tomorrow morning. On the dot.'

I went to go out, but the corporal called me back. 'Here, half a mo. How d'you spell Picquet? One K or two?'

'No K's at all Corporal,' I told him.

'Listen didn't I tell you not to be funny? I'll stick you on a chitty so help me if you ain't careful. How d'you mean, no K's. How can you spell Picquet without no K's?'

I explained. The corporal looked suspicious. 'Sure? You ain't trying to be funny?'

'No Corporal. P-i-c-q-u-e-t.'

'Okay.' He wrote it down. 'Need a bleeding dictionary to write this bastard out,' he muttered, and then looking up: 'All right, what're you waiting for. Scram. Gillo! And don't forget: 0830 tomorrow. Bring your small kit in case.'

I didn't like to ask him in case of what. I got out quick before he gave me scrubbing or spud-bashing or tried to take my teeth out maybe.

I didn't sleep too well that night, I can tell you. Next morning at 0830 there I was outside the orderly sergeant's bunk with my small kit: I'd found out from our sergeant what that was. There were quite a lot of other fellows there as well. It's funny how they pass you A1 into the army and then find out you're nothing of the sort. One of these fellows had flat feet, another weak lungs, and a third reckoned he was ruptured.

After a while the corporal came out. 'All right,' he said. 'Get fell in, the sick.'

We fell in and were marched down to the MI Room.

'Keep in step, you!' the corporal shouted at me. 'Christ, can't you keep step?'

Down at the MI Room it said on the walls NO SMOKING, NO SPITTING, and we sat around waiting for our names to be called out. At last mine was called and I went in. The MO looked up. 'Yes, what's wrong with you?'

I looked round. There were two fellows standing behind me waiting their turn. A third was putting on his trousers in a corner. More crowded in the doorway behind. I felt silly with all these fellows listening in. I didn't know what to say.

'Come on, out with it,' said the MO. 'Or perhaps it's something you'd rather say in private?'

'Well sir, I would prefer it.'

'Right. Come back at five tonight.'

I went out again.

'What'd you get?' the orderly sergeant asked me.

'He said to come back at five Corporal.'

'What's wrong? Got the clap?'

'No Corporal.'

'Crabs, maybe?'

'No, not crabs.'

'Well what the hell you want to see him in private for, then? Only blokes with VD see him in private as a rule. Unless they've crabs.'

At five I reported back to the MI Room.

'Right,' said the medical corporal. 'This way. Cap off. Don't salute.'

The MO said, 'Ah yes. Sit down and tell me about it.'

I did. He seemed a bit disappointed that I hadn't VD but in the end he examined my leg.

'Does it hurt? No? What about if you kneel on it? H'm, yes, there's something wrong there. You'd better see the specialist. Report here tomorrow at ten.'

The specialist was at a hospital some miles away from the camp. He said 'Try and straighten the leg. What, you can't? All right. Put your trousers on and wait outside.'

Pretty soon an orderly came out with a chitty. 'You're to have treatment twice a week,' he told me. 'Electrical massage. This way.'

I followed him down a lot of corridors and finally out into the grounds and up some steps into a hut with MASSAGE on a board outside it. There I lay down on a table and a nurse strapped some sort of pad on my thigh. After that they gave me a series of shocks from an electric battery. It lasted about half an hour.

'Feeling better?' the nurse asked me when it was over.

'No,' I said.

I could hardly walk.

'That'll wear off by and by,' said the nurse.

I drove in by an ambulance to the MI Room.

'Had your treatment?'

'Yes sir.'

The MO started to write something on a piece of paper. I was a bit nervous in case he used the red ink. But he didn't after all. He used blue ink instead. 'Give this to your orderly sergeant,' he said.

On the piece of paper it said 'Att. C.'

'Attend C!' said the orderly sergeant. 'Cor you got it cushy ain't you?'

'What's it mean Corporal?' I asked.

'Attend C? Excused all duties. Bleeding march coming off tomorrow and all.'

Two days later I went to the hospital again. After a week or two of treatment I'd developed quite a limp. The fellows all said I was swinging the lead. I limped about the camp doing nothing, in the intervals of having more electric shock. Then, after about three weeks, the MO sent for me again.

'Is your leg any better now?'

'No sir,' I said.

'Treatment not doing you any good?'

'No sir.'

'H'm. Well I'd better put you down for a medical board in that case.'

So I didn't even go to the hospital any more. I used to lie on my bed all day long reading a book. But I got tired of that because I only had one book and I wasn't allowed out owing to being on sick. There weren't any other books in the camp. Meanwhile the fellows were marching and drilling and firing on the range, and the man in the next bed to me suddenly developed a stripe. This shook me, so I thought I'd go and see the sergeant-major.

I was a bit nervous when I got to his office. The sergeant-major had an alarming appearance. He looked almost exactly like an ape. Only he'd less hair on him, of course. But he was quite a decent fellow really.

When I came in he was telling two clerks and an ATS girl how he'd nailed a native's hand to his desk during his service in India. He broke off this recital when he saw me standing there. 'Yes, lad, what d'you want?'

I explained that I was waiting for a medical board and meantime had nothing to do, as I was excused parades.

'But d'you WANT something to do?' the sergeant-major asked. He seemed stupefied.

'Yes sir,' I said. 'I didn't join the army to do nothing all day.'

The two clerks looked up when I said that, and the ATS stared at me with her mouth open. The sergeant-major breathed heavily through his nose. Then he said, 'Can you use a typewriter, lad?'

'Yes sir,' I said.

'Ah!' He jumped up from his table. 'Then sit you down here and show us how to use this ruddy thing. It's only just been sent us, see, and none of us know how to make the bleeder go.'

It was a very old typewriter, an Oliver. I'd used one before, so I didn't find it too difficult. Soon I was typing out long lists of names and other stuff full of initials and abbreviations that I didn't know the meaning of. Sometimes I couldn't read the handwriting, especially if one of the officers had written it, but the ATS used to translate for me.

Then one day the company commander walked in.

'Who's this man?' he said, pointing at me with his stick.

'Sick man, sir,' the sergeant-major said. 'Waiting a medical board.'

'Well he can't wait for it here. We're not allowed any more clerks. You've enough clerks already,' and he walked out again, after hitting my table a whack with his stick.

'All right, fall out,' the sergeant-major said to me. 'Back to your bunk.'

'Now we've no one to work the typewriter,' he said. 'Have to do it all by hand. Hell.'

Next day the orderly sergeant told me to go sick again. I'd got used to it by now. The other fellows called me the MO's right marker.

This time it was a new MO: the other one had been posted elsewhere.

'Well what's wrong with you?' he said.

I explained my case all over again.

'Let's see your leg.' He looked at it for a moment and then said, 'Well there's nothing wrong with that, is there?'

'Isn't there, sir?'

'No.' He poked at the scar, seized hold of my leg, bent it, straightened it a few times and then looked puzzled. 'H'm. There is something wrong after all. You'd better have a medical board.'

'I'm down for one already, sir.'

'What? Well why the devil didn't you say so then? Wasting my time. All right. You can go now.'

In the morning the orderly sergeant came into our hut. 'Get your small kit together,' he said, 'and be down the MI Room in ten minutes. You're for a medical board. It come through just now.'

At the hospital I sat for some time in a waiting room and nobody came near me. It was another hospital, not the one I used to go to for treatment. Then at last an officer came in. I stood up. He was a colonel.

'Carry on, carry on,' he said, and smiled very kindly. 'What's your trouble eh?'

'I'm waiting for a medical board, sir.'

'A medical board? What for?'

'I have trouble with my knee, sir.'

'Oh? What happens? Does it swell up?'

'No sir.'

'What, no swelling? H'm. Well come with me, we'll soon

have you fixed up.' I followed this kindly colonel to the reception desk. 'Take this man along to Ward 9,' he told an orderly.

So I went along to Ward 9 and all the beds in it were empty except for one man sitting up in bed doing a jigsaw puzzle.

'Watcher, mate,' this man said. 'What you got? Ulcers, maybe?'

'Ulcers? No,' I said.

Then a nurse came in. 'Ah, you're the new patient. This way to the bathroom. Here are the pyjamas you change into afterwards.'

'Pyjamas?' I said.

'Yes,' said the nurse. 'And directly you've bathed and got your pyjamas on you hop into this bed here,' and she pointed to one next the man with ulcers.

'But I don't want to go to bed,' I said. 'I'm not a bed patient. There's nothing wrong with me.'

'Then why are you here?'

'Nothing wrong with me like that, I mean. I'm waiting for a medical board.'

'Oh. Wait here a moment, please.' She fetched the orderly. The orderly said, 'SMO's orders he was to be brought here. Said it hisself. The SMO Ward 9, he said.'

'But this ward is for gastric cases,' the nurse said. 'This man isn't a gastric case.'

'I don't know nothing about that,' the orderly told her, and he went off.

The nurse said, 'There's some mistake. I'll see about it while you have your bath.'

So I had a bath and when I came out she gave me some blue clothes and a shirt and a red tie to put on and said I needn't go to bed.

'You'll have to stay here until we get this straightened out,' she said. 'Would you like anything to eat?'

'I would, thank you Nurse.'

'Well there's only milk pudding. This ward's for gastrics

you see.'

'You won't get very fat on that, mate,' the man with ulcers said.

He was right. I ate two lots of milk pudding but still felt hungry afterwards. Then later on the MO came round. A lieutenant, he was. Quite young. He looked at my leg and said, 'This man's a surgical case, Nurse. What's he doing in here?'

'SMO's orders, doctor.'

'Oh. Well he'll have to stay here then.'

'How long will it be before I get this medical board, sir?' I said.

'Medical board? Might be months. Meantime you stay here. Yes. you can have chicken. Give him some chicken, Nurse.'

So he went away and I ate the chicken.

'Wish I was you, mate,' said the man with ulcers.

It wasn't so bad being in the hospital except that you only got eight-and-six on pay day. Every morning I used to go down to the massage department. 'Electrical massage's no good for your trouble,' said the MO. 'We'll try ordinary massage.' So I had ordinary massage and then sat on a table with a weight tied to my leg swinging it to-and-fro.

'Now I know what swinging the lead means,' I said.

I used to have to lie down for two hours a day to recover from the treatment. I was limping quite heavily by the time the MO put his head in one morning and said 'You're for a Board today. Twelve o'clock down in my office.'

I waited outside the office nervously. I thought they might order me to have my teeth out. But they didn't. I was called in and there were three medical officers, one a lieutenant-colonel, who asked me a lot of questions and examined my leg, and then I went back to the ward.

'How'd you get on, mate?' asked the ulcers-man. 'What'd they do?'

'I don't know,' I said. 'They didn't tell me.'

But that evening the MO came in and said, 'You've been graded B2.'

'What does that mean, sir?'

'Garrison duties at home and abroad.'

'Can I go back to the camp then, sir?'

'Not until the papers come through.'

A few days later he sent for me. In his office. 'Something's gone wrong,' he said. 'We've slipped up. It seems you should have seen the surgical specialist before having the Board. But you didn't, so these papers aren't valid. You'll have to have another Board now.'

'When'll that be, sir?'

'I don't know. Don't ask me.'

So that afternoon I saw the surgical specialist. He was a major, although he seemed quite young. He was very nice and cheerful and laughed a lot.

'Lie down on the table,' he said. 'That's right. Relax. Now bend the knee. Now straighten it. Hold it. Hold it. Try to hold it steady. Ha ha! You can't, can you? Ha ha! Of course you can't. You've got no tendon in it, that's why. The patella tendon. It's bust. How long ago did you say the accident . . .? Sixteen years? Good lord, nothing we can do about it now. You'll have to be awfully careful, though. No running, no jumping. If you were to jump down into a trench your leg'd snap like a twig. Can't understand how they ever passed you A1. Ha ha! Well I'll make my report on you right away. Oughtn't to be in the infantry with a leg like that at all.'

I went back to Ward 9. It was supper time. Junket.

'Can't keep it down,' said the man with ulcers, and he proved this by bringing it up again.

Well then the MO went on leave.

'Now you stay here,' he told me, 'until the next Board comes off. Don't suppose it'll be till I'm back from my seven days. Meantime you stay put.'

'Yes sir,' I said.

But in the morning a new MO came round. He was a captain. With him was the Matron. 'Stand by your beds!' he called out as he came in.

The ward had filled up in the last week or two, but most of the patients were in bed, so they couldn't obey. The five of us who were up came belatedly to attention.

'Bad discipline in this ward Matron,' the captain said. 'Very slack. Who's the senior NCO here?'

There was only one NCO among the lot of us: a lance-corporal. He was up, as it happened, so he came in for an awful chewing-off.

'You've got to keep better order than this, Corporal,' said the captain. 'See that the men pay proper respect to an Officer when he enters the ward. If I've any further cause for complaint I shall hold you responsible. Also the beds aren't properly in line. I'm not satisfied with this ward, not satisfied at *all*. I hope to see some improvement when I come round tomorrow. Otherwise. . . .'

He walked on round the beds examining the patients in turn. The ward was electrified. He ordered most of the bed patients to get up and those who were up to go to bed. Except the lance-corporal, who had to keep order, and me. As for the man with ulcers, he was ordered out of the ward altogether. I was last on the list, standing by the end bed, when he came up.

'This man is fit to return to his unit Matron,' he said when he'd looked at me.

'But he's awaiting a medical board Doctor,' the matron said.

'Well he can wait for it at his unit. We're not running a home for soldiers awaiting medical boards. I never heard of such a thing.'

'Lieutenant Jackson said . . .'

'Never mind what he said. I'm in charge here now, and I've just given an order. This man will return to his unit forthwith.'

Then he walked out and the matron went too. Two nurses came in and helped the man with ulcers into a wheel-chair. 'So long, mates,' he said, then they wheeled him away. I don't know what became of him: he just disappeared. After that we straightened the beds and got them all in line.

'Keep order,' said the lance-corporal. 'Why the hell should I keep order. I'm not an NCO no more, they'll revert me soon's I get back. I'm Y listed, see? A bloody private, so why should I bother? Bleeding sauce.'

I wondered when they were going to chuck me out. Forthwith, he'd said, and forthwith turned out to be the next day.

I left about two o'clock. In a lorry. It dropped me at the station and I'd two hours to wait for a train. At last I got back to the camp and it looked all changed somehow, with no one about. Everything seemed shut up. I reported to the orderly sergeant's bunk. Sitting in it was a corporal I'd never seen before.

'Who're you?' he said. 'What d'you want?'

I told him.

'No one told us you was coming,' said this new corporal, scratching his head. 'All the others have cleared off. Jerry been bombing the camp, see? We've been evacuated. Last draft leaves tomorrow.'

'Am I on it?'

'You'll be on it all right.'

'Well where do I sleep? And what about my kit.'

'That'll be in the stores, I suppose. Buggered if I know. I'm from another company, I don't know nothing about you. Wait here, I'll see the storeman.'

But the storeman was out, and the stores were locked up. The corporal came back scratching his head.

'Buggered if I know when he'll be back. Gone on the piss I shouldn't wonder. You better find a place to kip down. Here's a coupla blankets, if that's any use to you.'

Eventually I found a barrack room that wasn't locked: all the other huts were closed up. There were two other blokes in this room, both out of hospital. 'Where're we going to, mate?' they asked me.

'Damned if I know.'

'Nobody bloody well does know, that's the rub.'

At last, after a lot of conjecture, we dossed down for the night. It was autumn by now and turning cold and my two blankets didn't keep me very warm. I slept in all my clothes. Jerry came over during the night but didn't drop any bombs, or if he did we didn't hear them.

Then in the morning the corporal appeared. 'I've found some of your kit left.' Most of it had been pinched. My overcoat was gone and another one, much too small, left in its place.

'I don't know nothing about it,' said the storeman.

'You better get some breakfast,' the corporal said. 'I'll sort this lot out for you.'

Breakfast was a bacon sandwich, all the cookhouse fires had been let out.

'Bloody lark this is, ain't it?' said the cooks.

'You're telling us,' we said.

Then we paraded on the square, about forty of us. Don't know where all the others came from. Other companies I suppose. A lieutenant was in charge of us.

'Where's your equipment?' he asked me.

'I've never been issued with it, sir,' I said.

'Never been issued with equipment!'

'No sir. I was excused parades. And then I've just got out of hospital. I have the papers here, sir, that they gave me.'

'Oh all right. I'll take charge of them.' He took the long envelope from me. Then a sergeant turned up and shouted Shun! 'By the left, quick—MARCH!'

We started off.

'Keep in step, there!' the sergeant shouted at me. 'Can't you keep in step? What the hell's the matter with yer!'

'I'm excused marching, Sergeant,' I said. I've just come from hospital.'

'Oh. All right lad. Fall out. Wait here.' He went up to the officer and saluted. ''Scuse me, sir, there's a man here excused marching, sir.'

'What's that? Excused marching? Well he'll have to

bloody well march. This isn't a convalescent home.'

'It's five miles to the station, sir.'

'Oh well, damn it, what d'you want done? Shove him on a truck or something. *Can't march*, indeed. He'd march soon enough if Jerry was after him.'

So the sergeant told a truck to stop and helped me to board it. It was full of kits and very uncomfortable, I nearly fell off twice. I felt a mass of bruises when we got to the station, and my leg had begun to ache. I sat down on a trolley and waited for the train to come in. It didn't come in for an hour, and the men who'd marched up meantime stood around and argued about where we were going. Some said Egypt, but others said no because we weren't in tropical kit. So then they said Scotland and THEN Egypt. I personally didn't care where we were going. I was fed-up with the whole business, and my leg ached badly : I'd hit my bad knee getting down from the truck.

Then the train came in and it turned out to be full of recruits from another regiment going to wherever we were going, a new camp somewhere or other, and so we'd nowhere to sit. We stood for a long time in the corridor and then I tried sitting on my kit but that wasn't a success because fellows kept falling over me and one of them kicked my bad leg. I was pretty browned-off by this time, so I got up and was going to sock him, but another chap got in front of me and said, 'You can't hit a sick man.'

'Who's a sick man?' I said. 'I'm a sick man.'

'So am I,' said the man I wanted to sock. 'I'm sick too. Hell I got a hernia so bad they daren't operate. I'm waiting my ticket.'

'Sorry, mate,' I said, 'I didn't know.'

'That's okay,' he said so we shook hands and he gave me some chocolate out of his haversack : we'd got bloody hungry by now.

'What about some grub?' everyone was saying. 'Where's the grub?'

By and by it came round in tins. A sergeant brought it.

'What's this?' we said.

'Beans. Take one.'

'Where's the meat?'

'You've had it,' said the sergeant. Everyone cursed. Then an officer came round, a captain. 'Any complaints?'

'What about some more food, sir,' we said.

'There isn't any. I've had none myself,' he said. 'Mistake somewhere.'

'You're telling us,' we said, but not to him.

It was dark when we got to this other town and the searchlights were up overhead. We formed up outside the station. Our sergeant appeared and recognized me. 'I'll see to you in a minute,' he said. But he couldn't, because all the transport had already gone. So I had to march after all. It was three miles, and after all that standing about I felt done in when we got to the new camp. We had a hot meal and I'd have slept like the dead if Jerry hadn't dropped a bomb somewhere near the barracks and woken me up.

'Bugger it,' I said. 'Now we'll have to go to the trenches.'

But they didn't blow the alarm after all, so we went off to sleep again.

In the morning I was down for sick, but the MO at this camp proved to be a much tougher proposition than any I'd yet encountered.

He said, 'What d'you mean, you've had a medical board? How can you have had a medical board? Where're your papers?'

'I gave them to the officer in charge of the draft, sir.' I said.

'Well I haven't got them. What was the officer's name?'

'I don't know, sir.'

'You don't know. My God you give your papers to an officer and you don't even know his name.' The MO held his head in his hands. 'God deliver me,' he said, 'from such idiocy.'

'I don't think I'm especially idiotic, sir,' I said.

'Your opinion of yourself is entirely irrelevant,' said the MO. 'And you must remember who you're talking to.'

'Yes sir,' I said.

'Silence!' said the medical corporal, who'd come up at this.

The MO said, 'Now what's all this nonsense about a medical board? What happened? Were you re-graded?'

'Yes sir. B2.'

'Let's see your pay-book. Corporal, get his AB64 Part I.'

I produced my pay-book.

'Not in it, sir,' said the corporal. 'A1 it says here.'

'I know,' I said, 'but . . .'

'Silence!' said the corporal. 'Speak only when you're spoken to.'

The MO had his head in his hands again. 'All this shouting,' he said. 'If that man gives any more trouble you'll have to charge him, Corporal.'

'Yes sir,' said the corporal.

'Now listen,' the MO said to me, speaking very quietly. 'You say you've had a medical board. You say you've been re-graded. Well you haven't. It's not in your pay-book. Therefore you've not been re-graded at all. You're lucky not to be charged with stating a falsehood, understand? Now don't come here again with any more nonsensical stories or you'll find yourself in trouble. Corporal, march this man out.'

'But sir . . .' I said.

'Come on, you!' the corporal said. So I went. Two days later we started training, and the new sergeant found out I couldn't march and sent me sick again. It was another MO this time and he had my papers, they'd turned up again, and he said I've got to have another medical board.

That was a month ago, and I'm still waiting. I've not done much training so far, and I've had to pay for all the kit I had pinched at the other camp, and all I hope is this: that when they give me the Board, I don't have to go sick any more afterwards. I don't care if they grade me Z2 or keep me A1, so long as I don't have to go sick. I've had enough of it. I'm fed-up.

# A Bit of a Smash in Madras

Absolute fact, I knew damn all about it; I'd been on a blind in Fenner's with some of the boys and I was on my way back when a blasted pi dog ran out in the road and I swerved the car a bit to avoid it. I don't remember the crash or anything, I must have hit into them and driven straight on to the bungalow without stopping. I was so damn tight I don't remember anything, but these fellows were coming out of Fenner's, the two of 'em, and they saw it all right and this bastard Krishnaswami recognized me: I'd a big open Vauxhall in those days and I was driving with the hood down.

The night watchman from Spinner's saw it too and he came across and there were these coolies pretty badly smashed about, one of them had a broken leg and God knows what, and Krishnaswami was shouting that he'd seen me and knew who I was. Mind you, he was properly sewn-up himself, and the other bloke with him was so bad that the station inspector refused to accept his evidence. But Krishnaswami had got the number of my car, so after they'd carted the two coolies off to hospital, the inspector came down to the bungalow to see me.

At that time I shared quarters with a chap called Stanton, he was with the company too, a damn decent chap, and when the peon told him this inspector was out there asking for me, he came into my room and there I was, of course, dead to the world. So Stanton went out and told the inspector I was asleep and could he come back later and the inspector said all right. When he'd gone Stanton woke me up and told me about it. Honest, it came like a bolt from the ruddy blue: I couldn't remember a thing.

'Accident?' I said. 'What the hell are you talking about? I haven't had an accident.'

'One of the coolies may die,' Stanton said.

'But it's nothing to do with me.'

'The inspector says he's got your number.'

'Holy smoke,' I said.

'You'd better snap out of it,' Stanton said. 'He's coming back presently,' so I got up and bawled for the peon to get my bath ready. This was five in the morning, mind you, and I felt foul. I'd an awful head and a mouth like a sewer from smoking. I couldn't understand what it was all about; I thought they'd got me mixed up with someone else.

After my bath I felt better, but I was still pretty bad. I kept drinking socking great cups of black tea, and about seven the inspector came back. He was a native, but quite a nice chap; I've forgotten his name. He brought two other men with him, and these stayed outside taking photographs of my car, which had a mudguard buckled and one of the headlamps knocked back. I'd already had a look at it, and it certainly seemed I had been in a smash, though I still couldn't remember anything.

Of course, directly these fellows started taking photos, I saw the red light, so when the inspector asked me if I'd make a statement, I said no, not without seeing a lawyer first.

'Very well,' the inspector said, 'but I'm afraid I shall have to ask you to accompany me to the station.'

'Is this necessary?' I said.

'I'm afraid so, sir,' he said. 'Purely a matter of form, you know,' so I said all right but could I call my solicitor's on our way down. The inspector said certainly and who was my solicitor?'

'Mr Shankran,' I said.

Of course the inspector knew Shankran; everyone in Madras did. I'd never had to employ him myself, but we'd always been good pals and I knew he'd always be ready to help me out of a hot spot. Besides, he was a damn smart lawyer: look what he did for Cornford that time he crashed into a Mohammedan funeral and killed five. Why, Cornford would have got life if it hadn't been for Shankran; as it was he got off with three years, and on top of that Shankran raised such an awful stink everyone was scared stiff of him; he had several officials sacked, two police sergeants reduced to the ranks, and even got the magistrate reprimanded—all through pull. I tell you, if Shankran couldn't get me off, nobody could.

But on the way to the station, I remembered that I didn't know his address, so I asked the inspector to pull up at Fenner's, which he did.

'By God, Adams old boy,' Fenner said when he saw me, 'you're in a mess this time.'

'I seem to be,' I said: luckily the inspector had stayed outside in the car.

'By God you are,' Fenner said. 'I've had the police round wanting to know all about you, what state you were in when you left, if you were sober, and God knows what. Course they got no change out of me.'

'Did they ask to see the bar chits?'

'Not yet. But you needn't worry: I've fixed those.'

'Thanks, old boy,' I said.

'Anything to oblige,' Fenner said, winking.

'Did you see the accident?' I asked him.

'No, but it sounds pretty serious from what I hear.'

'I'm just off to the station now.'

'Seen a lawyer yet?'

'No. I'm going to get Shankran.'

'Couldn't do better, old boy.'

'Matter of fact, that's what I came to ask you for—his address.'

So Fenner told me and I went back to the inspector and he drove me round to Shankran's bungalow. He was just having *chota hazri* when his boy announced us and he jumped up from the table as we came in, holding out his hand. He was a Brahmin, small and wearing gold rimmed glasses, and you couldn't tell his age from his looks.

'Hullo, hullo, hullo,' he said. 'Adams, eh? How are you keeping? Sit down, sit down. Boy, bring some gin! Sit down, Adams, don't look so worried!'

He seemed a bit surprised to see the inspector, but he said hullo to him too, and spoke a few words in Tamil, and the inspector smiled.

'Look here, Shankran,' I said, 'I'd like your advice. It seems I had a bit of a smash last night.'

'Oh? Well, well. Not a bad one, I hope? Ah, here's the gin. That's right, put it on the table. Help yourself, Adams, Inspector?'

The inspector said he wouldn't, being on duty. I felt better after I'd swallowed some gin.

'Now tell me all about it,' Shankran said. He spoke to the inspector in Tamil and the inspector went out on the veranda, leaving us together. I told Shankran what I knew, while he walked up and down saying 'Yes. Yes. Yes,' sucking at a cigarette without touching it to his lips, the way Brahmins do.

'Yes. Yes,' he said. 'Of course I'll do my best for you. Trust me. Yes. Inspector!'

The inspector came in.

'How badly are these coolies hurt?' Shankran asked him.

'One of them is not expected to live, sir.'

'H'm. H'm. That's bad. Yes.' Shankran turned to me. 'Pity you couldn't come here at once, directly it happened. There'd have been no case, I would have squashed it from the start. Now, of course—h'm.' He sucked at his cigarette, thinking. Then suddenly he turned to me again, holding out his hand. 'All right,' he said. 'Don't you worry. I'll see you through. Make no statements to anyone. Keep mum and meet me in Fenner's to-night, nine o'clock.'

He came to the door with us, telling me again not to worry, and we drove off. He was a damn good scout, Shankran, and except for his skin a good deal whiter than some of those swine that swank about the club thinking they're sahibs. I felt better now the case was in his hands.

We got down to the station and went in and there were a few native police standing about in boots and puttees, but nobody else. The inspector sat down at his desk and was starting to ask me a few questions when suddenly there were voices raised outside and that swine Holt, the Assistant Commissioner, came storming in.

'Arrest that man!' he shouted as soon as he saw me. 'Put him under arrest!'

'But Mr Holt——' I started to say.

'Be silent,' he shouted, and to the inspector: 'Detain him, don't let him get away. He's a dangerous man!'

Of course this was damn ridiculous and unprecedented to boot, treating a European that way. Truth was, I'd had a bit of trouble with Holt over the licensing of buses: he was Traffic Commissioner as well and he didn't like me. He was only doing this to get his own back.

'Can I have bail, sir?' I said.

'Bail? Yes. A thousand rupees,' and with that he stamped out of the station. Well, of course the inspector didn't put me in a cell; I was simply shut in a room on my own. I'd just thought I should be phoning the office, when who should roll in but old Major Brant: he'd been with me the night before and had heard about the accident from Fenner.

'Well, Adams, old boy,' he said, 'in a jam again?'

'By God I am. It's that bastard Holt. He put me under arrest.'

'Won't they let you have bail?'

'A thousand chips.'

'That's all right, old boy. I'll fix it for you.'

So he went bail for me and the inspector let us out. We went down to Fenner's and Brant said: 'Boy, bring Master a large brandy.' So I drank three large brandies altogether and Brant said he'd testify I was sober the night before, because a short time before I left I'd been playing the big drum in the dance band and it's difficult to keep time when you're tight— although I had done it apparently. What's more, Brant said, I had been dancing with his wife earlier on, and he certainly wouldn't let his wife dance with a drunken man. He winked at me and I thanked him and got off to the office. When I came in there the secretary had a message the Old Man wanted to see me.

'What's the meaning of all this, Adams?' Sir Alec said.

'Well, sir, I had a bit of a smash last night.'

'So you said last time you drove your car into a tree and smashed it up completely. Were you drunk?'

'No, sir.'

'Why didn't you stop then?'

'I must have lost my nerve.'

'Humph!' Sir Alec said. 'Well, this is Dr Menon, the company solicitor, who will act for you.'

Dr Menon came forward and shook hands. He was a Hindu, Oxford degree, BBC accent, and all in European dress, even to the green felt hat lying on the desk: people don't wear topees the whole time out East the way you read about in books. I knew Menon slightly: he was a slimy skite and I wouldn't trust him an inch. I didn't let on I'd already been to Shankran.

Menon suggested we should go down to the scene of the accident, and I said all right, without telling him I didn't know where it was. I knew it was somewhere near Fenner's because the inspector had told me so, and we drove down there. Of course all traces had gone by this time, and Menon said he could do nothing more at the moment.

'It all depends on the condition of the coolies,' he said. 'I will inquire at the hospital and let you know later.'

'Righto,' I said.

## II

That night I went into Fenner's to wait for Shankran. I was sitting outside drinking a double scotch when a chap came up to me called Turpin, awful little squirt he was, supposed to be a jockey, though he never seemed to do any riding. Matter of fact, I found out afterwards he'd been warned off.

'Evening, Mr Adams,' this chap said to me.

'Evening,' I said. I'd never spoken to the little bastard before and wondered what in hell he wanted.

'Sorry to hear about your smash last night,' he said. 'It was a bad break.'

'Yes.'

'Nasty thing to happen.'

'Yes.'

'Suppose this coolie croaks. You'll be in the cart.'

'Yes.'

'But maybe I can help.'

'How?' I said.

He looked round to see no one was listening, then leant across the table. I moved back a bit: the little bleeder stank of booze.

'Look here,' he said. 'It happens I know the bloke that's making all the bother. Name of Krishnaswami. He's the bloke you want to look out for.'

'How d'you mean?' I said: I hadn't heard of Krishnaswami until now.

'He's the bloke that saw it all. Took your number. Told the police.'

'I see. I didn't know they had a witness.'

'You bet they have. He's the star turn.'

'Well, what about it?'

'He might be fixed,' Turpin said, looking at me and putting a finger alongside his nose.

'But if he's given his evidence?'

'He could slip out of that easy enough. He's got pull, see? His dad's Trade Commissioner back home. A big bug. He could pull strings.'

'Ah.' I began to see daylight. Turpin and Krishnaswami were in cahoots, and Turpin was the pilot-fish. But I didn't let on I'd spotted their little game, and simply nodded to what he'd said.

'Suppose you talked to Krishnaswami, see? Just a friendly chat. It wouldn't hurt you.'

'Where can I meet him?'

'He'll be here in a tick. He said he was coming at eight.'

'All right.'

'I'll get along then. If Krishnaswami comes in, shall I send him over?'

'Yes, do.'

'Right you are.'

He went out, and I guessed he'd gone to fetch Krishnaswami. Sure enough in about five minutes, this bloke blew in, complete with white bum-freezer and smoking a cheroot. I'd often seen him about, without knowing who he was. He always seemed to have plenty of cash to sling about. He was a thick-set chap with a little moustache and a brown spot on the white of his right eye. He looked sly, and he was, as things turned out.

'Excuse me,' he said, 'but am I addressing Mr. Adams?'

'You are.'

'May I sit down?'

Certainly.'

He gave a little bow and sat down opposite me.

'What'll you have?' I said.

'A brandy, if I may.'

He sat there smiling and looking smug until the boy brought his brandy. Then he said: 'Mr Adams,' and stopped.

'Yes?' I said.

'It seems that my action in giving evidence last night has caused you much inconvenience,' Krishnaswami said. 'I should like to apologize for the trouble to which you have been put.' He spread his hands and smiled. 'Believe me, I am sincerely sorry.'

'That's all right,' I said.

'You are very kind. But perhaps if you would allow me to explain, you will understand the motives actuating my conduct. I feel sure you will understand.'

'Carry on.'

'Mr Adams, I am an Indian! Those coolies whom your car injured are Indians also—my own people. I am an enlightened man, a democrat. I do not believe in the caste system. It is barbarous and should be abolished. To me, all men are brothers. Those coolies are human beings like ourselves, are they not?'

'Oh, absolutely,' I said.

'Imagine, then, my feelings when on emerging from Fenner's, I saw these men struck down by your car and left bleeding and mangled in the roadway, while you yourself drove on without heed. Indians, Mr Adams, my own people! Natives, it is true, but not animals, to be slaughtered like cattle. I knelt down beside them, I was bathed in their blood. One had sustained terrible injuries to his head, it seemed as though he might die there in my arms. You can understand my anger, Mr Adams, and why, having noted the number of your car, I immediately denounced you to the police. Also, I must admit, I was at the time slightly intoxicated. Under the influence of liquor. It had gone to my head. Had I but reflected, I should not have taken the course which I did. But I acted on impulse. Upon the spur of the moment. Now I realize that I was wrong, that if you drove on it was from some other reason than callousness, and I am prepared, so far as I am able, to make amends. I cannot, alas, retract my statement to the police, but there are ways and means by which its effect may be softened.' He pulled a handkerchief out of his sleeve and started to mop his forehead. He'd got very heated talking about the coolies. He drank some brandy and went on. 'If for instance you were to offer some compensation to the family of the injured man——'

'Would that do any good?'

'In my opinion, yes. It would be a point in your favour when the case is brought to court.'

'How much money should I offer?'

'Something in the nature of five hundred rupees.' He looked at me sideways out of the eye that had the brown spot in it. 'If you were to give some such sum into my hands, I would see that it was distributed to the best advantage and in a manner which would rebound to your credit.'

'Oughtn't I to give it them myself?'

'No, I think perhaps it would come better through me—one of their own people, you know. I should of course make it quite clear that you were the donor, and that I was merely acting as intermediary.'

'Well, I tell you what. I'll sleep on it and let you know. How's that?'

'Admirable. I am staying at the Laburnum, just round the

corner. Here is my card. You can always get in touch with me there.'

'Right.'

'And with regard to my evidence, I think we might achieve some compromise. My father, as you are doubtless aware, is Trade Commissioner in England at the moment. He would gladly exert his influence on your behalf.'

'Thanks.'

'I am pleased to be of service,' Krishnaswami said. 'Will you join me in a drink?'

'No, I won't have another now, thanks.'

'Just to show there is no ill-feeling.'

'No really, thanks. Not now.'

'As you wish,' Krishnaswami said. 'But I see you are a good sport, you do not bear malice. And perhaps you are wise not to drink too much. The police have an unworthy suspicion that you are a man of intemperate habits. Mr Holt, the commissioner, is your enemy. Beware of his spies. You are being watched at this very moment!'

'How d'you know all this?'

Krishnaswami smiled, smoking his cheroot. 'We natives have many systems of communication unknown to the European. Besides, news travels fast in the East. If you observe that table behind you, you will see that I am speaking the truth.'

I looked behind me. There was an awful crowd of Mohammedan sods sitting at that table: they looked more like cut-throats than detectives, but they were watching me right enough.

'Agents of Mr Holt,' Krishnaswami said. He got up from the table and bowed. 'Till our next meeting, Mr Adams.'

'So long,' I said, and watched him walk out, strutting, with the cheroot cocked up at a jaunty angle in his mouth. I looked at the card he'd given me. H. B. KRISHNASWAMI, it said, BACHELOR OF ARTS, OXON, and written underneath, 'Laburnum Hotel, Madras.' I took another look at those Mohammedans. Detectives be damned. More likely some of Krishnaswami's pals, keeping an eye on me. It'd take more than them to stop me drinking. 'Boy,' I called, 'bring another whisky. A large one.'

Soon after this Shankran rolled in, all smiles as usual.

'Well, well, well! How's it going?'

'Not too good,' I told him.

'Now, now, don't get downhearted. Never say die, you know. This case isn't as bad as it seems, I've been making inquiries. It appears the police have a witness. A man named Krishnaswami.'

'I know. I've just been talking to him.'

'What!'

I told him what Krishnaswami had said to me. Shankran listened, holding a cigarette with his hand cupped round it, sucking up smoke from time to time. 'Yes. Yes. Yes,' he said, and when I'd finished: 'It's as you thought. This Krishnaswami is a crook. I have him taped, I've been on his track for some time. That's why I was pleased when I came in just now. If Krishnaswami appears in court I shall unmask him as an impostor. His evidence will be discredited.

'But isn't he the son of Sir Somebody Krishnaswami then?'

'No, no. That's all bunk. Absolute nonsense. He's an imposter.'

'He said I was being watched by detectives. At the table behind.'

'What? Those ruffians. Bunk, my boy, bunk. Krishnaswami's after your cash.'

'That's what I thought.'

'You were right. But don't worry, we can circumvent him. He doesn't present a serious obstacle. No. The main thing is that coolie. If he dies, Holt will make it hot for you.'

'He put me under arrest this morning.'

'I know, I know. And Major Brant bailed you out.'

'News travels fast in the East,' I said.

Shankran said: 'I got it from the inspector. He and I are good friends. He will keep me posted with all details and developments as to police work.' Suddenly he looked very serious. 'But if that coolie dies. . . .' He shook his head.

'What about the other one?' I asked.

'Oh, he's all right. A broken leg, that's all. We needn't worry about him.' Shankran tapped on the table. 'And listen, on no account give Krishnaswami any money. Stall him, you understand. Procrastinate. But give him nothing. Take no one's advice but mine.'

'Sir Alec has called in Dr Menon, for the company.'

'Menon? I know him. One of these kid-glove lawyers. No pep. Not the man for this case. Pay no attention to him.'

'All right.'

'I'll deal with Krishnaswami. For the rest, pray to God that coolie doesn't die. Pray to God. I will pray for you myself tonight.' He was serious.

'Holy smoke!' I said.

'Boy, bring some gin!' Shankran said.

## III

There were two mosquitoes had got in my net that night, and I couldn't sleep. Every time I dozed off, one of the bastards'd come singing round and sting me, and at last I had to get up and swat them. Even so I couldn't sleep for thinking of that coolie. It was bloody hot and I was sweating and I thought, suppose he does die? I didn't want to get three years like Cornford. I don't mind telling you I did pray that night, I was in an awful state. At last I managed to sleep, and woke late in the morning feeling lousy. I fined the blasted boy an anna for each of those mosquitoes and got off to the office. I hadn't been there long before the Old Man sent for me. I went up and he had Dr Menon with him, who looked serious.

'About this accident of yours, Adams,' Sir Alec said. 'Did you know the police have a witness?'

'Yes, sir, I said. 'I've spoken to him.'

'Is it true he is the son of the Trade Commissioner in England?' Dr Menon said.

'He told me he was.'

Menon nodded. I could see he was impressed.

'What did he speak to you about?' Sir Alec said.

'He suggested that I should offer compensation to the injured man's family sir.'

'Humph! How much?'

'Five hundred chips.'

'Humph. What d'you think, Menon?'

'It wouldn't do any harm to parley with them sir,' Menon said. 'Have you got his address, Mr Adams?'

'Yes. Here's his card.'

'Well, we might go round there and see him this evening, eh?' He looked at Sir Alec, who grunted 'Good idea,' so I agreed.

That evening Menon and I went round to Krishnaswami's hotel, back of Mount Road. He was in right enough, very smooth and pleased to see us. It was a bloody sight to see those two, Menon and him, both talking Oxford-English and trying to outdo each other at it. By God, you should have heard them. Krishnaswami let off a little bit about his father and I could see Menon believed him. He swallowed it whole. At last, after a lot of this, we got down to brass tacks. Krishnaswami still stuck out for five hundred chips and Menon seemed to think it'd be a good thing if I shelled out.

'But look here,' I said. 'The police are prosecuting me, not this fellow's family at all. How will it help to give them five hundred?'

'It would make a good impression on the court,' Menon said.

'But in any case the sum seems a bit stiff,' I said, and so it was. Why, what the hell, five hundred chips was pretty near a whole month's screw.

'Oh come, Mr Adams,' Krishnaswami said. 'When I think of that poor coolie, with his blood and brains bespattering the roadway, when I think of his poor family, of the terrible worry and uncertainty which they must be undergoing, I sometimes wonder whether any sum of money, however large, could be adjudged sufficient compensation.'

'Well anyhow,' I said, 'he's not dead yet, because I phoned

up the hospital this afternoon and they say he's getting along nicely.'

I'd been keeping this up my sleeve as a trump card, and I could see it was a setback for Krishnaswami: he didn't like it at all. Then Menon came in with another one.

'Well,' he said, 'we will consider your proposal, Mr Krishnaswami. I personally am in favour of it. If Mr Adams will appoint some responsible person to distribute this sum among the man's family, I have no doubt that such an action would influence the court favourably.'

Krishnaswami didn't like that either. He'd counted on getting hold of the dough himself. He bowed and showed his teeth, but it wasn't a smile. He said: 'Perhaps Mr Adams would prefer to consult his *other lawyer*, Mr Shankran, before committing himself to any course?'

'Mr Shankran?' Menon said. He frowned.

'I think I am correct, Mr Adams, am I not?' Krishnaswami said. 'Mr Shankran is acting for you also?'

'Yes,' I said.

I wondered for a moment how the hell he knew, and then I remembered those Mohammedans.

'News travels fast in the East,' I said.

Krishnaswami smiled and bowed. He knew I'd caught on, but he didn't care. He saw the game was up. Menon was still frowning. He didn't say anything more about Shankran, but he was upset all the same. Going downstairs, I tried to explain to him how it was, but he turned away and said: 'It is most unprofessional having two solicitors. You should have informed me before now.'

In the car he'd evidently thought up something, because he said: 'I wonder if it would be possible to see Mr Shankran this evening. Since this state of affairs has been allowed to transpire, perhaps it can be turned to advantage. Mr Shankran and I should compare notes as soon as possible.'

'We can see if he's in,' I said.

He was. We found him sitting at a table covered with briefs, busy on a big case, he told us.

'Dr Menon and I have just seen Krishnaswami,' I said.

'Oh, yes? What happened?'

Menon, still upstage and on his dignity, said: 'Apparently Mr Adams consulted you first, before Sir Alec called me in. I think therefore that we should pool our knowledge and work together as far as possible from now on.'

'Yes, yes. Quite. A pleasure, Dr Menon. What did Krishnaswami say?'

Menon told him.

'Are you satisfied that this man has no ulterior motive in suggesting compensation?' Shankran said.

'For my part, I am perfectly satisfied,' Menon said. They argued about it for some time, but Shankran wouldn't agree; he still didn't like the idea. At last Menon got up to go. He'd said good-bye and was at the door, when he turned round again as if he'd remembered something.

'Oh, yes. One moment, Mr Shankran.' He turned to me. 'I am sure you will excuse us, Mr Adams. Just a technical point.'

'Sure,' I said, 'don't mind me,' so they went out on the veranda together while I mixed myself another whisky and soda and as I was drinking it I could hear them out there talking away in Tamil. Presently they came back, both smiling, and Menon seemed in a better temper.

'That's settled then,' he said. 'If you should decide in favour of compensation, will you let me know, Mr Shankran?' and Shankran said he would, and Menon went out. He didn't shake hands with me, just said 'Good-bye,' and I think he was still a bit put out. Directly he'd gone, Shankran stopped smiling and turned round on me.

'The dirty bainchut,' he said. 'D'you know what he told me outside?'

'I've no idea.'

' "Don't worry, Shankran," he said, "Get as much out of him as you can. I'm paid by the company, I won't ask you for a cut." You see? The corrupt bainchut. They're all the same out here: squeeze you for your last anna. By God,

Adams, you can thank your stars I'm straight!' He tapped on the table again. 'As for Krishnaswami, if he comes near that court I'll smash him. But he won't, depend upon it. Those five hundred rupees, he wants them for his hotel bill. It's the amount he owes the proprietor!'

'What!' I said. 'How do you know?'

'I found it out,' Shankran said. 'It's my business to find out things. Krishnaswami's up to his nose in debt. He's a twister!'

He took off his glasses and wiped them. He was so furious he started sweating hard, and the sweat ran down his nose on to his glasses so that he couldn't see. He wiped the glasses and said: 'However, he won't appear in court. He knows I'm after him!'

'You don't think Menon's working with Krishnaswami, do you?' I said.

'Menon? Oh, no. He's a twister too, but not that kind. Hasn't got the guts.'

'You don't think so?'

'I'm sure of it, my boy, sure of it. No. You needn't worry about that. As for the case, it'll go off all right if that coolie recovers.'

'He's doing well so far. I'm going up to see him at the hospital tomorrow.'

'That's fine,' Shankran said. 'But remember, don't give him any money. I'll tell you when the time comes to pay out.'

'Righto,' I said.

## IV

I got up to the hospital next day and there was this coolie with his head and face bound up in bandages and all his family weeping and wailing round the bedside. The other coolie who had a broken leg was there too, but he didn't seem to have any family, or at least I didn't see them anyway.

The mother of the broken-headed coolie came across and spoke to me. Of course it was all in Tamil and I couldn't understand the half of it, but I told her in English how sorry I was, and I think she understood, because she made a salaam and pointed to her boy and said a piece more, weeping all the time. I felt awful. The old woman didn't sound angry, only very sad, but she couldn't stop crying. I bloody near wept myself, I don't mind telling you. I spoke to the coolie, but he didn't answer: he was lying back with his eyes closed where you could see them through the bandages, and he looked pretty bad to me. I felt terrible. I spoke to the other coolie and he grinned up at me and seemed quite cheerful, so I said a bit more to the old mother who salaamed again, still sobbing, and the rest of the family crowded round all chattering and some of them salaamed too. They could tell I was sorry. Then I got out and told the matron to give the coolies anything extra they wanted and charge it up to me.

'That's very good of you, Mr Adams,' she said, 'but I think they are quite comfortable. They have all they want.'

'The one with the broken head looks bad. Will he live?'

'Certainly. He's quite out of danger now,' she said, so I thanked her and went out. Driving back to the bungalow I still felt awful about it, though.

A week went by and I heard nothing more, except I had a summons from the police saying I was to appear on various charges in three days time. Then one morning Sir Alec sent for me.

'Adams,' he said, Dr Menon was here yesterday. He says he wants to give up the case as you already have a solicitor acting for you. Is that so?'

'Yes, sir,' I said.

'Who is he? A good man?'

'Yes, sir. Mr Shankran.'

'Humph! I've heard of him. Sails a bit near the wind sometimes, doesn't he?'

'He's a smart lawyer, sir.'

'Humph. Didn't he act for Cornford?'

'Yes, sir.'

'Think he'll get you off?'

'He seems pretty certain of it.'

'I'm glad of that. Sure you don't need Menon then?'

'No, sir.'

'Very well,' Sir Alec said, 'if you're satisfied.'

## V

I couldn't find Shankran anywhere. He'd gone off on a case and nobody seemed to know where he was. I was due to appear next day and didn't know what the hell to do. I sat in Fenner's sopping up straight Scotch and feeling awful. Then suddenly, towards the end of the evening, Shankran came in. By God I was never so glad to see anyone in my life.

'Hullo, hullo, hullo,' he said. 'How are you? I've just come back from the hills. Been chasing a witness. Boy, bring some gin!'

'Listen,' I said. 'My case comes off tomorrow at twelve. Have you got everything fixed?'

'Tomorrow? I can't appear for you tomorrow. I'm up to my eyes. Rape. A very difficult case. I've bribed the chief witness but there are still two I've got to get at. Tomorrow's impossible. I shan't be here.'

'Well, what the hell's going to happen?'

'Don't worry. You won't appear either.'

'But I've had the summons!'

Shankran shook his head. 'You won't appear. You're ill. You can't appear if you're ill.'

'What do you mean—ill?'

'You're sick. You've got dysentery.'

'I haven't at all.'

'Of course you have. Don't be silly. We'll get the case postponed. Meet me tomorrow morning and I'll fix it for you.'

So I met him next morning and he drove me right down to George Town, through the bazaar and a lot of stinking little streets and stopped at a chemist's shop that had posters up on the walls outside, advertising cures for siph.

'Up here,' Shankran said, so we went up some awful filthy stairs and into a doctor's waiting room full of natives covered in sores. Shankran sent in his card and the doctor saw us straightaway. He was a Hindu with a big black beard.

'Ah, yes. Mr Adams. How do you do? Dysentery, isn't it? I'll make the certificate out at once.'

He sat down and wrote a certificate saying I was suffering from dysentery and we thanked him and went.

'That's settled,' Shankran said. 'Drop me at the court as we go by, I'll just file the certificate. Don't be alarmed if you don't hear from me for a while, I've got to get after those witnesses. Curse the corrupt bainchuts. Baksheesh, that's all they think about in this country.'

## VI

Fenner said to me one night: 'Seen Krishnaswami lately?'

'No,' I said.

'Well, you won't either. He's shot the moon. Blown off to Bangalore.'

'By God. Is that so?'

'It bloody well is. He owes that fellow at the Laburnum five hundred chips.'

'By God. Does he owe you anything?'

'No. But that little blighter Turpin does, and he's gone too. They've done a bunk together.'

'By God,' I said. 'Have another drink?'

## VII

Well at last the case came off. I met Shankran the night before and he gave me a whacking long list of answers I had to make in court.

'Better memorize those,' he said. 'Learn them off by heart. You won't have much trouble, I know the magistrate. He's a gentleman. You won't have to go in the box. As for witnesses, Krishnaswami's gone. He got out when I threatened him with exposure. The night watchman from Spinner's saw the smash but I've fixed him all right. Major Brant will of course speak for you. The inspector's on our side as well. You'll have to give him three hundred chips by the way, when it's all over.'

'D'you think we'll win?'

'Of course we shall. Without Krishnaswami they've got no case at all. It'll be a walkover.'

The court was very hot and crowded, with bags of natives sprawling about the corridors, all chattering to beat the band, gobbing and chewing betel nut, and peons with red sashes and great brass plates on their chests strutting up and down bawling for silence and making more row than all the rest put together.

Inside, some native police were keeping order and it looked pretty much like the American courts on the cinema, with benches all the way down and a high dais for the magistrate to sit at. I saw old Brant and several of the boys, but no sign of Krishnaswami. Holt wasn't there, of course, being commissioner, but all the coolie's family were, and soon after an ambulance rolled up and the coolies themselves were carried in on stretchers.

'Have you got the answers off pat?' Shankran asked me.

'Yes,' I said.

Then the magistrate came in and we all stood up. He was a Mohammedan and Shankran knew him well. He rapped with the gavel and we all sat down again. Mine was the first case called. The inspector gave his evidence first, for the prosecution, then Shankran called Major Brant, for the defence.

After he had spoken, Krishnaswami's name was called. No answer. The usher walked up and down shouting 'Mr Krishnaswami!' but Krishnaswami didn't show up. The inspector was called back to the box. He read out the statement made by Krishnaswami, to the effect that I had caused the accident and furthermore had callously driven on, being at the time under the influence of drink.

Shankran jumped up. He was sweating hard. He wiped his glasses and the back of his neck and shouted: 'Do you deny that this witness was himself intoxicated at the time of giving his evidence, and that moreover one of his companions was in such an unseemly condition that you refused to accept his statement?'

The inspector didn't deny it.

'Therefore the case for the prosecution rests solely upon the evidence of two men who were themselves in a state of intoxication, and who have since left the city?' Shankran said. 'Thank you, that is all.' He sat down again.

'You say these witnesses cannot be found?' the magistrate said.

'No, your worship,' the inspector said. 'Their present whereabouts are unknown.'

'H'm. Does the defendant plead guilty or not guilty?'

'Guilty, your worship,' Shankran said, 'on the charge of causing the accident; not guilty on the charge of intoxication.'

'Will the defendant please approach?'

Shankran nudged me, and I went forward and stood in front of the dais.

'You plead guilty to the charges against you?'

'Except to that of intoxication, your worship,' I said.

'What caused your car to collide with these men?'

'A pariah dog, your worship. It ran out in the road, and in my efforts to avoid it, caused the accident.'

'Why did you drive on, instead of stopping to assist the men you had injured?'

'I lost my nerve, your worship.'

'Why didn't you report to the police?'

'Same reason, your worship.'

'H'm. Well, in the absence of further witnesses, the case will have to be adjourned in order that the question of compensation be discussed among the parties concerned.'

Shankran jumped up again, wiping his glasses like mad.

'Your worship!' he said. 'Cannot the question of compensation be discussed without delay? My client has suffered considerable inconvenience as a result of this case and we would sooner proceed to its conclusion without further postponement.'

'Very well,' the magistrate said. He looked over at the coolies. The one with the broken leg had it done up in plaster of Paris and the other one had some of the bandages taken off his face and looked a bit better.

'Let us say then,' the magistrate stroked his chin, 'the sum of three hundred and fifty rupees.'

He repeated it in Tamil and looked at the coolies and at the old mother who was sitting with the family on the front bench. She nodded and started to cry again and the rest of the family began to argue and talk in Tamil.

The magistrate rapped for order and said: 'You are also fined one hundred and fifty rupees for driving an automobile to the common danger and fifty rupees for failing to report an accident to the police. These sums should be paid to the clerk of the court. Case dismissed,' so it cost me eight hundred and fifty chips altogether, including three hundred for the inspector, and on top of that came Shankran's fee. By God, it was worth it though. I went on the binge for a bloody month afterwards, I was so relieved at getting off. In fact that's what got me the sack eventually, not the accident at all. Sir Alec was damn decent about it on the whole, he said he couldn't keep me in the circumstances, but he gave me a damned good reference just the same. That's how I come to be home again.

Don't know of any good jobs going, do you?

# Five Finger Exercises

'I don't believe it,' Jocelyn said.

'It's quite true,' she said. 'Honour bright. I'm sixteen.'

'You can't be,' Jocelyn said. 'You must be older than that.'

'Well, I'll be seventeen soon,' she said with satisfaction.

'Even so,' Jocelyn said, 'you're not sixteen now. You simply must be more than sixteen.'

'It's very rude of you not to believe me.'

'But it does sound incredible.'

He thought she looked fully twenty-three when he first saw her looking at an illustrated paper in the lounge, before lunch. They did not take any notice of each other; Jocelyn stared out the window at the steady-falling rain and thought My god, the Sussex Riviera, comparing it unfavourably in his mind with Monte Carlo or Cannes. He did not look at the girl at all; she might not have been there so far as he was concerned. He stared out at the rain which splashed in puddles on the drive. Then the luncheon gong sounded and they went through to the restaurant. Walking behind her Jocelyn noticed the set of her shoulders in the blue openwork jumper that she wore, but without interest, abstractedly. After lunch they sat in the lounge again. Jocelyn talked to an old lady named Mrs Bliss, who was the only other person staying in the hotel. She was very withered, with untidy white hair and a glass eye. She spoke dogmatically and continuously about her past glories and titled relations; her thin drawl drifted tirelessly on as the rain dripped down the windowpanes outside. Jocelyn said 'Yes' and 'Quite!' and 'Definitely,' having found it a good plan to agree with everything that old people said, as that sometimes prevented them from saying it more than once.

While they talked the girl sat across from them, reading a bulky novel which she held upon her knee. Presently she rose and went out.

'What a quiet girl,' Mrs Bliss said. 'I haven't heard her say a word. I expect she's terribly shy, poor thing.'

'She didn't look shy to me,' Jocelyn said.

He did not see her again until dinnertime. Mrs Bliss never came down in the evenings so they were alone in the lounge afterwards. For something to do, Jocelyn offered her a cigarette.

'Thank you,' she said. 'I don't smoke.'

'Isn't it dreadful weather?'

'Yes. I suppose it's still raining.'

'Yes.'

'I tried to go for a walk this afternoon but it rained so hard I went to the pictures instead.'

'What was on?'

'It was a gangster film. You know : full of machine guns and molls.'

'And tough guys saying Okay Chief.'

'That's right.'

Jocelyn laughed. 'D'you like the pictures?'

'Not much.'

'I suppose you're keen on dancing and that sort of thing.'

'Well, I haven't done a lot of it. I only left school last year you see.'

'Last year?'

'I ran away.'

'Good god.'

It was at this point that Jocelyn enquired her age and received his second surprise. He looked at her more closely. She was a big buxom girl and she had a round face. She had a smooth golden skin, a snub nose, and straight hair, bobbed and held back from her forehead with a circular comb. She had changed into a long yellow frock that went well with the colour of her skin. Jocelyn saw that she was younger than he had at first supposed, but she still looked more than sixteen.

'And how old are you?' she asked him.

'Guess.'

'Thirty.'

'Got it first time.'

The girl nodded her head complacently.

Jocelyn said: 'Tell me. Why did you run away from school?'

'I just got tired of it. I ran away and took a job in London.'

'But don't your people object?'

'They don't know where I am.'

'Well, I'm damned. You're a most extraordinary girl aren't you?'

'I'm pretty extraordinary.'

'Good. I like extraordinary people.'

'You're not very ordinary yourself.'

'Of course I'm not.'

'When I saw you first I didn't think you were English.'

'I've lived a lot abroad.'

'Where? In Paris? I've been to Paris.'

'Yes, I was in Paris for years studying art.'

'Are you an artist then?'

'Of sorts.'

'I thought you were.'

'Why did you think that?'

'You look very Bohemian. Not respectable.'

'Do you like respectable people?'

'No. They're too dull.'

The evening passed pleasantly. The girl, whose name turned out to be Jill, told Jocelyn some amusing stories about the department store where she worked, and in return he recounted several of his experiences on the continent.

Jill said: 'You *have* had a hectic life. Don't you find it very boring down here after all that?'

'A bit. I shall be going back to London soon. I have a studio there.'

'I suppose you paint women in the nude.'

'Occasionally.'

Jill smiled. She had good teeth. She had widespaced grey eyes and a wide mouth with full lips. Jocelyn, who held unconventional views about girls' looks, found her attractive. He wished that she were not so young as this made things more complicated than they would otherwise have been. To establish contact he took her hand and began to tell her fortune by the lines on her palm, predicting all kinds of unlikely events for the future. Outside it continued to rain heavily. At last Jill drew away her hand, which Jocelyn had been holding all this time, and said she must go to bed.

They went up together; their rooms were not far apart. Outside her door Jocelyn said: 'Goodnight, my dear,' and as she smiled at him he bent his head to kiss her. She stepped back and evading his arm, slipped into her room and gently closed the door.

Jocelyn retired to bed rather annoyed.

Next morning it was bright sunny weather, although everything was still wet from the rain. Jocelyn did not see Jill until after lunch, when he came upon her in the lounge, reading *The Good Companions*. He sat down beside her and immediately opened siege. 'Why were you so silly last night?'

'You mean I wouldn't let you kiss me?'

'Yes.'

'Men like you always want to kiss girls. I knew you wanted to long before that, when you were reading my hand.'

'Why wouldn't you let me?'

'I wanted to see you blow up.'

'I never blow up. I'm a very good tempered man. At the same time I'm very persistent. I always get my way.'

'You're very conceited. That's one of the reasons why I wouldn't let you kiss me.'

'Are you going to let me do it now?'

'No.'

He leaned over and took her wrists. She was wearing a scarlet openwork jumper and he could see her flesh through it. Her breasts were prominent, with pointed nipples. She had a strong body and well-shaped. Jocelyn had always liked heavily built girls. He looked down into her face. She was smiling with her full lips pursed up and did not look at all frightened or disconcerted. He kissed her cheek and felt the skin firm and smooth under his lips. She turned her mouth away.

'Dear me,' she said, 'you certainly *are* persistent.'

'Have other men tried to kiss you?'

'Oh, yes. One of the salesmen in our department is always trying.'

'And do you let him?'

'No.'

'Darling.'

At last he succeeded in kissing her mouth. It was closed and completely unresponsive.

'Now are you satisfied?' she said.

'Far from it.'

He was kneeling by her chair and he pulled her down and put his arms round her shoulders.

'It'll be funny if Mrs Bliss comes in and catches us like this,' Jill said.

'She's gone for a walk.'

He pressed his lips against hers several times. The result was again disappointing. He said: 'Do kiss me, darling. You should be able to with a mouth like that.'

'I'm afraid I haven't your experience.'

The sun struck through the glass of the window and made a pattern on the carpet. Jocelyn drew her forward so that she was sitting on the floor beside him, with her back against the chair. 'Now kiss me.'

'I don't think I can.'

She did not know much about kissing but she improved a little as the afternoon progressed. At tea time they were interrupted by the entrance of Mrs Bliss. She did not notice anything peculiar about them, although they were still sitting on the floor; she was as usual too occupied with her own affairs. Tea was brought in by a waiter. Mrs Bliss told Jocelyn and Jill of the walk she had taken, describing the scenery with a wealth of unnecessary detail. Jill ate a number of cream cakes and returned to reading *The Good Companions*. Mrs Bliss talked to Jocelyn about her girlhood in Ireland, touching briefly on various men, all wealthy and goodlooking, who had wanted to marry her.

When she went up to change for dinner, Jocelyn said to Jill:

'We'll come in here afterwards, shall we?'

'If you like.'

'Keep on your jumper; I love you in that.'

'I'm glad somebody appreciates it.'

Later they spread cushions in front of the fire and sat down on the floor. As he was kissing her, the lock of hair which he wore over his forehead, to show he was an artist, fell forward into his eyes and she smoothed it back with her hand. He kissed her throat and neck and felt her body firm and heavy against his as he strained her to him. She drew away with a gasp. 'Let me get my breath back.'

'You're very sweet, Jill. I love you.'

'How many girls have you said that to?'

'You funny thing. Don't you believe me?'

'No. You just want someone to kiss.'

Jocelyn laughed and put his cheek against hers. 'Do you like me, Jill?'

'Course I do. Else I wouldn't let you do this.'

'Say you like me then. Say "darling".'

'I never say "darling". It's one of the things I can't say.'

'Why not?'

'I just can't.'

'Let me kiss you while you smile.'

Very much later, Jocelyn said: 'The fire's gone out.'

'I've got a gas one in my room.'

'Lets go up.'

'All right.'

The gas fire lit with a plop and the sticks of asbestos began to glow red.

'Don't let's have the light on,' Jocelyn said.

He led her over to the bed. They lay back across it and he started to kiss her. She was less shy in the dark.

'Kiss me properly, Jill.'

'How's that?'

'Not bad. Try again.'

'Mm.'

The gas fire glowed and hummed in the darkness. The

eiderdown quilt on the bed became warm from the impress of their bodies. Jocelyn put his hands on her breasts through the woollen mesh of her jumper. She shivered slightly and said: 'You know too much for a man.'

'It's just as well.'

He continued to stroke her breasts and she began to breathe quickly. She held him to her with her arms round his neck and her lips worked slowly under his.

'Am I doing better?' she asked him presently.

'Very much better. You're a wonderful girl. You'll be at the top of the class soon.'

'Thank you, professor.'

'Take off your jumper, darling.'

'I thought you liked me in it.'

'I want to see you without it.'

'All right.'

She sat up and wriggled out of the jumper, dropping it on the chair beside the bed. He kissed the firm flesh of her shoulders and breasts, which gleamed faintly in the dark. Suddenly she buried her face on his chest and he could feel her trembling all over against him.

'Don't be frightened, darling,' he said. 'It's nothing to be afraid of.'

'I'm not afraid.'

'What's the matter then?'

'Nothing's the matter.'

Afterwards he said: 'You've got a lovely body, darling.'

'Please don't laugh at me.'

'I'm not laughing at you. Really. I'm speaking as an artist. You'd make a very good model.'

'D'you think so?'

'You'd make a lovely model. You must come and sit to me in London.'

'Oh, I should love that. Will you really? I've always wanted someone to paint me.'

She rolled over and kissed him several times. She was overjoyed. He held her in his arms. What he had said about her body was quite true. She had a magnificent body.

'When will you come to London?' she said.

'Fairly soon.'

On Monday morning Jill came into the lounge, dressed for the journey. She looked different in her hat and coat and very grown-up. Jocelyn took her hands and said: 'I'm sorry you're going, dear. I wish you could stay.'

'Truly?'

'Yes, truly.'

'I wish I could stay too. But we'll meet again soon, shan't we?'

'Of course we shall.'

He kissed her and she kissed him back in the way he had taught her. 'Have you enjoyed your holiday, my sweet?' he said.

'Yes. Everything. I've enjoyed it all frightfully.'

'Good.'

She smiled up at him. 'And have I been a good pupil?' she said.

'A splendid pupil. You're a credit to the school.'

'I never was a backward girl,' Jill said.

He kissed her again and the sun was warm on her face and the porter came in to say the taxi was waiting outside.

'I'll come and see you off,' Jocelyn said.

In the afternoon, at tea, Mrs Bliss said: 'Has that little girl gone?'

'She went this morning.'

'She was rather peculiar, wasn't she?'

'Yes, she was rather. She was only sixteen.'

'Really? Is that all? It reminds me,' Mrs Bliss said, 'of an experience I had in Ireland when I was a girl . . .'

Two days later, Jocelyn received a letter addressed to him in a large round handwriting.

JOCELYN DEAR,

How are you. It is very cold in London. I started work well on Tuesday morning. I jammed my little finger in a swing-door. It looks so funny now, it's got a huge bandage on it. I quite shocked the first-aid man because instead of crying I swore. I didn't even know some of the words before, they just came naturally. I felt rather proud of myself afterwards. I'm afraid I'm not a very good letter writer, this one seems to be all about myself. Please write and tell me all that is happening at the seaside, I wish I were there today. I feel most jealous of you, being there. I haven't forgotten my five-finger exercises yet, tho' I haven't gained any further experience. (Take that which way you please.) Don't get conceited because I have written to you, I've seen so many respectable people today that I had to provide an outlet to my feelings by writing to someone who was not!

With lots of love and kisses,

JILL.

PS. I hope you come to town soon. (No conceit about this, please.)

PPS. A girl told me yesterday that one of the salesmen in our department is rather fast. I don't quite know what this means. but if it means 'quick work' then you must be fast.

# Happy as the Day is Long

Directly I came into the shop I saw the Baron was pretty tight. The Baron had been trepanned and had a silver plate in his skull. When this plate pressed on his head and hurt him, he used to drink whisky to dull the pain. At these times he always got tight.

He was a little man with a wrinkled yellow face and supposed to be French, though he spoke English with an Italian accent. He was a dealer in antiques and the shop belonged to him.

When he saw me come in, he staggered forward a few paces, almost overturning the oil stove that stood in the middle of the floor, and shouted: 'Hey, you rascal! Why you not been to see me, hey?'

He swayed to-and-fro, keeping his balance by clutching hold of an antique table. He was wearing a long blue overcoat with a velvet collar. He slammed me hard on the back with his hand and shouted again: 'Why you not been to see me? Where you been hiding, hey?'

'I've been ill,' I told him.

'Hey? Ill? Oh, I am sorry.' The Baron's manner changed. He lowered his voice and putting his hand on my shoulder, said: 'I am so very sorry. But you are better now, yes?'

'Yes,' I said, 'I'm better now.'

The Baron's eyes filled with tears: 'I am so glad,' he said. 'I am so very glad.'

There were other people in the shop besides the Baron. These included Mrs Neville-Stanforth and the Baron's secretary, a small woman who wore a green hat. A middle-aged man whom I didn't know was sitting quietly on a chair in the corner, smiling to himself.

Mrs Neville-Stanforth said: 'Hullo, Sylvester! All right again now?'

'Yes, thanks,' I said, 'going strong.'

I shook hands with the Baron's secretary. She stood behind a table with cakes and cups on it. There was also a bottle of Scotch, half empty, and some glasses. The Baron came forward unsteadily and said: 'I am so glad to see you, my dear friend.' He flung out his hand towards the table and shouted at his secretary: 'Give the boy a drink, no?'

'I was just going to, monsieur.'

The Baron glared at her fiercely. Mrs Neville-Stanforth said: 'Hadn't you better sit down my dear?'

'Sit down?' The Baron stared at her. 'What for I sit down? You sink I cannot stand? You sink I am trunk?'

'No, no, of course I don't think you're drunk.'

'I am not trunk,' the Baron said with dignity. He pointed suddenly at the man in the corner and shouted: 'Why for you grin? You sink I am funny, yes?'

'I think you're very funny,' the man in the corner said with a chuckle. His voice was low and rather husky.

'He sinks I am funny!' The Baron turned indignantly to me. 'You do not sink I am funny, no?'

'That's all right, old chap,' the other man said. 'Just you sit down and don't worry your head.'

'Sit down! Sit down! Why for I cannot stand, hey?'

'Don't ask me, old chap,' the other man said, 'ask yourself.'

I took the drink the secretary held out to me and sat down by the stove.

'Would you like some cake?' the secretary said.

'Thanks,' I said, 'just a slice.'

I hadn't had anything much to eat all day, and the cake tasted good. I was glad I'd called on the Baron: when you're down to your last ten bob, a free meal and drink isn't to be sneezed at. It was difficult, though, having to eat the cake as if I wasn't really hungry.

Outside, in the King's Road, Chelsea, it was raw and cold and the cold came in through the half-open door from the street outside. The oil stove didn't do much about heating unless you actually sat on it.

'Will you have another slice of cake?' the secretary said.

'Yes, I think I will, thanks.'

Mrs Neville-Stanforth had at last persuaded the Baron to sit down. He sat astride a hard chair with his arms leaning on the back of it, as though he were riding a horse.

'What about that job you were after?' Mrs Neville-Stanforth said. 'The one with Hatrick I mean. Did you manage to get it?'

'No,' I said.

'D'you know Hatrick then?' the man in the corner asked me.

'I've met him once or twice.'

'I know Hatrick,' the Baron said. 'He is a rascal, that one.'

'I'm sorry you didn't get the job,' Mrs Neville-Stanforth said.

'So am I,' I said. 'Damn sorry.' I finished off the glass of whisky.

'I understood it was all settled,' Mrs Neville-Stanforth said. 'I thought he'd practically given you the job.'

'So he had,' I told her. 'But I got ill, you see. I was in bed three weeks, and when I got up I found he'd given it to someone else.'

'He is a rascal, that Hatrick,' the Baron said.

'Of course I couldn't expect him to wait for ever,' I said.

'What was the job?' the man in the corner asked.

'Painting decorative panels for one of his houses.'

The door came open and two ladies walked into the shop. A blast of cold air came in with them and the flame of the oil stove shot up with a humming sound. The Baron sprang to his feet. He became entangled in the legs of the chair and finally it fell over and he kicked it out of his way. He staggered over to the ladies, who were looking rather surprised.

'Yes?' he said in a menacing manner, 'Yes?'

One of the ladies looked wildly around and picked up a vase, at random. 'How much is this, please?' she asked.

'That?' The Baron took the vase from her and looked at it, holding it at arms length away from him. 'That it tree guineas! Tree!' He shook the vase at her and glared menacingly. 'Tree!'

he shouted again.

For a moment it seemed as if the lady would be stampeded into buying the vase, but her companion showed more presence of mind. 'No,' she said firmly. 'That is too expensive. Thank you very much.'

'Tree guineas!' the Baron shouted, waving the vase after them as they hurried out.

The Baron's secretary bent forward and picked up the overturned chair. 'Oh, dear, oh dear,' she said. She looked very distressed.

Mrs Neville-Stanforth said in an undertone to the man in the corner: 'Can't you get him out of here? He'll drive everyone away in his present state.'

'Leave it to me,' the man said.

The Baron closed the shop door with a great deal of noise and replaced the vase on the table where it stood. He said: 'All day they come in, they look round, they buy nossing. I am sick of such peoples. They are no good. I tell to them "Get out" if they will not buy. So!'

He came back to the table and stood swaying to-and-fro. I reached out and took the last piece of cake from the plate. I was still damned hungry.

The Baron's secretary said: 'Oh, I'm so sorry. I didn't offer you ... will you have another drink?'

'Thank you, I will.'

'That is right,' the Baron said. 'I am pleased you have come, my friend.' He patted me on the shoulder and grinned. 'I too will have another drink, hey?'

'Come and have one in the pub,' the man in the corner said. 'That bottle's nearly empty.'

'Alas,' the Baron said, 'I cannot leave the shop.'

'I'll look after the shop if you like, monsieur,' the secretary said, trying not to sound too eager.

'No,' the Baron said, 'I must be here myself in person.'

'Come on old chap,' the other man said, 'we'll only be gone a few minutes.'

I finished the cake and my second drink and held out my

hands to the stove. It wasn't so cold with the door shut, but the stove didn't give out much heat.

'I consent on one condition,' the Baron said. 'That my dear friend here,' he patted my shoulder, 'come also with us. Yes?'

'Will you come along?' the man in the corner asked me.

'Sure,' I said, 'I'll come.'

'There you are,' the man in the corner said.

'Wait just one moment,' the Baron said. He tipped the last of the bottle into his glass and drank it off neat. Then he said: 'So!'

'All set?' the other man said. He rose to his feet.

The Baron looked at his secretary. 'You will see after the shop?'

'Yes, monsieur.'

The Baron started to give her minute instructions regarding the price of certain valuable antiques on sale in the shop.

'Come on,' the other man said, 'don't be all night about it.'

'Yes, yes, I come,' the Baron said.

'Goodbye, my dear,' Mrs Neville-Stanforth said to me.

'Goodbye,' I said.

'I come back soon,' the Baron said to his secretary, turning at the door. The other man seized his arm and hustled him out. It was bitter cold in the street and the sky was smoky and reddish from the reflected glare of neon-signs. The Baron linked his other arm in mine and we crossed the road. The pub was on the other side, almost opposite the shop.

The landlord was just opening the side door into the saloon bar when we got there.

'Well, well,' the landlord said, 'you're on time you are. And no mistake.'

Evidently the Baron and the other man were well-known to him.

'It's gone five, Joe,' the other man said looking at his watch.

'Only just,' Joe said.

We followed him into the saloon; it was warm and cosy inside. The landlord switched on the lights and went behind the bar. The Baron rapped on the counter with a coin.

'What you drink, hey?' he asked us.

'Whisky,' we both said.

'And me also,' the Baron said.

'White Horse, Haig, Johnny Walker, Black and White,' Joe said. 'Which would you like?'

'It's no matter,' the Baron said. 'They are all whisky, yes?'

'I'll have White Horse,' the other man said. 'Because you can tell it blindfold.'

'And you, sir?' Joe said.

'I'll have Irish,' I said.

'Are you an Irishman?' the other man asked me.

'No,' I said, 'not particularly. Why?'

'I thought I'd discovered a fellow countryman,' the other said.

'Are you Irish then?'

'Sure I am,' the other said. 'I come from Dublin. My name is Casey.'

'Not so!' the Baron said banging on the counter. 'You not Irish. You are a Jew!' He said to me: 'Do not believe this man. Always he tell he is Irish but it is not so. He is an old Jew!'

'That's right,' the other said goodhumouredly. 'I am a Polish Jew. I come from Warsaw.'

'Why for you tell you Irish then?' the Baron asked him belligerently.

Joe put the drinks on the counter and watched us with a grin.

'This man is a Jew!' the Baron told him. 'A Polish Jew!'

'That's right,' the other said, winking at Joe.

'Do not believe when he tell he is Irish,' the Baron said. 'It is a lie!'

'Well, cheerio,' the other said, picking up his glass.

'A la vôtre,' I said to the Baron.

'Cherry-o,' the Baron said with dignity.

I had never been able to persuade him to talk French with me. He sat there in his velvet collared coat, his wrinkled yellow face looking almost asiatic. It was impossible to guess at his true nationality. He was a very small man and his legs dangled short of the ground as he sat up on the high stool at the counter, lifting his glass solemnly to each of us in turn.

'You know,' the other man said to me in his husky confidential voice, 'I'm not really a Jew. That's just his joke. I'm an Irishman from Dublin. My name is Casey.' He put a hand in his pocket and produced a card with 'Tim Casey' engraved on it in big letters. 'You see?' he said.

I took the card and looked at it. Underneath the name 'Tim Casey' was inscribed the address of a firm of interior decorators.

'So you're in the same line as Hatrick,' I said.

'That's right,' Tim Casey said, leaning back against the bar. He said: 'I'm pretty well-known in the trade. Ask anyone you meet if they've heard of Tim Casey. They'll tell you. By God, I've lost a fortune over Art, I have.'

'Is that so?'

'It's been my ruin,' Casey said. 'Are you an artist?'

'Yes.'

'There's no money in Art,' Casey said.

'Don't I know it.'

'I'll bet you do,' Casey said, chuckling. 'Hatrick now, *he* makes it pay. He's a business man. I'm not. I haven't the head for it. We Irish rarely make good business men. We're too simple. Too free and easy.'

I finished my whisky, wondering how I could pay for the drinks when it came to my round. I'd only got a ten bob note and that had to last me till the end of the month. There was a calendar up behind the bar, advertising a brand of cider. The date was 15th February.

'Same again?' Casey said, looking at my empty glass.

'Thank you,' I said.

'I'm hungry,' Casey said. 'I want something to eat. Will you have something too?'

'All right.'

Casey turned to the Baron, who hadn't spoken for some time. He sat huddled on his stool, holding his head in his hands.

Casey said: 'Same again, old chap?'

The Baron just nodded, dully.

'What's the matter?' Casey asked him. 'Feeling blue?'

'I have pains,' the Baron said. 'Pains in my head.'

'A spot of whisky'll soon put them right,' Casey said. He gave the order to Joe. 'Let's have some sandwiches too,' he added.

'Cheese, ham, or tongue?' Joe said taking a plate from out of a glass case.

'Ham, I think,' Casey said. 'What about you?'

'Yes, I'll have ham,' I said.

'Have a ham sandwich,' Casey said to the Baron, who shook his head. 'Come on. It'll do your pains good.'

'You sink so?' the Baron said, looking up.

'I'm sure of it.'

'Ver' well. I will have a ham.'

'Three ham sandwiches,' Casey said to Joe. 'Here you are,' he said to the Baron. 'Get outside that. You'll soon feel good again.'

'Sank you,' the Baron said gravely. He took a bite of the sandwich and a gulp of whisky. He said: 'You are a Jew but you are generous. You have pay for my drink. So!'

'That's right,' Casey said. 'We Polish Jews are always generous.' He winked at me as he said it.

'You are a generous Jew,' the Baron said.

'You bet I am.' Casey winked again. 'That's just his joke,' he explained to me huskily.

I nodded, eating my sandwich. I was wondering if I could perhaps touch Casey for a quid. Of course if the worst came to the worst there was always Fleurette, but I didn't want to go to her. We'd had the hell of a bust-up just before I got ill and it would take a bit of getting over. Besides, I hate borrowing money from women, because they never let you forget it. Especially Fleurette.

So I considered Casey. He might have been a Jew or again he might not. You couldn't tell from his face; there are plenty of Irishman with thick noses.

'Have another sandwich,' Casey said, pushing the plate over towards me.

310

'Thanks, I will.'

'Do,' Casey said, 'it's on me.'

Joe went along behind the bar and switched on the radio; it played a syncopated tune.

'Are you fond of music?' Casey said.

'Do you mean dance music?' I said.

'No, real music.'

'Yes,' I said, 'are you?'

'And then some,' Casey said. 'You mightn't believe it, but I had a great career ahead of me once, as a singer.'

'Really?'

'Yes,' Casey said. 'I had a beautiful voice. Really beautiful.'

'What happened?'

'The war,' Casey said. 'I was gassed. Now I can't sing a note. Not a bloody note.'

'I say, what rotten luck.'

'It was,' Casey said. 'I'd have been a great singer if it hadn't been for that war.'

'What was your register?'

'Tenor,' Casey said. 'I'd have been a great Irish tenor. Like Count McCormack.'

'Or Jack Doyle.'

'That's right,' Casey said.

'Did you ever meet James Joyce in Dublin?'

'No. Who's he?'

'Another Irish tenor.'

'I never met him,' Casey said. He shook his head. 'Ah, if I could only be young again. I'd give all the money I've got in the world if I could be your age, with your opportunities. I'd be happy as the day is long.'

'Would you?'

'By God I would,' Casey said. 'You don't know how lucky you are.'

'No,' I said, 'you're right about that.'

'How old are you, if you'll pardon me asking a personal question?'

'Twenty-six.'

'Twenty-six!' Casey said. 'Twenty-six! I'd give every penny I possess to change places with you. To be young and carefree and happy again.'

'How d'you know I'm carefree and happy?'

'If you're not you ought to be,' Casey said. 'You've got all the world before you. What more do you want?'

'Lots of things.'

'Such as?'

'Well, money, for one.'

'Ah, that's a thing we all want,' Casey said. 'But remember, money can't buy happiness.'

'It could for me at the moment.'

'You can make money,' Casey said.

'How? You say yourself that there isn't any in Art.'

'No, that's true,' Casey said. 'But there are other ways of making money. If I were you, if I had my life to live over again, I should chuck Art. Believe me, it doesn't pay, and I'm one who knows.'

'So am I.'

'There you are then. Why not give it up? Become a bank manager or something.'

'That's not so easy, either.'

'Everything's easy when one's got youth,' Casey said. 'Look at me. I'm over fifty. The best part of my life's behind me. But what couldn't I do if I were twenty-six again? Eh? I ask you that.'

I couldn't think of an answer offhand and Casey continued: 'When I was twenty-six I had everything—youth, health, strength, the promise of a great future. I was handsome, too. Look at me now and you can imagine what I was like then. Eh?'

I looked at him. There was nothing about his appearance to indicate that he had ever been good looking, but I nodded, for politeness' sake.

'I had everything, I tell you,' Casey said. 'Now I have nothing. All gone. Youth's a stuff will not endure.' He removed his hat sadly and I saw then that he was completely bald. Bald as a coot. He passed a hand over his head and said: 'I had thick curly hair once, as thick as yours. Now even that's gone and I have only memories to look back upon.'

He shook his head again; he looked more like a Jew with his hat off. He said: 'In Dublin they used to call me the Tiger.'

'Why?'

'It was a tribute,' Casey said. 'A tribute to my youth and strength.'

'I see.'

The radio behind the bar continued to play dance music. The Baron sat huddled on his stool, staring vacantly into space. Joe was leaning on the counter, reading the sporting page of an evening paper.

Casey said: 'I'm telling you this so that you'll realize what it means to waste one's opportunities. I've sacrificed myself in the service of Art. See that you don't make the same mistake. You're young and healthy: take time by the forelock. Go in and win.'

'Meantime,' I said, 'I've only ten bob in my pocket.'

'Ten bob?'

'That's all.'

A subtle change came over Casey's expression. He suddenly looked very shrewd. He said: 'Ten bob isn't much certainly.'

'It's got to last till the end of the month.'

'What's the date today?'

'The fifteenth.'

'Oh, that's not so bad,' Casey said.

'It's pretty bad. Thirteen days.'

'Time passes quickly when one's young. The end of the month'll be here before you know it.'

'So will the end of the money.'

'It'll last you,' Casey said with conviction.

'How d'you know it will?'

'I'm certain,' Casey said. 'I've got a feeling it will. We Irish get these feelings you know, and we're usually right.'

'Are you?'

'Nearly always.'

'That's a comfort, anyway.'

'It'll last if you're careful,' Casey said. 'If you don't go throwing it away. That's always been my trouble—generosity. Chucking money about like water.' He turned to the Baron. 'How are you feeling now?'

The Baron shook his head dully.

'Pains bad?' Casey said.

The Baron nodded.

'Never mind. Have another drink. You'll feel better then.' Casey turned to me. 'Like another?'

'Thanks.'

'Same again all round,' Casey told Joe.

I said: 'I suppose you don't happen to have any jobs going?'

Casey looked at me very shrewdly, rubbing a hand over his head. 'No, I'm afraid not, old chap,' he said. 'Of course if I hear of anything . . .'

'Of course,' I said.

'Well, cheerio,' Casey said.

'Cheerio,' I said.

The Baron lifted his glass and gulped the whisky down.

'Better?' Casey asked him.

'No,' the Baron said.

'Cheer up,' Casey said, 'you'll be all right again tomorrow.'

'You sink so?'

'I'm sure,' Casey said.

'Have you got a feeling about it?' I asked Casey.

'Yes,' Casey said.

'That's all right then,' I told the Baron. 'The Irish are always right about these things.'

'I'll say we are,' Casey said.

The Baron looked at the clock above the counter; it marked a quarter to six.

'I must return to the shop,' the Baron said. He got down off the high stool. His movements were still unsteady, but he was much more subdued; his pains seemed to have sobered him a lot.

'Right-ho,' Casey said, putting on his hat.

'Good night gentlemen,' Joe said.

'I'll be seeing you, Joe,' Casey said.

'I bet you will,' Joe said.

We all went towards the door.

'Wait a sec,' Casey said. He stopped in front of a fruit machine that stood near the door. He said: 'I must try my luck with this. We Irish are like that, you know; we can't resist a gamble.'

He put a sixpence in the slot and pulled the lever; the machine whirred and the numbers clicked into place, 1-7-0.

'Damn the thing,' Casey said. He put in another sixpence without success. He put in four sixpences altogether, without winning anything at all. Then he turned to me. 'Now you put one in.'

'I can't afford to.'

Casey took a sixpence from his pocket and handed it to me. 'Here you are,' he said. 'Go on. You can pay it back at the end of the month.' He chuckled.

I put the sixpence in and pulled the lever. 0-0-7 turned up.

'No luck,' Casey said. 'Never mind.'

He opened the door and we went out into the street where it was still bitterly cold. The Baron turned to me and held out his hand. 'I'm glad you come to see me, my friend. You come again, hey?'

'Certainly.'

'Soon?'

'Soon,' I said.

'You not forget?'

'No, I won't forget. And I hope your head gets better quickly.'

'Sank you,' the Baron said, 'you are kind.'

In the dim smoky light of the street his face looked yellow and strained, but he seemed much soberer now.

'So long, old chap,' Casey said to me. 'Look in sometime, you've got my card. If there's any jobs going . . .'

'Yes,' I said, 'and I can pay back the sixpence.'

'Don't worry about that,' Casey said with a wave of his

L

hand. 'And remember,' he tapped my chest lightly with his finger, 'you've got youth, and that's everything. Money doesn't matter when you've got that. Take it from me. I'm one who knows.'

'So long,' I said.

Casey took the Baron's arm and they crossed the road. I turned up my coat collar and started to walk away down the King's Road, past the cinemas, the tobacconists, and the cheap confectioners, wondering what I should do next. It was damned cold; I could feel it right through my gloves and overcoat.

There was only one thing to do: ring up Fleurette. She'd come across all right, once we'd patched up that row. Walking along, feeling the cold, I cursed Casey for a stingy swine. Still, I'd had two sandwiches and three drinks out of him, even if I had had to listen to his bloody nonsense about youth and health and money not mattering.

It was all very fine for him to talk, but money *can* buy happiness when you haven't got any. It could buy happiness for me right now, at this very moment.

I turned into the square where the telephone-boxes stood. I went into one of the boxes and the glass door shut the cold out behind me. I hesitated, looking at the telephone, thinking curse him, curse him for a mean goddamned swine.

Then I picked up the phone and dialled Gerrard one-six-double-o.

# The Swag, the Spy and the Soldier

PART ONE

*The Story*

Then war broke out and the amusement park closed down.
The swings and roundabouts were silent, covered in tarpaulin.
From dismantled stalls the painted faces of the Aunt Sallies
grimaced, gaping in vain for flung coconuts. The bumper cars
no longer jolted round the track striking electric sparks; the
distorting mirrors reflected nothing. Dead bulbs in daylight
still spelt out ZOO over the papier-mâché entrance, but inside
the cardboard grottoes echoed with emptiness; the animals—
the polar bear, the Algerian rat, the owl, the shrieking savage
cockatoo—had been evacuated.

And Sandy O'Connor, like the rest of the staff, was out of
work.

When I first met him he was shouting numbers hoarsely
from the housey-housey stall, wearing a long white linen coat
and a leather pouch containing change slung by a strap from
his shoulder. Some of the shillings and coppers occasionally
found their way from this pouch into Sandy's pocket: the
fairground boys called this fiddling. You couldn't blame him,
working fourteen hours a day (fifteen on Saturdays) for a wage
of two-ten a week. By fiddling Sandy made this salary up to
about six nicker and a few hundred fags. It was a recognized
practice: the bosses shut their eyes to it; sometimes, very
rarely, someone was made an example of and given his cards.

Sandy at this time was nineteen, rising twenty. He was
stockily built and square jawed. His oblong face had a fresh
colour and his eyes that lashless look peculiar to people with
reddish hair. His thick pink lips, which seemed puffed up, bee-

stung, twisted sideways when he spoke, always out of the corner of his mouth and very quickly in a Scotch-Irish accent. He came from Glasgow, where his home life had not been happy. Most of his time there seemed to have been spent knocking out his elder brother, who was a right bastard. He got fed-up finally and cleared out to earn his own living. This he had done in various ways up and down the country. He'd worked on a race-track, in a pin-table saloon, in a glass-blowing factory, where for some reason the faces of the workers eventually turned yellow; in the intervals of these occupations he had lorry-hopped and slept in casual wards all over England. He had been in the army, but not, so far, in prison.

## II

I was passing the amusement park the day Sandy got sacked. I saw him come out. He was smoking and he snapped away the butt of his cigarette and spat back over his shoulder at one of the gigantic grinning cardboard dummies that stood on either side of the entrance. He scored a direct hit. Then he muttered: 'Fog 'em.'

'What's wrong, Sandy?' I asked him.

'Got my cards,' he said. He had them in his hand. He spat again, this time into the gutter, and said: 'I'm for a cup o' char.'

We walked in brilliant sunshine down the deserted esplanade. Pillboxes had already been put up and a dannert wire apron fence encircled the pier arcade. Sandbags were stacked round the shops and notices announced CLOSED on all sides.

We sat down in a café that wasn't closed. 'What d'you mean to do?' I asked him.

'Oh, I'll make out all right,' he said, stirring his tea. 'Once I get up the Smoke. Plenty graft going up there. Smashing jobs.' He'd two weeks' wages on him, plus a quid he'd fiddled. 'I'll take some time off first,' he said. 'Reckon I've earnt a rest.'

He never had it. He got boozed up instead. I met him next day; he hadn't a bean. 'Dead skint,' he said. 'Somebody rolled me. If I could only get my hands on that bastard!'

'Where'd you sleep?' I asked him.

He jerked a thumb towards the amusement park. 'In the dobbies.' But despite this he still looked natty, his trousers were knife-creased, his sandy hair as usual brilliantined back. The only thing, he wasn't shaved. The blond stubble glittered along his chin where the sun caught it. He said: 'I'm off to sign on the Labour.'

'What'll you do meantime,' I asked, 'without money?'

He shook his head. He slouched along, hands in pockets. He was depressed. I said: 'You anywhere to stay the night?'

'Oh, I'll find some place to kip down, don't worry,' he said.

I'd have lent him a quid but I was hard-up myself. The money I'd earned that summer writing radio plays had nearly run out, and I'd no idea where the next lot was coming from. The Jansens, whom I shared a bungalow with, were hard-up too, but on the other hand we had a spare bedroom.

'You'd better put up with us,' I told him.

He shook his head: 'I wouldn't want to be a trouble.' It took the hell of a time to persuade him, he was stubborn as a mule. But in the end he came. 'I'll pay you back first fifteen bob I draw,' he said.

'That's all right,' I told him. 'Come on.'

'I got one or two things to pick up, first,' he said. 'Be back right away.'

I watched him walk rapidly off towards the amusement park. He disappeared inside and came out a few moments later lugging an enormous valise, which he'd evidently parked there. 'All set now,' he said. We boarded a bus bound for Greenleaves.

The bungalow stood isolated at the end of a long rutted road which in winter, when it rained, became almost impassable: a lake of liquid yellow mud. This condition had its advantages for us. Creditors hesitated to approach. Cars got stuck halfway up, bicycles were no use at all. Now, in September, the road was baked hard with sun and Greenleaves showed no signs of life as we neared it. It was practically in a state of siege. We came in the gate, up the path, Sandy changing hands with his valise. Except for a few bushes in the back garden, there seemed no reason why the bungalow should be called by that name. Sun-dried grass, mowed by Erik Jansen into the semblance of a lawn, surrounded it. The mower itself, rusty and decrepit, stood up abandoned by the porch. The green paint of the front door had broken out in blisters.

I banged on the door. Subdued voices inside the house ceased instantly. There was dead silence. I banged again and shouted through the slit of the letter-box. There was a shuffle of slippers in the hall and the door opened a chink. Jansen peeped round it at us. He wore Russian silk pyjamas with an eagle embroidered on the chest. A curious small smoking-cap was perched on the back of his head. A lock of yellow hair fell forward into his eyes from under the cap. He pulled the door wide and said: 'Thought you were the Macfisheries' man again.'

'This is Sandy O'Connor,' I said. 'He's coming to stay with us.'

'Splendid!' Jansen said, shaking hands. 'Splendid! Welcome to Greenleaves.' He led the way into the living-room, shouting 'Food' and 'Eva'. Eva, Jansen's wife, sat in a chair by the fireplace, with a turban round her head, darning a sock. She sprang up, startled. For a moment she thought the bailiffs were in.

'Food!' Jansen shouted. 'Food for our guest, Sandy O'Connor.'

Eva shook hands with Sandy, who in these surroundings seemed subdued. Books were piled up everywhere, there was an easel in the corner; the remains of a meal and the manuscript of Jansen's novel littered the table. Sandy looked round furtively at the gramophone, the typewriter, the colour-prints on the wall. He swallowed. He muttered something about a wash and shave.

'That can wait,' Jansen said. 'You must be famished. Eva! Food! We must prepare a feast.'

Eva was at a loss. 'There's only bread and cheese,' she said.

'Bread and cheese?' Jansen said in surprise. 'That all?' He

looked round at the table as though expecting a colossal spread to materialize before his eyes. Bread and cheese confronted him instead. He coughed.

'There may be some jam,' Eva said. 'If you haven't eaten it all.'

'Jam!' Jansen said, recovering. 'Of course there's jam. Bread and cheese and jam. Which will you have?'

Sandy hesitated. Then he said: 'I'll have bread and cheese *and* jam.'

'Fine!' Jansen said. 'Fine! Sit you down.' He started to saw at the loaf. 'It's all very informal here,' he explained. 'Bohemian. We lead a Bohemian existence.' He poured out some tea. 'It's a bit stewed,' he said. 'Black as your hat.' Sandy said he liked it black. Jansen said: 'Splendid. Very fortunate, especially as there's no milk.'

Eva said: 'No more milk until we pay up. Man told me this morning.'

'Money-grubbing materialist,' her husband said. 'We'll take our custom elsewhere. We'll go to Sait's.'

'We owe Sait's two pounds ten.'

'Do we? That's a blow. Still, there must be other dairies.' With a sweep of his hand he dismissed the subject as sordid. Little Eva, his daughter, aged two, toddled in from the passage dragging a decapitated rag doll by the neck behind her. She was introduced to Sandy, but did not pay much attention. So many strange people came in and out of the house that the presence of this new additional uncle passed her by almost unnoticed. Sandy ate bread and cheese and jam steadily. Jansen picked up his manuscript and read out a chapter of the novel. Sandy stopped chewing. He said: 'Did you write that?'

'Yes,' Jansen said. 'I'm a writer. So's he,' pointing at me. 'We are both writers.'

'What about your wife?' Sandy asked. 'She a writer, too?'

'She's a sculptress.' Jansen pointed at a masked harlequin, carved out of wood, which stood gloomily staring down from the top of a bookcase. Sandy looked at the harlequin and nodded. He jerked his head towards Eva, playing on the couch with her doll.

'And her?' he said. 'She a writer?'

'Writing runs in the family,' Jansen said. 'When she gets a little older she'll be a great writer.'

'She'll may be a sculptress,' Sandy said.

'She'll be a sculptress *and* a writer,' Jansen said proudly.

So the future of little Eva was settled.

Sandy stood up from the table. He slapped his pockets in search of cigarettes, but found none. He went over and opened his valise. It seemed to be principally full of bright-coloured shirts and bottles of Brylcreem. He dug underneath these and produced a hundred Players. We were overjoyed; there were very few fags in the house.

'All I could get me hands on,' Sandy said. 'I'd rather have Craven A by rights.'

He dug in the valise again; he hadn't finished. A giant panda was fished out and handed to little Eva. I'd seen it before, as one of the principal prizes on the housey-housey stall. There were cries from the Jansens of 'Say thank you.' Little Eva didn't respond. She put a finger in her mouth and stared at the panda with an awed expression. Sandy was still fumbling among the shirts. He started to fling them backwards as a dog, digging, flings earth back from a hole. Two bottles of perfume came to light next. But just as Sandy was offering Eva Jansen one of them a knock came at the door.

Everyone went immediately to ground, Jansen under the table. Further knocks followed, then the sound of footsteps crunching away down the gravel path. From a crouching position Jansen peered out through the window. He stood up. 'All clear!' he said as the gate closed.

'Who was it?'

'The wireless man.'

This was one of our most frequent and importunate visitors. He was always on about the instalments we owed. To celebrate his departure Jansen switched on the wireless itself. The news came through on National. It was nothing much. Sandy asked if he could take off his coat. It was a sign that he was

settling in. He sat there in his shirt-sleeves, smoking and nodding his head in time to the dance music which followed the
news. Jansen did the honours. He showed Sandy his hunting
trophies, the silver riding cup he'd won at the Concours
Hippique, the hole a rat had gnawed in the living-room door
last winter.

In the middle of this my girl friend, Helen Baker, arrived.
She was mistaken for a creditor at first, but at length admitted.
She'd brought us a chocolate cake. Sandy presented her in
return with the second bottle of perfume. She accepted it, but
was suspicious. She stared in astonishment at the shirts, the
cigarettes and the panda.

'Where's he get all this stuff?' she asked me while Sandy
was being shown his room.

'Ask no questions, hear no lies,' I told her.

She shook her head gloomily. 'You'll all end up in jail.'

And as things turned out she was very nearly right.

### III

Sandy slept on a camp-bed in the attic, among the mouldering
boxes full of false hair, tinsel crowns and sticks of grease-
paint, relics of the time when for a short period Eva Jansen
had been on the stage. Jansen had formerly used the attic as a
refuge, a place to retire to in moments of stress, when creditors
made a mass attack or his wife, during a family quarrel, flung
the bread-board at him. It was reached by a trapdoor and a
ladder which could be drawn up after ascent, like the draw-
bridge of a castle.

Sandy used the attic for sleeping in only. During the day,
between signing on at the Labour and looking for jobs, he used
to walk restlessly about the living-room or sit hunched up in
a chair smoking Craven A and snapping the cork butts into
the fireplace. He became more and more restless as the prospect of getting work receded. He handed all his dole money
over to us, only keeping back enough for a packet or two of
fags. He often talked of joining up. Only the fact that he'd
already deserted from the peace-time army deterred him from

this course. He stood for hours staring out of the window and swearing softly under his breath. Often he'd cross over and peer closely at the books on the shelves. These seemed to fascinate him. He'd stand there and gaze, his thick lips moving silently, spelling the titles over to himself.

One day he actually took a book down. It was *Brighton Rock*. He read it through at a sitting. This started him off. He became a tremendous reader. He read book after book, anything that came to hand. The tough books and those dealing with working-class life were the ones he liked best. He used to comment on the authenticity of the slang used in the dialogue. Expressions he used—'Charva', and 'Scarper' and 'Palone'—became part of the lingua-franca of Greenleaves. There was also rhyming slang: a thief became a tea-leaf, tea itself was Rosy Lee. Sandy climbed the apples and pears to bed; we ate at the Cain and Abel.

Meanwhile the last late summer broke up; rain poured down in a solid sheet outside; there was a flood; when this subsided, the road leading to Greenleaves had resumed its winter condition and the hire-purchase touts employed by typewriter, gramophone and radio companies could no longer get at us. Visits from the local tradespeople also ceased; on the other hand, our letter-box became choked with bills, solicitors' letters, demands and threats which we did not bother to open.

The financial position had not improved. Jansen's novel wasn't finished; my short stories returned regularly; the job I'd been promised at the BBC did not materialize owing to wartime curtailment of staff; moreover, I was expecting my call-up papers any moment. But even these didn't materialize.

The Great Bore War went on. We heard Haw-Haw on the radio; 'We'll Hang Out Our Washing on the Siegfried Line'; gallant little Finland; *on les aura*. We took it in turns to go out in my mackintosh and Jansen's rubber boots; I used to wade downtown in these to see Helen, as it was now almost impossible for her to visit us. I'd come back to find Sandy crouched over the fire reading and the others gone to bed depressed.

Then one evening when we were all together Sandy suddenly announced that he'd like to try his hand at a short story himself. He licked the stub of pencil and bent determinedly over one of my abandoned notebooks, which had a few blank pages in it. He wrote steadily for about an hour. When he read us the result we were astounded. It was a story called *The Spike*, about life in a casual ward, and told entirely in dialogue. We thought it very good indeed.

Sandy was encouraged. He set to and wrote several more stories. He used to write three or four short stories in an evening. He filled notebooks with his pencilled script, printed always in block letters and abounding in spelling idiosyncrasies and contractions that none but I could decipher. I typed some of the best stories and sent them round to editors. They came back, but then so did mine. Undeterred, Sandy started on his autobiography. It was called *Dog-End*. It seemed to us to have the makings of a best-seller, or at any rate a banned book.

Then as a sideline Sandy took up surrealism. A book he got out of the public library began it. He sketched out some extraordinary designs of his own and Eva painted two of them for him. One was called Birth of a Nation, the other The Parson Preached a Sermon on Palm Sunday. The Parson had to be painted on plywood, as Eva had only one canvas left, and the Birth of a Nation occupied that. I planned to take these down to the owner of the local art shop, who was keen on modern painting.

Then everything fell through. We struck a particularly bad patch. The tradesmen with one accord cut off our credit. We were behind-hand with the rent. There were no fags and very little food in the house. Outside it was freezing hard. We'd plenty of coal, but you can't eat coal. Sandy got restless again and began to walk up and down, muttering 'Fog it' through clenched teeth. He gave up reading and writing; he didn't even sketch.

'Art don't seem to be much cop,' he said.

One night he put on my mackintosh and went out. He didn't say where he was going. By midnight he had not returned; I began to fear he'd done himself in. Then I heard him crunching ice underfoot on the path. He tapped on the window for me to open the door.

'Where in hell have you been?' I asked him.

He held a finger on his lips for silence. His face was flushed, and at first I thought he'd been on the beer. He closed the living-room door and leaned against it, breathing hard. Then, speaking even more rapidly than usual in his thick, slurred voice, he said: 'I done a job.'

He began without further ado to empty his pockets. In a trice the table became completely covered with a miscellaneous collection of bracelets, wrist-watches, alarm clocks, shaving sets, cosmetics, scent sprays, jars of sweets, slabs of chocolate and boxes of cigarettes. I gaped down at these in a daze.

'Where'd all this come from?'

'Ssh!' Sandy said. 'Don't make a loud mouth about it.'

Then out came the whole story. He'd done a bust, burgled the amusement park. Apparently they had the whole stock stored up there. Sandy had eluded the nightwatchman; he knew a way in via the Zoo. He'd cased the gaff; he wasn't no amacher tea-leaf; no one'd be the wiser. It might be days before they found anything out. Meantime we were all sitting pretty.

He offered me a fag from one of the stolen boxes. Tomorrow he'd think up ways and means of selling the stuff. There was the barracks, for instance. One or two of those watches'd go over big, tosheroon apiece. He wanted to wake Jansen and cut him in a three-way split then and there. I said no, Eva'd be furious. Sandy said maybe you're right. He snapped away his cigarette butt and shovelled the loot back into his pockets, leaving a hundred Players for me on the table.

He said: 'See you in morning,' and climbed to his attic. He pulled up the ladder and closed the trapdoor behind him.

## IV

Next morning an uproar in the passage outside awoke me. It was Jansen locking his wife and child in the kitchen. Eva shouted and hammered on the door. Little Eva shouted too, but joyfully. I could hear her dancing up and down. She thought it great fun.

I got out of bed and put my dressing-gown on. The living-room door was also locked. 'What the hell's going on?' I shouted.

Jansen opened the door. 'Come in quick, I don't want Eva to know.' He locked the door again behind me. 'What you think of this lot?' he said. 'Look, watches!'

'I've seen them,' I said. I was feeling a bit sour. The stolen goods were spread out on the table and Sandy sat there arranging them in separate heaps. 'These ought to fetch a tidy packet,' he said.

'What's my cut?' Jansen said. His eyes shone. He evidently fancied himself in the rôle of a fence: Fagin or Jonathan Wild.

'Ten per cent,' Sandy said.

'Not enough,' Jansen said. 'After all if the swag's found here, I take the rap.' He lit a stolen cigarette and started to wind up the alarm clocks in a row. He wound up a watch and held it close to his ear, listening to the tick. He buckled it on to his wrist, broke off a bar of chocolate and sprayed scent on himself. He and Sandy began to argue about his cut. Jansen waved his hands and stroked an imaginary beard. All the alarm clocks went off at once. I said: 'For Christ's sake!'

We could hear both Evas shouting and hammering in the kitchen.

'I'd better let her out now,' Jansen said. 'Hide the loot quick.'

'I'm away,' Sandy said. He gathered the stuff up and disappeared aloft.

'What's the idea?' Eva asked indignantly as the door was unlocked. 'Why'd you shut us in? What were all those clocks going off?'

'None of your business,' her husband told her. 'Here, take this lipstick and shut up.'

'Where'd it come from?' Eva said suspiciously. 'Not another of your schemes?'

'You want to know too much,' Jansen told her.

That afternoon Sandy borrowed a bike and rode over to the barracks. He sold seventeen watches at half-a-crown each, an alarm clock, three bracelets and a scent spray. Out of all this I got seventeen and eightpence cash.

'A pretty good day,' Jansen said, pocketing his share. 'Now we'll have tea.' He went to let Eva out.

'What *is* this?' she said. Nobody answered her.

## V

Next day was Helen Baker's birthday. I'd been saving a very elaborate embroidery case, which had belonged to my mother, as a present for her. Helen herself met me at the door of her house. At sight of the embroidery case she started back in horror.

'No, no! Don't bring that here! The police have only just left.'

'Police?' I said. 'What police? What're you talking about?'

'The burglary!' Helen hissed. 'For God's sake hide that thing and go quick.'

'I don't get it,' I said. 'What's happened?'

What had happened was this. The police had found a jemmy left behind by Sandy at the amusement park. This tool had the name of Helen's brother engraved on it. Detectives had been round asking questions. Since Helen's brother was now in the navy, he'd a perfect alibi; nobody could account for the presence of this clue on the scene of the crime. Only Helen knew that Jansen had borrowed the engraved jemmy that summer to do some carpentering. She immediately assumed that Jansen was the burglar and that my embroidery case was part of the swag. She hadn't thought of Sandy. When I told her she was even more horrified.

'You've got to get rid of the stuff at once.'

'Telling me,' I said. I got on a bus back to the bungalow. I burst in on Sandy, who sat by the fire, head in hands.

'I know, don't tell me,' he said. 'The fogging jemmy. Couldn't think where I'd left the fogger at first. I went back last night when you was in kip, but they'd a copper on the door. I scarpered quick.'

'Well,' I said, 'we've got to get busy. They'll be along here any minute.'

We carried the swag out into the back garden. Jansen and Sandy started feverishly to dig a hole. I kept an eye on the gate. Little Eva, locked with her mother in the kitchen, left off playing with the panda, to which she'd by now become accustomed, and watched with interest from her high chair overlooking the window.

'Mummy, mummy,' she said. 'Look, Daddy dig.'

'Yes, darling,' her mother said bitterly. 'Buried treasure.'

The ground was hard as hell and digging a hole deep enough took ages. I felt it was good practice for the hard labour to which we might all soon be sentenced. At last the loot was buried; by that time it was dark. We kept only the cigarettes.

Afterwards we sprawled exhausted by the fire. Eva could be heard singing her daughter to sleep next door. Once Sandy said: 'I never been in the nick.'

'Now you'll have the opportunity,' I told him.

'Ah, for fog's sake,' he said.

After this nobody spoke. It was a night of terror. We started at every sound, listening for the clump of official boots. But no one came.

No one came next day either. We gathered glumly round the local rag. 'An arrest may be expected at any moment.' Nobody expected it more than we did. But after two days it began to look as though we weren't going to be arrested at all. After a week we deemed the danger past. We started to make a joke of it. Only Helen didn't seem to find it funny.

Sandy was never quite the same either. He felt he had brought disgrace on the house. He did no more writing or sketching; he just sat about. One day he came in with a letter in his hand. The letter was from a mate of his, geezer called Cohen, who'd been a ponce and was just out of jug. He offered Sandy a smashing job in some gaff up the Smoke.

Two days later this man drove up to Greenleaves in an

enormous scarlet racing car. Sandy climbed in with his valise; we assembled at the door to wave goodbye. The car splashed and jolted off through the puddles with Sandy waving from the back seat. It turned the corner and we heard the whine of its powerful engine receding in the distance out of sight. It was the last we expected to see of Sandy.

He said he'd write, but he didn't. The Parson and the Birth of a Nation remained propped up on the easel in the living-room for a time, until Eva got fed up dusting them. There was also the danger that little Eva would scrape off some of the paint and eat it. So the paintings vanished upstairs to the attic and were soon followed by his notebooks and the manuscript of his autobiography. The swag mouldered in the earth outside.

Weeks passed and we often wondered what had become of him. But it was not for another month, when Jansen looked round for his hunting trophies and silver riding cup in order to pawn them, that he discovered the disappearance of these.

PART TWO

*The Sequel*

Looking out from the window of our hut, you could see, over to the left, craters in the chalk where the bombs had dropped. Jerry used to come over and drop them on the camp every night.

I'd been in the army about two months. During the day, when we were not being bombed, I worked as a clerk in the company office.

One morning the Orderly Corporal came in with the mail. Only one letter for me, forwarded on from Greenleaves, a long official envelope with OHMS stamped on top. It looked like income tax. I thought: some hopes. I tore the envelope open. Inside was a sheet of notepaper in unfamiliar hand-writing, starting off 'Dear Sir'. At the top it said: 'Ref. Pte. O'Connor, F.' I didn't at once connect this with Sandy. I'd forgotten about him. I had other things to think about.

The letter went:

'You are doubtless aware that the above-named man is to be tried by District Court-Martial on Friday next, 23rd inst., on a charge against the Defence Regulations. I have been detailed as Defending Officer, and in order to assist me, O'Connor has informed me that you hold certain manuscripts of short stories he claims to have written.

If you are able to produce these, will you forward them to me at above address at the earliest possible moment, please.'

The letter was signed 'G. Cook (Major), OC 'D' Coy, Blankshire Regt.' At first I couldn't understand what it was all about. I thought it was one of Jansen's jokes.

The Quarter Bloke sat at another table reading the paper. 'What d'you make of this, sir?' I asked him. He took the letter and ran his eye down it. Then he said: 'O'Connor? Here you are. In the paper and everything.'

He passed over the paper he'd been reading. It was there right enough. PRIVATE SOLDIER ON SECRETS CHARGE. A section underneath was headed: 'DIRECT USE TO ENEMY', ALLEGATION. I read with amazement: 'Details of factories and bombing objectives; two sketches of an RAF station; extracts from notebook read in camera; the court adjourned.'

My name was there, too, misspelt but perfectly recognizable. I didn't care much for the description of myself as an 'amateur novelist'; I had by now certainly published stories, but I'd never written a novel. Still, perhaps that was what they meant.

'This O'Connor,' the Quarter Bloke said. 'Is he a Fifth Columnist?'

'Not so far as I know.'

The paper said Sandy stated he was collecting material for a book about the war when it was over. This seemed awfully

likely. That his notebook contained information 'of direct use
to the enemy' I didn't for a moment believe. Even in the army,
nobody would be silly enough to entrust Sandy with information of this nature. A German dictionary and a driving licence,
found during a search of his kit, appeared also to constitute
evidence against him: God knows why.

'You'll have to testify,' the Quarter Bloke said.

'Can I use the typewriter, sir?' I asked him.

'Sure. Go right ahead.'

I sat down and slammed out two letters: one to Jansen
asking him to unearth the manuscripts and forward them to
the defending officer; the other to Major Cook himself. I said
I thought things were coming to a pretty pass if writers could
have their notebooks confiscated and be put on trial for collat-
ing the material necessary to their craft. Suppose my own kit
was searched? They might even court-martial *me* as a Fifth
Columnist. I took a very poor view of the whole affair.

While I was typing, the CSM looked in. 'Busy?' he asked.

The Quarter Bloke explained: 'One of his mates is in a jam.
On court-martial for a secrets charge.'

'Go on?' the CSM said. 'Not that O'Connor? I bin reading
about it. Reckon 'e's guilty?'

'No, sir,' I said. The CSM came behind me and read the
letter as the typewriter keys tapped it out. 'Who's that to?'
he asked.

'Defending officer, sir.'

The CSM chuckled. He said: 'You want to watch out that
you ain't clapped in clink yourself, m'lad,' and to the Quarter
Bloke: "Ow about a game o' darts?'

They started to play. I stuck the two letters in their
respective envelopes. The Quarter Bloke got double-top. He
told me: 'You can fall out now.'

It was 12.30. Cookhouse blew as I came out on the veranda.


## II

Next day, Sunday, the news was all over the camp. I was

pointed out in the canteen; crossing the barrack-square; in the cookhouse.

'See that bloke? 'E's a Fifth Columnist!'

'Aye, name in the paper an' all.'

*'Sunday Pictorial.'*

*'News of the World.'*

'It don't say nothing in mine.'

'Fifth Columnist? Rotten bastard.'

'Nah, mate, you got it wrong. His mate's the Fifth Columnist, not im.'

'Private bleeding O'Connor. 'Ere it is: page seven.'

Copies of the Sunday paper were passed from hand to hand. This said that as my presence was essential to Sandy's defence, the hearing had been again adjourned until next Saturday.

On Monday morning I was sent for by the Company Commander.

'You are detailed to attend as a witness at a Court-Martial to be held at Chelsea Barracks on Saturday. You will be ready to proceed tomorrow to D Company, Blankshire ITC, and there report to the Officer Commanding. Here are your train-timings, rail-warrant, and other documents. Sergeant-Major, see this man has a haircut immediately.'

'Yessir. About turn! Quick march!'

Out on the veranda the CSM said: 'Now you nip over to the barber's and have all that 'air off. All of it, mind, else you'll be on a bleeding court-martial yourself soon's they see you.'

I went over to the barber. 'Cut it short,' I told him, 'I'm on a Court-Martial Saturday.'

'King hell. What you bin up to, chum?'

'Nothing. I'm only a witness.'

I reported back to the CSM.

'Now go and draw equipment from the stores. Get it scrubbed and brasses shining like buggery by tomorrow. Parade here, full pack, the whole works.'

Inwardly I cursed. The thought of lugging that load across London in this hot weather was intolerable. Besides, I hardly knew how to connect it up. One of the blokes in our hut, who'd been a batman, came to my rescue. He polished the brasses, packed my kit, and got everything ready.

Next morning, after a heavy raid and a night in the trenches, I dragged myself across the square to Company Office. It was drizzling damply. The pack on my back bowed me double beneath its weight. The straps cut into my shoulders. I'd been issued with fifty rounds of ammo by the CSM: an injudicious action on his part, considering my present mood. I felt quite capable of shooting up the camp with it.

At last I embarked in a truck with a corporal bound for the same destination as myself. He'd been detailed to bring back an absentee apprehended in that area. We drove through the drizzle and got on a train which was a long time starting.

Later the drizzle ceased and sunlit fields flowed backwards past the windows of our compartment. The corporal, taciturn at first, suddenly became communicative and showed me a snap of his wife and kids. 'What're you on, chum?' he asked me.

'Witness at a court-martial.' The story was too long to tell, so I took out a press-cutting and passed it on to him. The corporal read it carefully.

'But this don't say nothing about you. This says a novelist. You ain't no novelist.'

'No.'

The corporal gave it up. He sat back in his corner looking a little offended. He thought I was taking the piss.

Presently we reached a station where we had to change. The platform was crowded with soldiers who'd just been released from detention. These assumed at first that I was a prisoner travelling under escort. One of them shared a compartment with us on the London train.

'Got a fag, mate?' he asked me. I gave him one. 'Ta,' he said. 'First smoke I've had in twenty-eight days. I'm shit out, see? Ain't got bugger all. Give me a bob they did, the bastards; a bleeding bob, that's all. I bin to Dunkirk and that's what I get: twenty-eight days' glasshouse and a bleeding bob.' He pulled up his trouser-leg and showed me a scar on his calf. 'Shrapnel, see? I bin out with the BEF and that's what they give me. Bleeding glasshouse and a bob.'

'But surely they didn't give you the glasshouse for going to Dunkirk?'

'Nah, course not. I mucked off home for a month, see?'

The compartment was terrifically hot. The corporal went to sleep with his mouth open and the glasshouse man continued to recount his experiences in detention.

'Do everything at the double there. Full bleeding pack an' all. Ain't no ruddy picnic, I assure you.'

We got to Waterloo and into another train. Then we walked about in narrow streets and broiling heat, looking for a bus. Our equipment and ammunition boots weighed us down; the blinding sun got into our bones, melting them to water. At last a bus was sighted. It deposited us some distance from the barracks and again we had to walk. Sweat streamed stickily down our faces. My throat felt as though an iron bar had been fixed across it: I'd a sharp burning pain in my back. We passed a high wall with spikes running along the top. This evidently enclosed the ITC. Summoning up a spurt of energy, the corporal shot ahead, presented his pass to the guard, and disappeared through the gates.

I followed through a doorway stacked with sandbags into the guardroom. Inside it was dark and cool after the sun and the RPs were playing darts. The corporal vanished immediately in the wake of another corporal carrying a bunch of keys. No one took any notice of me. I began to wonder if they would not imprison me as an accessory. I recalled gloomily what the jankers-man had said about the glasshouse.

After a time the provost-corporal returned. I came to attention. 'Reporting as witness in the O'Connor case, corporal.'

'Oh, so *you're* that bloke. Come this way.'

I followed him down a cold stone passage between cells. I wondered if he intended to lock me up straight away. The corporal stopped in front of a cell halfway down and stooped his head to the square aperture in the door. He called out O'Connor. There was a scuffle of feet inside and Sandy's oblong face, with the long square chin and thick bee-stung lips, appeared squinting sideways up in the opening.

'Hullo, Sandy,' I said.

Sandy's mouth dropped open. His lashless eyes were fixed in an unbelieving stare. Then his face became animated, the eyes lit up, the teeth flashed in a tremendous grin.

'Be Christ it's good to see you,' he said.

'You look very well, Sandy,' I said. And so he did. Nor was he stark naked and wearing chains, as in my imagination I had pictured him. His reddish hair was Brylcreemed and his face fresh-coloured as before.

'You look well too,' he said.

'My looks belie me,' I told him.

Then we talked about his Defending Officer. 'Smashing geezer. Gives me all I want. Books, everything.'

'Splendid. We'll soon have you out of here now.'

"'E won't want to leave,' the provost-corporal grinned. 'They live on the fat o' the land here. Eh, Sandy? Ain't that so?'

'That's so, Corp,' Sandy grinned back at him. 'Fat o' the land.'

He seemed in high spirits. The corporal conducted me back down the passage. 'Satisfied? Everything okay?'

'Fine,' I said. 'What d'you make of this case, corporal?'

'Bleeding balls-up, between you and me.'

He took me over to D Company Headquarters. It was in another part of the ITC and in process of construction. A smell of damp plaster and camouflage paint pervaded it. Pails and ladders stood about everywhere; the stone huts had no doors or glass in the windows and they were not yet wired with electric light.

I'd been detailed to sleep in the Orderly Sergeant's bunk. The Orderly Sergeant was a corporal. He said: 'I dunno where the hell you're going to kip. We only got three beds in here, and one of 'em's broke.'

Then I was taken before the acting CSM. He viewed me

336

with disfavour. 'So you're here at last,' he said. 'Well, Major's orders are: don't do no talking to no one. 'Bout O'Connor, I mean. Keep your trap shut, see? Get it? Right. Report back here 0900 hours tomorrow morning for interview with the major. Meantime: trap shut. All right. Fall out.'

Well, it was evident I wasn't to be locked up, anyway. I had a wash and went back to make up my bed. It had a large rent in the canvas and one of the legs was splintered, but I felt I'd rather anything than sleep on the floor. 'Am I allowed out?' I asked the Orderly Sergeant.

'Sure. Till 2359. Sign in the gate coming back.'

I went to a cinema and when I came out there was an alert on. The searchlight beams swung and pointed and planes throbbed overhead. I checked in at the gate and crossed the barrack-square, which seemed enormous in the searchlight rays. A dull panting of asthmatic engines indicated the presence of Jerry somewhere in the sky. Ack-ack rumbled over to the west.

I found the Orderly Sergeant's bunk with difficulty. The blackouts were up and it was pitch-dark inside. I struck a match; the hut was empty. Nobody had come in yet. The camp-bed creaked and sagged ominously as I climbed into it. I could feel the canvas splitting. Jerry chugged almost immediately above. It was a sound I'd become used to in the other camp. I'd have felt lonely without it. I fell asleep and was awakened by a man falling over me. This happened at intervals until the hut was filled with a sound of steady stertorous breathing and I went to sleep again.

The hell of a crash woke me. I was certain a bomb had been dropped on the barracks. I sat up and my bed collapsed under me with a splintering sound. A voice said out of the breathing dark: 'Ain't nothing, mate. You get used to that. Nowhere near. Miles away.'

I lay down again but it was some time before I went off to sleep. My bed was now flat on the ground, but I was too tired to do much about it. I woke next morning at eight. Luckily, no one rose early in the Orderly Sergeant's bunk. Breakfast was brought up from the cookhouse by a man called Paddy. After eating I had to brass myself up to meet the major. I started on this task while Paddy, seizing a broom, set himself to sweep the floor, shouting in an unintelligible accent for assistance. No one paid the slightest attention; the Company Runner, seated bolt upright on his roll of bedding, polished and polished a pair of boots, crooning all the time an unending obscene parody of a nursery rhyme, something about Miss Muffit and a spider, a rock and Robinson Crusoe. The Orderly Sergeant sat down at a table and began to write furiously. Paddy continued to sweep up; the air was full of flying particles of dust and horse dung. The Company Runner crooned:

> *Then up came a spider,*
> *Sat down beside her . . .*

From the other huts issued a stream of men carrying rifles and scrambling in a mad rush to get on parade. The voices of sergeants shouting 'Outside!' could be heard. It was 0900 hours. I dropped my button stick and made a dash for Company Office. But first came Company Evidence; it took ages. Nearly the whole Company seemed to be on a charge. Then the acting CSM called my name; he shouted 'Shun!' I marched in, right-wheeled, stood to attention in front of a desk.

I liked the major on sight. He looked like Charlie Chan. He had horn-rimmed spectacles and a thick drooping dark moustache. He ignored my salute and stood up to shake hands. He said to sit down. 'All right, Sergeant Major, wait outside.'

'I was so glad to hear from you.' He pushed over a box of cigarettes.

'It'll be an awful blow to the prosecution. They don't really believe you exist. They think O'Connor invented you, to lend colour to his story. By the way, have you brought the MSS?'

'They're on the way, sir.'

'Good. He really does write? The prosecution doesn't believe that either.'

'The prosecution seems awfully unbelieving.'

'Well, it does seem incredible.'

Then he told me the story. It was long and not easy to follow. Sandy had not been a model soldier. He had already absented himself at least twice. Before one of these flights he'd dropped his notebook in a Naffy. Some woman had picked it up and, bewildered by the contents, which she imagined to be in code, had taken it along to the civil police. Meanwhile, Sandy had been picked up by the red-caps, and the notebook, forwarded on by the police, had led to a search of his kit and the discovery of further notebooks, sketches, maps, and a German dictionary.

'Of course it's all rot,' the major said. 'There's no reason why he shouldn't have a German dictionary. Why, I've got one myself.'

'What about the RAF sketches, sir?'

'I'll show them to you.' The major took a few sheets of paper from a tray on his desk. Groups of buildings, pylons and hangars, rather out of drawing, were sketched on them. There was also an unfinished sketch of a plane, evidently made by Sandy when, with another unit, he had been stationed near a drome.

'These couldn't be of any value to the enemy.'

'No. Does he sketch, normally?'

'Yes. I've two of his pictures at home. Paintings.'

At this the major became tremendously excited. Jansen must be sent for, with the paintings. I suggested that Helen Baker might also be a useful witness. I saw no reason why she should not spend a few days in London at the army's expense. The major said he'd send her a wire.

Then he showed me Sandy's notebooks. I turned the pages. There was no connected narrative, but merely page after page of notes, which Sandy's habit of making contractions rendered almost indecipherable. I could not make head or tail of them. Isolated phrases of stilted German dialogue, plainly copied from the back pages of his dictionary, appeared here and there enigmatically. Columns of figures were scrawled in the margins: a habit of Sandy's when he was thinking something out.

There were certain dates and items of information relating to bombed British factories written underneath them in a journalistic style. I was completely baffled.

At this point a lance-corporal, who'd been a barrister in civilian life and was helping to prepare Sandy's defence, entered with some pages of typescript in his hand. These were copies of statements used as evidence against Sandy. One from an adjutant; one from the military policeman who at some time or another had arrested Sandy and who suspected him of having (sic) communistic or fascist tendencies. A lot more statements from people obscurely connected with the case. A letter from a woman whose son had lately been buried. The exact date of the burial was important, I forget why. I think Sandy had absented himself without leave to attend the funeral, but I don't really remember now.

Then Sandy was brought in. He was in splendid form. It was evident he got on smashing with the major. He sat down. He smoked a fag and, like old times, flicked the ash in the fireplace. He said not having smokes was the one thing that got him down in detention. I said: 'Now look here, Sandy, what the hell have you been up to? Are these really notes for a novel?'

'Sure. I was going to write it when the war's over, see? I took notes on everything I seen. Realism; atmosphere; same's you always told me. Bits in the paper too I copied out. All this stuff about factories they're kicking up a caper about, it's all bin printed; they're the dates written down, proof plain. But would they believe that? Not a word. No, they was dead set on me being a spy. Put handcuffs on an' all. I bin waiting on this court-martial a couple o' months now.'

'What about all this German?'

'Oh aye. I got a character, a Jerry, don't speak nothing but his own language. So I got me a dictionary to work out the di-log. I told 'em all that but they wouldn't listen, the ignorant soandsos. Would have it I was a Fifth Column. Now is it likely, if they'd the brains of a louse?'

'Well,' the major said, 'I think it's in the bag now. Soon as the MSS arrive I shall want to take down a statement from you both. Meantime,' he said, coming with me to the door, 'make yourself at home. I'll give you a permanent pass so you can go out any time of day. Anything you want, just ask.'

'Thank you, sir,' I said. Out of the corner of my eye I saw Sandy scoop up a handful of fags from the open box and stuff them down the front of his shirt. He winked at me as the door closed.

### III

The intervening days passed quietly except for incessant sirens; mornings with the major looking over the MSS and making sure the statements tallied; afternoons having tea with Helen, who'd arrived in answer to the major's wire; evenings at the cinema; altogether a pleasant rest from the usual routine of army life. The major had even provided me with a new camp bed to sleep on.

Then came Saturday; I buckled on my belt and bayonet; we drove to the court in a camouflaged civilian car; a sympathetic RP sitting next to the driver; Sandy and I at the back. A great deal of sun flashed back off glass in this suburb we were passing through; it seemed to be full of gigantic garages; Sandy, with a fag on, talked happily out of the corner of his mouth about his future; he seemed quite confident he would get off. What he wanted to do was go abroad, see some action; parades and bullshit got on his wick; why couldn't they put him on fogging draft.

Only the idea of seeing Jansen again appeared to worry him, as we drove past the furniture shops in the King's Road; I could understand that, remembering the disappearance of the hunting trophies and the riding cup. But Jansen, waiting for us at the barracks with the paintings wrapped up under his arm, wasn't one to bear malice; all he had for Sandy was a hearty handshake. There was just time for this before Sandy was led away through a door with a sign on it: COURT-MARTIAL IN PROGRESS. KEEP SILENCE.

I was the first witness called for the defence. I marched in uneasily, afraid that my belt and bayonet would fall off me. I stood before a table with a crimson blanket covering it. I saluted the President, who wore a crimson sash. He had white hair and smiled at me benevolently. I took the oath and sat down on a form facing the court. Major Cook stood up and said did I see Sandy O'Connor among those present. He nodded towards Sandy sitting between two RPs. I said I recognized him perfectly. I gave my evidence. A snuffy little man, who turned out to be a journalist, scribbled assiduously in short-hand at my elbow. The siren went as I was speaking; the President smiled. I stopped. The MSS were handed up by Major Cook and passed around. The President read a chapter of *Dog-End* with great attention.

Then the Prosecuting Officer stood up to cross-examine me. He coughed and stroked a short fair moustache. Did I really consider it possible that a boy like O'Connor, without—ahem—the advantages of education, could ever become an author? Surely it was necessary to have some—ahem—knowledge of grammatical rules before authorship could be embarked upon? I asked him sternly whether he had ever heard of the prole-tarian school of literature. He had not. He said was it a corres-pondence school? I put him right on this point. The journalist asked me if I would mind repeating the name of the school, he hadn't quite caught it. The President chipped in. Was it true, he asked the Prosecuting Officer, that the notes on bombed British factories made by the accused had previously been printed as common knowledge in the daily press? The Prose-cuting Officer coughed and said he now understood that to be the case. He sat down deflated. The President smiled at me and said: 'Well, I don't think we need trouble this gentleman—I mean this Private,' he smiled again, 'any longer.'

So I saluted and marched out, and Jansen was called. He turned out to be the star turn. The paintings caused a sensa-tion. 'What did you say this was called?'

'The Birth of a Nation.'

They nodded gravely. 'And this?'

'The Parson Preached a Sermon on Palm Sunday.'

'I beg your pardon?'

'The Parson Preached a Sermon on Palm Sunday. Excuse me, sir, you've got it the wrong way up.'

Then Helen Baker's statement was read out; she didn't appear in court herself. After this it was all over bar shouting. An acquittal on the secrets charge was certain. There were still two charges of absence, but the major hoped to get these squashed as Sandy had already spent two months in close arrest awaiting court-martial. He also promised to send Sandy abroad on the very next draft. This cheered Sandy up no end; we all shook hands and wished him the best of luck and came out into the bright glare of noon where Helen awaited us, wearing sunglasses and twirling a parasol. The All Clear blew as we came out.

Later, we all got drunk at the Café Royal. Jansen paid; he had a publisher's contract in his pocket; besides, he'd put it down as expenses when he sent Major Cook his bill. 'The Army pays,' he said, emptying his glass and ordering another. 'Drink up, it's on the Army.'

'D'you remember the swag?' he said. 'My God, those were the days. Good old Sandy. Remember those watches? And when he pinched my cups, too. My God, he was some lad.'

We all drank a toast to Sandy, solemnly standing to attention: 'To the great Tea Leaf!'

Everyone in the café stared disapprovingly.

## IV

Two years later I received a letter from Sandy. It had stamped on it PASSED BY CENSOR and bore an address in the Middle East Forces.

'DEAR OLD PAL,' the letter said,

*'I have made many attempt to write you though I have never quite got down to it. The reel reason was to say I have not forgot the great help you give me on my Court-Martial. I only hope some day I get the chance of repaying that debt. You must wonder even now how I got myself mixed up in that espial. I only hope we meet again so I can tell you. I*

expect by this time you will be wearing a pip or two. If not, why not. Have you any news of Jansen, I am always looking for his book out here, but it doesn't seem to have got this far yet.

'How is your own writing coming along, it is hard writing in the army, I know as I have tryed it myself. I have met a great many geezers who do a bit of writing as a hobby, they are all of the opinion you can't write and be a soldier same time. Myself I think that's all balls, though I am sometimes wondering if it is worth carrying on. Well, Pal, cherro and good luck. I will be hoping to hear from you.

S. O'CONNOR,
One of the Tea Leaves
from Green Leaves.'